S0-AKG-857

RADIO

COLLECTOR'S

GUIDE

1921-1932

THE AUTHOR AND SOME COLLECTIBLES

RADIO COLLECTOR'S GUIDE

1921-1932

Ralph H. Langley's
"SET CATALOG AND INDEX"

Edited and Expanded by

Morgan E. McMahon

MCMAHON'S

PUBLISHED BY **VINTAGE RADIO**

We wish to thank many friends for their help and guidance in collecting and verifying facts, particularly Earl England, Joe Horvath, Erv Rasmussen, Richard Sepic and Carl Sivertson. We also appreciate information gleaned from the Antique Wireless Association.

Photos are from the collections of Dan Heath, Paul Giganti, Louie Irvine, Morgan McMahon and Richard Smith. Other photo contributors (all rights reserved) are:

> Automatic Radio
> Doubleday and Company; Radio Broadcast Magazine
> Gernsback Publications; Radio News
> Zenith Radio Corporation

Production by H. Juhl Graphic Art Services, Cerritos, California

Printed by Griffin Printing and Lithography, Glendale, California

FIRST EDITION
SECOND PRINTING, 1974

Copyright © 1973 by VINTAGE RADIO. All rights reserved.
Published by VINTAGE RADIO, Box 2045, Palos Verdes Peninsula,
California 90274

Printed in U. S. A.
International Standard Book Number O-914126-03-2

CONTENTS

AUTOMATIC RADIO SR.
1930 AUTO

ATWATER KENT 10B 1924 BREADBOARD

DE FOREST RADIOHOME
1922 BOX CRYSTAL SET

NATIONAL MB-32 1931 CHASSIS

KELLER-FULLER RADIETTE
1930 MANTEL COMPACT

RCA RADIOLA X REGENOFLEX
1924 CONSOLE TABLE

COLONIAL 1931
CLOCK CABINET

CROSLEY BANDBOX
1927 METAL TABLE

PHILCO 90
1931 CATHEDRAL COMPACT

STROMBERG-CARLSON TREASURE CHEST
1929 TABLE

GILFILLAN
PORTABLE 1925

FREED-EISEMANN NR-5
1925 TABLE

TYPICAL VINTAGE RADIOS

SUPER ZENITH VIII
1924 6 TUBES $260.00

FRESHMAN MASTERPIECE
1925   5 TUBES

FALCK
"NO—BATTERY RADIO"
5 TUBES AC $150.00 1927

RCA RADIOLA 30
1927 8 TUBES AC $575.00

ATWATER KENT 44
POOLEY RADIO-CELLARETTE
1928 8 TUBES AC $536.00

GRIGSBY-GRUNOW
MAJESTIC
1928 8 TUBES AC $138.00

STROMBERG-CARLSON 638
1929 8 TUBES AC $380.00

PHILCO 86
NEUTRODYNE PLUS
1929 8 TUBES AC $275.00

ALL-AMERICAN MOHAWK
LYRIC
1929 10 TUBES AC $169.00

TYPICAL CONSOLE RADIOS

THIS BOOK

Collecting historical wireless, radio and television sets is a fun hobby for everybody. It's a challenge to chase down those hand-crafted early wireless sets, 1920's battery sets, 1930's "cathedral" and console models, and early television sets. Collections can range from one-radio conversation pieces to rooms full of historical equipment. There's a real kick in discovering an unusual old set in an unexpected place. The old radios don't even have to work to have value.

This book fills the need for information on radio sets made form 1921 through 1932. It is an ideal aid to the collector, historian and dealer. It is bound in a soft cover and convenient size for the roving collector.

This book began with a tabulation written by Ralph H. Langley in 1933 and published by John F. Rider. It was something less than a best-seller at that time, but was a good basis for our Guide. Mr. Langley's list was put together from the published claims of advertisers, the only information available at that time. We have carefully researched all presently available material to verify facts, improve information, and add models not originally listed. We have added several hundred previously unlisted models, with several thousand pieces of corrected or previously unlisted information.

PLEASE READ THE "EXPLANATION" SECTIONS BEFORE YOU PUT THIS BOOK TO WORK. Each line of the tabulation has a wealth of information if you know how to read it. There are two sections (1921-30 and 1931-32), each with its own format and explanation. The 1921-30 section has been considerably expanded and reworked; the 1931-32 section is reproduced directly from Mr. Langley's original list.

One word of caution: There were numerous variations within each model number in the earlier sets. Don't be surprised if your set is somehow different from another of the same model number. This is particularly true of Atwater Kent receivers.

We recommend that you use the book "Vintage Radio" along with this Guide. It is a pictorial history of wireless and radio, with pictures of many of the radio sets described in our tabulations. "S. Gernsback's 1927 Radio Encyclopedia" is another enjoyable and useful book. Both are published by Vintage Radio Co.

Please let us know if you have more information, or if you have corrections to our listings. We are always interested in upgrading the Guide. Address comments and inquiries to Vintage Radio, P. O. Box 2045, Palos Verdes Peninsula, Calif. 90274.

COLLECTING

(Reproduced from the book Vintage Radio)

The collector is the strongest force in preserving the history of radio. He may have a single old radio in his den as a conversation piece. Or he may build a separate building to house his large collection. The Antique Wireless Association, a group of serious collectors, has an outstanding collection in Holcomb, New York.

There are many kinds of collectors. Some of us collect facts and interesting stories, and are the historians of the wireless-radio era. Some collect old technical publications. Some collect old radio programs, broadcast business publications and memorabilia of radio stars of the past.

Collectors of early-day wireless equipment have a very challenging job of locating and restoring the various parts that made up the wireless stations. In wireless days, (mostly pre-1920), most transmitters and receivers were assembled from separate pieces, rather than being bought as units. One problem is that it is impossible for the uninformed person to recognize that the piece of "junk" in his attic is a piece of wireless history. Wireless collectors continually prowl antique stores, swap meets, junk shops and garage sales in hopes of finding wireless components. Once the parts get into the hands of collectors, they are enthusiastically traded from hand to hand as each collector tries to enrich his own specialized collection. There is no "dollar market" in wireless parts; collectors prefer to trade rather than sell. When a collector does sell, the price is a stand-alone figure based on that transaction only. One word of caution; there are some beautiful replicas, which can be easily mistaken for the real thing.

The radio era brought complete transmitters and receivers. These items are more easily recognized, and can be more easily appreciated by the general public. Workmanship on many of the receivers is as fine as can be found on any top-grade furniture. The novice is captivated by the weird collection of knobs, dials and switches, and by the hand-crafted cabinets. Sophisticated collectors can get a tremendous thrill from seeing a rare Federal radio, or by filling in one more vacancy in a string of Atwater Kent radios.

Again, there is not a firm dollar market value in radio transmitters and receivers. A radio is worth what a collector can afford to pay for it. "Asking" prices vary widely; you may find a lovely old radio for $20, and then find someone next door asking $100 for the weathered hulk of a defunct set.

Wireless and radio add-on components make good collections. Some people collect headphones, of which hundreds of kinds were made. Others collect speakers, which have many kinds of insides and which range from weird to poetic in their styling. Vacuum tubes make perhaps the most interesting collection for the technical man. They are the key elements in the progress of radio, ranging from 1904 Fleming valves to 1929 screen grid tubes.

Most old radios do not operate after many years in storage. The paper-dielectric wound capacitors are bad, or will go bad shortly after batteries are connected. Sometimes they can be saved by starting at a low voltage and gradually increasing the voltage over a period of days. The remedy for bad capacitors (or condensers, as they were called), is not to replace them with equally old ones that will go bad just as quickly. Rather, one must replace the old foil windings with new ones. Most windings are tarred into the cans. The first thing to try is to freeze the condenser; the tar will usually shrink away from the can and the insides will slide out. Failing this the condenser can be heated and the tar poured out.

Transformers are another problem. In the old days, paper insulation contained traces of sulphur, which deteriorated the windings over the years. Old transformers may fail at any time. The old transformers can be re-wound, or a newer transformer can be put inside the old case by the non-purist.

WARNING: Do NOT attempt to hitch up voltage or repair antique wireless or radio equipment unless you know what you are doing. You can do irreparable damage to both yourself and the equipment. This is especially true of early A-C power supplies.

There are some excellent books on the radio industry and its people. "Vintage Radio" and "S. Gernsback's 1927 Radio Encyclopedia" are companion pieces to this guide. Erik Barnouw's series "A Tower in Babel," "The Golden Web" and "The Image Empire," (Oxford University Press, N.Y.) is a very interesting factual history of broadcasting. Ron Lackman's "Remember Radio" (G. P. Putnam's Son's, N. Y.) and Jim Harmon's "The Great Radio Comedians" and "The Great Radio Heroes" (Doubleday & Co., Garden City, N. Y.) are entertaining and informative memory trips. Lawrence Lessing's "Man of High Fidelity" (Bantam Books, N. Y.) is the story of E. H. Armstrong's amazing career. Tapes and records of old radio programs are also very enjoyable. These can be found in record shops or in the classified sections of antique periodicals.

If you are seriously interested in radio history and collecting, write to the Antique Wireless Association, Holcomb, N.Y. 14469; The Antique Radio Club of America, 516 Country Lane, Louisville, Ky. 40207; or the Canadian Vintage Wireless Association, P.O. Box 51, Station R, Toronto Ontario, M4G 2E6.

Every day, valuable pieces of wireless and radio history are thrown onto the trash heap. Perhaps you, the reader, can help your relatives, friends, and neighbors dig up these modern-day antiques out of attics and basements. It's a great way to start a hobby, or to get these bits of history into the hands of true collectors.

GOOD HUNTING!

AGE GUIDE

There are useful clues to the age of early-time sets. Early wireless equipment looks like experimental scientific equipment. Radios of the early and mid-1920's were battery sets with many knobs and dials. Early A-C sets built in the mid-1920's were simply battery sets with power supplies replacing the batteries. True A-C sets, with built-in power supplies and A-C tubes were introduced in 1927.

Console models became popular in the late 1920's when radio became part of the home scene. Well-constructed consoles were the showpieces of the home in the 1930's and 1940's. Smaller A-C cabinet "cathedral" radios (also known as "midget" or "depression" models) became widely used in the early 1930's as bad times made money scarce. These evolved into the box-shaped table radios that are sold today. Small AC-DC radios with plastic cabinets made the $9.95 "cheapie" available to every room in the home in the late 1930's.

Patent numbers appear on many radios built up through the mid-1930's. They are a good clue to age, since the item must have been made later than the latest patent shown.

January	Number	January	Number
1900	660,000	1926	1,580,000
1902	720,000	1928	1,660,000
1904	770,000	1930	1,760,000
1906	830,000	1932	1,850,000
1908	890,000	1934	1,940,000
1910	950,000	1936	2,010,000
1912	1,020,000	1938	2,100,000
1914	1,080,000	1940	2,180,000
1916	1,150,000	1942	2,270,000
1918	1,240,000	1944	2,340,000
1920	1,320,000	1946	2,390,000
1922	1,410,000	1948	2,430,000
1924	1,500,000	1950	2,500,000

Tube types give another rough guide to age. Four-prong tubes, most often −00A, −01A, WD-11 and −99 were used in the 1920's. Early A-C sets from 1927 to 1929 used four and five prong A-C tubes like the 26, 27 and 71A. The 24A tube, with its grid cap connection on top, hit in 1928 and was widely used well into the 1930's. Six and seven prong tubes were introduced in many sets in 1932. "Octal" tubes with plastic-keyed bases hit in 1935. Many of these tubes were made of metal rather than glass. "Loctal" tubes with metal bases were introduced in WWII. Miniature glass tubes were used in compact and portable sets starting in 1941, and were used in many sets after 1945.

One word of caution: Model numbers don't usually follow in time sequence. It's dangerous to assume that a radio is older because it has a lower model number.

CROSS-REFERENCE LIST

Sometimes the name on a radio set doesn't give a clue as to its manufacturer. This list will aid you in finding the manufacturer in this book.

Brand Name	Manufacturer
ABC	Wireless Equipment Co.
Ace	Crosley Radio Corp.
Acratone	Federated Purchaser
Aeriola	RCA
Airline	Montgomery Ward & Co.
Ajax	Commonwealth Radio Mfg. Co.
Amaco	American Apparatus Co.
American Bosch	United American Bosch
Amrad	American Radio & Research Lab.
Angelus	Davison-Haynes
Apex	U. S. Radio & Television Corp.
Auto-Dial	J. M. P. Mfg. Co.
Auto-Lite	Electric Auto-Lite Co.
Baird	Shortwave & Television Labs, Inc.
Bosch	American Bosch, United American Bosch
Clarion	Transformer Corp. of America
Claritone	U. S. Radio & Television Corp.
Code	Service Electric Co.
Counterphase	Bremer-Tulley
Day Fan	General Motors Radio Corp.
Deresnadyne	Andrews Radio Co.
De Wald	Pierce-Airo Inc.
Dubilier	DuMont Electric Co. Inc.
Erla	Electrical Research Labs.
Eveready	National Carbon Co.
Falck	Advance Electric Co.
Find-All	Allied Engineering Inst.
Freed Eisemann	Freed Television & Radio Corp.
Freshman-Belmont	Belmont Radio Corp.
General	General Television & Radio Corp.
Geneva	Cordonic Mfg. Co.
Hamilton-Lloyd	Pioneer Television Co.
Hetro Magnetic	Mercury Electrical Co.
ICA	Insuline Corp. of America
Imperial	Fink Industries
LaFayette	Wholesale Radio Service Co.
Lemco	Lee Electric & Mfg. Co.
Lyric	All American Mohawk Corp.

Majestic	Grigsby-Grunow Co.
Mars	Radio Sight & Sound Corp.
Master-Craft	La Mar Mfg. Co. Inc.
Mayflower	Clago Radio Corp.
Miraco	Midwest Radio Corp.
Mission	Consolidated Radio Mfg. Co.
Motorola	Galvin Mfg. Corp.
Neco	Newark Electric Co.
Neutrowound	Advance Auto. Accessories Co.
Newlands	Incandescent Supply Co.
Oard	(Sold by) Atlantic-Pacific Radio Supply
Perasco	Perry Radio Supply Co.
Peter Pan	Jackson-Bell Co. Ltd.
Pfanstiehl	National Phanstiel Mfg. Co.
Philco	Philadelphia Stg. Batt. Co.
Radak	Clapp-Eastham
Radiette	Keller-Fuller Mfg. Co.
Radiocraft	DeForest Radio Co.
Radiodyne	Western Coil & Electrical Co.
Radiola	RCA
RCI	Radio Chassis Inc.
Regent	High Frequency Labs.
Sentinel	United Air Cleaner Corp.
Silvertone	Sears Roebuck & Co.
Sky-Hawk	Republic Industries
Sparton	Sparks-Withington Co.
TCA	Transformer Corp. of America
Telmaco	Telephone Maintenance Co.
Tiffany-Tone	Horn, Herbert H.
Tom Thumb	Automatic Radio Mfg. Co.
Transitone	Philco
Ultradyne	Traul Radio Co.
United Am. Bosch	American Bosch
Victor	RCA
Visionette	Western Television
Walton	Northwest Specialty Co.
Wavemaster	Kellogg Switchboard & Supply Co.
Zenette	Zenith Radio Co.

EXPLANATION OF 1921-1930 TABULATION

MANUFACTURER: The manufacturer's company name is given. When more than one name was used, they are cross-referenced in the listing. When a trade name was used, that name is also shown. (Majestic for Grigsby-Grunow, for instance).

YEAR: The year shown is that in which the model was introduced in national advertising. They are calendar years, not model years.

MODEL NUMBER AND NAME: Most models had model numbers or model names, although some used only the company name. If every model used the same trade name, that name is shown with with the corporate name under Manufacturer.

PRICE: Figures given are the first advertised Eastern prices. In the 1921-30 period they did not usually include tubes, batteries or other accessories.

STYLE: This column gives the general style of the receiver:

A	Automobile
B	Breadboard
B/P	Blueprint only
C	Console
CC	Clock cabinet
Ch	Chassis only
CL	Consolette (small floor-model console)
CT	Console, table
D	Desk-type floor cabinet
GE	Glass-enclosed
HB	Highboy cabinet
KD	Knocked down (unassembled cabinet)
Kit	Unassembled parts kit
LB	Lowboy cabinet
M	Midget, mantel or cathedral (compact table console)
MC	Metal Console
Mldd	Moulded
MT	Metal Table
P	Phonograph panel
Por	Portable
RP	Radio-phonograph combination
S	Spinet-type floor cabinet
T	table model

DIALS (D): Number of primary tuning controls. Usually, this is the same as saying "how many big knobs or big dials".

TUBES (T): Number of tubes, including rectifier. Special ballast or regulator tubes are not included. Some manufacturers did not include BH rectifiers in their tube count.

POWER (P): Type of power supply providing operating voltage. Don't put too much faith in the difference between B, E and S, since different manufacturers used different definitions. True dry battery sets used special low-drain tubes like the '99 types.

A	Alternating current (AC) supply
B	Dry Batteries
D	110-volt direct current (DC) supply
E	Either storage or dry batteries
S	Storage battery for filament supply

CIRCUITS AND STAGES: This column is intended for the enthusiasts who understand the technical side of radio. The type of circuit is stated using the description most closely describing the circuit:

A	Single-stage audio amplifier
AA	Two-stage audio amplifier
AAA	Three-stage audio amplifier
C	Crystal receiver
D	Vacuum-tube detector
DA	Detector and one audio stage
DAA	Detector and two audio stages
Neut	Neutrodyne circuit TRF receiver
PT	Pre-tuner
Reg	Regenerative receiver
RF	Untuned radio frequency amplifier
RFA	Tuned radio frequency amplifier
RFL	"Radio Frequency Laboratory" circuit TRF receiver
Rfx	Reflex receiver
SG	Screen-grid circuit TRF receiver
SH	Super-heterodyne receiver
SReg	Super-regenerative receiver
TRF	Tuned-radio-frequency receiver

The number of stages is given in the following order (a,b,c,d):

a.	Untuned RF amplifiers
b.	Tuned RF amplifiers
c.	Intermediate-frequency (IF) amplifiers
d.	Audio amplifiers

It is assumed that the circuit expert realizes that all receivers use a detector stage, that all super-heterodyne circuits use an additional "first detector" and local oscillator, and that all AC sets use at least one rectifier tube or equivalent. Hence, these stages are not tabulated.

A push-pull output stage is indicated by an asterisk (*), and a push-pull parallel output stage by a number sign (#). Single-ended parallel output stages are not separately identified.

For example, - 2 - 2 means a TRF receiver with two tuned RF stages and two audio stages. - 3 - 2* means a TRF receiver with three tuned RF stages and two audio stages, the output stage being push-pull. - - 2 3 would be a super-heterodyne with two IF amplifiers and three stages of audio amplification.

In the 1921-30 tabulation, a blank indicates no available information. This differs from the 1931-32 tabulation.

MANUFACTURER	YEAR	MODEL NO. & NAME	PRICE	STYLE	D	T	P	CIR. & STAGES
ABLET CO. CHAS. R.	1923	"Navy Type"	595.00					
A. C. DAYTON CO.	1923		5.00	Box	1	0	-	C - : - -
	1924	Super Polydyne Six	43.35	T	2	6	S	TRF - 3 - 2
		Copp #4	98.00	Kit	3	4	E	TRF - 1 - 2
		Copp #5 (R-12)	115.00	T	3	4	E	TRF - 1 - 2
	1925	XL 5 Polydyne	115.00	T	3	5	E	TRF - 2 - 2
		XL 10	185.00	C	3	5	E	TRF - 2 - 2
		XL 15	120.00	P	3	5	E	TRF - 2 - 2
		XL 5	72.50	KD	3	5	E	TRF - 2 - 2
		XL 5	125.00	GE	3	5	E	TRF - 2 - 2
		XL 5	250.00	C	3	5	E	TRF - 2 - 2
		XL 5	56.00	C	3	5	E	TRF - 2 - 2
	1926	XL 20	79.00	T	2	5	E	TRF - 2 - 2
		XL 25	135.00	T	2	5	A	TRF - 2 - 3
		XL 30	139.00	T	2	6	B	TRF - 2 - 3
		XL 25	210.00	C	2	5	A	TRF - 2 - 3
		XL 30	255.00	C	2	6	A	TRF - 2 - 3
	1927	XL 30	85.00	C	2	6	A	TRF - 2 - 2
		XL 25	149.00	T	2	5	E	TRF - 2 - 2
		XL 25	252.00		1	5	E	TRF - 2 - 2
		XL 50	135.00	T	2	6	E	TRF - 3 - 2
		XL 60	285.00	C	2	6	E	TRF - 3 - 2
		XL 70	165.00	T	2	7	E	TRF - 4 - 2
		XL 70	315.00	C	2	7	E	TRF - 4 - 2
	1928	XL 61	65.00	T	1	6	B	TRF - 3 - 2
		AC 63	98.00	T	1	7	A	TRF - 3 - 2
		AC 65	123.00	T	1	7	A	TRF - 3 - 2
		AC 66	148.00	T	1	7	B	TRF - 3 - 2
	1929	XL 72 Navigator	79.00	T	1	9	A	PT - 4 - -
		AC 98	108.00	LB	1	9	A	PT - 4 - -
		AC 9960 "	148.00	LB	1	9	A	PT - 4 - -
		AC 9970 "	165.00	LB	1	9	A	PT - 4 - -
		AC 9980 "	185.00	HB	1	9	A	PT - 4 - -
		AC 9990 "	188.00	RP	1	9	A	PT - 4 - -
		AC 99100"	234.00	T	1	9	A	PT - 4 - -
		XL 71	69.00		1	7	B	PT - 4 - 2
ACME APPARATUS CO.	1922	Acmefone Loudspeaker Receiver						Rfx
	1923	Acmefone						Rfx
	1924	"						

MANUFACTURER	YEAR	MODEL NO. & NAME	PRICE	STYLE	D	T	P	CIR.	& STAGES
ACME APPARATUS CO. (cont.)	1925	A		Kit		4		Rfx	- 3 - 3
		S		Kit		5		Rfx	- 3 - 2
ACME ELEC. & MFG. CO.	1928	AC 7	58.00	Ch		7	A	TRF	1 2 - 2
		AC 7	65.00	T	2	7	A	TRF	1 2 - 2
		AC 7	99.00	LB		7	A	TRF	1 2 - 2
		AC 7	65.00	T		7	A	TRF	1 2 - 2
	1929	77	115.00		1	7	A	TRF	- 3 - 2
		78	130.00		1	8	A	SG	
		88	139.00	LB	1	8	A	SG	- 3 - 2*
		88	155.00	HB	1	8	A	SG	- 3 - 2*
ADAMS-MORGAN CO.	1916	L,S,X	22, 30, 35	B	-	-	-	PT	- - -
	1921	RA 6 Paragon	35.00	T	2	1	-	Reg	- - -
		2-5-U	70.00	T	1	1	-	Reg	- - -
		RA 10 Paragon	75.00	T	3	0	-	RegPT	- - 2
		RA 10-DA2 "	140.00	2T	3	3	-	Reg	- - 2
	1922	RD 5-A2 "	65.00	2T	3	3	S	RegDAA	- - 1
	1923	DA 2 "	135.00	T	0	3		Reg	
		RB 2 "	75.00	T	3	1		Reg D	
	1924	RD 5 "		T			S	Reg D	- - -
		RA 0		T					
		Paragon Two	27.50	T	1	2		Reg	
		Paragon Three	48.50	T	1	3		Reg	
		Paragon Four	65.00	T	1	4		Reg	
		Paragon III	175.00	T					
	1925	2 Paradyne	27.50	T	1	2	S	RegDA	- - 1
		3 Paradyne	48.50	T	1	2	S	RegDA	- - 1
		4 Paradyne	65.00	T	1	2	E	TRF	- 1 - 2
ADIRONDACK MOUNTAIN SERVICE CO.	1925	Heteromagnetic	82.50			5	S	Neut	- 2 - 2
ADLER MANUFACTURING CO.	1924	Cabriole 10	300.00	RP	3	5	S	Neut	
		Royal Neutrodyne							
		201A	215.00	T	3	5	S	Neut	- 2 - 2
		199	205.00	T	3	5	B	Neut	- 2 - 2
	1925	Floor #1	350.00	C	3	5	S	Neut	- 2 - 2
		Phonograph Panel	135.00	P	3	5	S	Neut	- 2 - 2
ADROIT TOOL CO.	1925		60.00					TRF	
			75.00					TRF	

MANUFACTURER	YEAR	MODEL NO. & NAME	PRICE	STYLE	D	T	P	CIR. & STAGES
ADROIT TOOL CO. (cont.)	1925	R 5 P Adrola	125.00					TRF
	1926	R 5 8 "	60.00					TRF
		R 5 C "	75.00					TRF
			125.00					TRF
	1927	Adrola All Electric	230.00	T			A	
ADVANCE AUTOMOBILE ACCESS.	SEE	Neutrowound						
ADVANCE ELECTRIC CO. (Formerly Falck)	1930	77	69.50	M	1	6	A	SG - 2 - 2
		88	59.50	M	1	6	A	SG - 2 - 2
		89			1	6	A	SG - 2 - 2
ADVANCE RADIO RESEARCH LAB.	1926	HF 3	72.00					TRF
		TR 5	39.50					TRF
		R 5 Neutro	100.00					TRF
		7 B Super Power	140.00					TRF
		8 A Super Power	185.00					TRF
		8 Super	225.00					TRF
AEOLIES CORP.	1924							RF
AER A DYNE MFG. CO.	1925 / 1926	7-0-5	75.00					
AEREX	1922	King		Box	2	-	-	C - - - -
AERIAL ELEC. CO.	1925	Crystal Mystery	10.00		2	-	-	C - - - -
	1926	Crystal King	8.00		2	-	-	C - - - -
		Comb. 1	10.95		2	-	-	C - - - -
		Comb. 3	19.50			-	-	C - - - -
AERIOLA	1924	10		Box	2	-	-	C - - - -
AERODYNE CO., THE	1925	Aerodyne	38.75	T	1	6	S	TRF
	1926	"	38.75	T	1	7	S	TRF - 3 - 2
		SIX		1	5	S	TRF - 3 - 3
	1927	Special		T			S	TRF
							S	TRF
AERO PRODUCTS	1928	International S. W.	55.30	Kit	1	4	B	Reg. 1 - - 2
		Standard S. W.	49.95	Kit	1	3	EorA	Reg. - - - 2

18

MANUFACTURER	YEAR	MODEL NO. & NAME	PRICE	STYLE	D	T	P	CIR. & STAGES	
AEROVOX WIRELESS CORP.	1923	Crystal	16.00			-	-	C	- - - -
	1924	TD2A			1	3		DAA	- - - 2
AINSWORTH-GATES RADIO CO. (Ainsworth Radio Co. in 1925)	1924	Ranger Five	95.00						
		Ranger DeLuxe	175.00						
	1925	Torodyne	100.00	T	3			TRF	
AIRLINE RADIO CO	1926	6							
		8							
		9							
AIR-OLA RADIO CO.	1925	Just-Rite Reflex	120.00	C	1			RF	
		"	215.00		1			RF	
		Console	250.00		1			Rfx	
AIRO MASTER CORP.	1925	#60 Chest	60.00		3			TRF	
		70	60.00		3				
		75 Concert	75.00	CT	3			TRF	
		130	130.00		3			TRF	
		150 Console	150.00	HB	3			TRF	
AIR-WAY ELECTRIC APPLIANCE CORP.	1923	F	50.00		2			RF	
		G	100.00		2			RF	
	1924	#41	65.00	T	2	4	S	TRF	- 1 - 2
		42	100.00	T	2	4	S	TRF	- 1 - 2
		51	125.00	T	3	5	S	TRF	- 2 - 2
		52	375.00	C	3	5	S	TRF	- 2 - 2
	1925	#61	98.50		2	5	S	TRF	
		62	137.00		2	5	S	TRF	
		63	197.00		2	5	S	TRF	
		61D	98.50		2	5	B	TRF	
		62D	137.00		2	5	B	TRF	
		63D	197.00		2	5	B	TRF	
	1926	#61	98.50		2	5	S	TRF	
		62	137.00		2	5	S	TRF	
		63	197.00		2	5	S	TRF	
		61D	98.50		2	5	S	TRF	
		62D	137.00		2	5	S	TRF	
		63D	197.00		2	5	S	TRF	
AJAX ELEC. SPECIALTY CO.	1924	Crystal				-	-	C	- - - - -

19

MANUFACTURER	YEAR	MODEL NO. & NAME	PRICE	STYLE	D	T	P	CIR. & STAGES
AJAX ELEC. SPECIALTY CO. (cont.)	1925	Marveltone	45.00		3	-	-	TRF - - -
		ACS Crystal	5.00		1	-	-	C - - -
		CST Junior Crystal	3.00		1	-	-	C - - -
	1926	Marveltone	60.00		3	-	-	TRF - - -
		Crystal	2.50		-	-	-	C - - -
AKRADYNE RADIO CORP.	1926				2			
					3			
ALADDIN MFG. CO.	1925	Aladyne	75.00		2			TRF
		"	100.00		2			TRF
		#510 Aladyne	75.00	SC	2	4		TRF
		RF4	75.00		2			TRF
	1926	Aladyne	60.00		2			TRF
		"	90.00	SC	3	5		Neut.
		Super Five						
ALBRIGHT & CO., J.E.	1924	I Martinola	15.00		3			
		II	20.00		3			
ALGONQUIN ELEC. CO. INC.	1927	WT-7	150.00		3	5		Th - 3 - 3
		TA-7	250.00	T	3	5	S	Th - 3 - 3
		RF5						TRF - 2 - 2
ALL AMERICAN MOHAWK CORP. (All-American Radio Corp.) See also Mohawk Corp. of Illinois	1925	Senior	42.00		2	5	S	Rfx - 2 - 2
		Junior			2	6	S	TRF - 2 - 3
	1926	R	90.00	T	2	5	S	TRF - 2 - 2
		Duet	115.00	T	1	7	S	TRF - 3 - 3
		R Hi Boy	115.00	HB	1	7	S	TRF - 3 - 3
		Sovereign	435.00	HB	1	7	S	TRF - 3 - 3
		Loraine	335.00	T	1	6	S	TRF - 2 - 3
		Forte	210.00	D	1	7	S	TRF - 2 - 3
		Sextet	175.00		1	6	A	TRF - 2 - 2
		226	100.00		1	5/6	B/A	TRF - 3 - 2
	1927	115	170.00	A	1	6	S	Rice - 3 - 2
		44	70.00	T	1	6	A	Rice - 3 - 2
		55	125.00	HB	1	9	S	TRF - 4 - 2
		80	135.00	T	1	10	A	TRF - 4 - 2
		90	145.00	T	1	10	A	TRF - 4 - 3*
		77	150.00	T	1		A	TRF
		Duet	160.00	T	2	6	A	TRF - 2 - 3

MANUFACTURER	YEAR	MODEL NO. & NAME	PRICE	STYLE	D	T	P	CIR. & STAGES
ALL AMERICAN MOHAWK CORP. (cont)								
		66	245.00	C	1	7	A	TRF - 3 - 2
		88	210.00	HB	1	9	A	TRF - 4 - 2
		Sextet	220.00	HB	2	6	A	TRF - 2 - 3
		Forte	270.00	T	1	9	A	TRF - 4 - 2*
		99	285.00	C	1	7	A	TRF - 3 - 2
		Loraine	360.00	HB	1	9	A	TRF - 4 - 2*
	1928	Sovereign	460.00	C	1	9	A	TRF - 4 - 2*
		60	125.00	C	1	7	A	TRF - 3 - 2
		61	165.00	C	1	7	A	TRF - 3 - 2
		62	172.50	C	1	7	A	TRF - 3 - 2
		65	137.00	C	1	7	A	TRF - 3 - 2
		66	245.00	C	1	7	A	TRF - 3 - 2
		70, 73, 75	140.00	C	1	8	A	TRF - 3 - 2
		77	128.00	T	1	8	A	TRF - 3 - 2
		80	128.00	T	1	9	A	TRF - 4 - 2*
		83	250.00	T	1	9	A	TRF - 4 - 2*
		84	295.00	T	1	9	A	TRF - 4 - 2*
		85	195.00	T	1	9	A	TRF - 4 - 2*
		88	425.00	RP	1	10	A	TRF - 4 - 2
	1929	93 Lyric	169.00	C	1	10	A	TRF - 4 - 2
		95	199.00	HB	1	8	A	TRF - 3 - 2
		SG1	187.00	LB	1	7	A	SG
		94	153.00		1	8	A	SG - 3 - 2*
	1930	96	155.00		1	7	A	SG - 2 - 2
		D11	99.50		1	7	A	SG - 2 - 2
		D19	119.00		1	7	A	SG - 2 - 2
		D29	139.00		1	7	A	SG - 2 - 2
		D39	199.00		1	8	A	SG - 2 - 2
		D69	169.00		1	8	A	SG - 3 - 2
		H19	134.00		1	8	A	SG - 3 - 2
		H29	154.00		1	5	S	SG - 2 - 2
		H60	184.00		1	6	D	SG - 3 - 2
		Battery Model	99.50					
		DC Model			1			
ALLEN-ROGERS-MADISON INC.	1928	Ultradyne Six	139.75					
AMBASSADOR SALES CO.	1926							
AMBER ENGINEERING INSTITUTE	1926							

MANUFACTURER	YEAR	MODEL NO. & NAME	PRICE	STYLE	D	T	P	CIR. & STAGES
AMBER MFG. CO.	1925	512C Marv-o-dyne	98.00		3	5	E	TRF - 2 - 2
		Skylark	58.00		3	5	E	TRF - 2 - 2
		T Marv-o-dyne	90.00	T	3	5	E	TRF - 2 - 2
		D Marv-o-dyne	125.00		2	6	S	TRF - 2 - 3
		DC Marv-o-dyne	185.00	C	2	6	S	TRF - 2 - 3
		Marv-o-dyne	110.00		2	5	S	TRF - 2 - 3
AMBLER-HOLMAN	1924	TR 5	75.00	T	3	5	B	TRF - 2 - 2
	1925				3	5		TRF - 3 - 2
AMEREX ELEC. CORP.	1924	Ace	59.00	C	3	5		TRF - 2 - 2
	1925					5		TRF - 2 - 2
AMERICAN APPARATUS CO. "AMACO"	1925	CN7	20.00		2	2		Reg. -
		CNW-6 Amacodyne	20.00	Por	1	1		Reg. -
		CN8	80.00		1			TRF -
		CN8 Amacodyne	60.00		1			TRF -
		CN9 Amacodyne	80.00		1			TRF -
	1926	E-6 Amacodyne	150.00	Por	1	6		RF - 3 - 2
		E-6-B Amacodyne	150.00	CL	1	6		RF - 3 - 2
AMERICAN BOSCH MAGNETO CO. (United American Bosch Corp., American Bosch Corp.)	1925	16 Amborola	150.00	T	3	6	S	TRF - 2 - 3
	1926	27 Amborada	310.00	C	2	7	S	RFL - 4 - 2
		35 Cruiser	100.00	T	2	5	S	RFL - 2 - 2
		35 Imperial	85.00	T	2	5	S	RFL - 2 - 2
		35 Royal	140.00	C	2	6	S	TRF - 2 - 2
		46	68.50	C	1	6	S	RFL 1 2 - 2
	1927	57	340.00		1	6	S	RFL - 4 - 2
		57AA			1	6	S	RFL - 4 - 2
		57AC			1	6	S	RFL - 4 - 2
		66	99.50	T	1	6	S	RFL 1 2 - 2
		66AA			1	6	A	RFL 1 2 - 2
		66AC	155.00	T	1	6	S	RFL 1 2 - 2
		66ACAA		T	1	6	S	RFL 1 2 - 2
		76	175.00	C	1	6	S	RFL 1 2 - 2
		76AC			1	6	S	RFL 1 2 - 2
		76L	195.00	C	1	6	S	RFL 1 2 - 2
		87	195.00	T	1	7	A	RFL - 4 - 2
		96	295.00	C	1	6	A	RFL 1 2 - 2
		96DC Cruiser	295.00	C	1	7	D	RFL 1 2 - 2*

22

MANUFACTURER	YEAR	MODEL NO. & NAME	PRICE	STYLE	D	T	P	CIR. & STAGES
AMERICAN BOSCH MAGNETO CO. (cont.)		107	440.00	C	1	7	A	RFL - 4 - 2
		107AA			1	7	A	RFL - 4 - 2
		116	170.00	T	1	6	A	RFL 1 2 - 2
		116AA			1	6	A	RFL 1 2 - 2
		126	135.00	T	1	6	A	TRF 1 2 - 2
		126AA			1	6	A	TRF . 2 - 2
		136	195.00	C	1	6	A	RFL 1 2 - 2*
		146	139.00	C	1	6	A	TRF 1 2 - 2*
		156	195.00	C	1	7	D	RFL 1 2 - 2*
		166	119.00	T	1	6	A	TRF 1 2 - 2
		176	149.00	C	1	6	A	TRF 1 2 - 2
	1928	28	132.00	T	1	8	A	TRF 1 2 - 2
		28A	170.00	C	1	8	A	TRF - 3 - 2*
		28AA	197.00		1	8	A	TRF - 3 - 2*
		28C	237.00		1	8	A	TRF - 3 - 2*
		28D3	212.00	C	1	8	A	TRF - 3 - 2*
		28-25	170.00	C	1	8	A	TRF - 3 - 2*
		28-33-B3	212.00	C	1	8	A	TRF - 3 - 2*
		28-33-B4	187.00	C	1	8	A	TRF - 3 - 2*
		27-7C	212.00	C	1	8	A	RFL - 4 - 2
		28-7D	212.50	C	1	8	A	TRF - 3 - 2*
		28-7E	187.00	C	1	8	A	TRF - 3 - 2*
		29		C	1	8	A	TRF - 3 - 2*
		29AA	230.00	C	1	8	A	TRF - 3 - 2*
		29B	295.00		1	8	A	TRF - 3 - 2*
		29AS			1	8	A	TRF - 3 - 2*
		29W825	225.00		1	8	A	TRF - 3 - 2*
		29W826	232.00	C	1	8	A	TRF - 3 - 2*
		297A	230.00	C	1	8	A	TRF - 3 - 2*
		297B	237.00	C	1	8	A	TRF - 3 - 2*
		29D1	225.00	C	1	8	A	TRF - 3 - 2*
		29D2	232.00	C	1	8	A	TRF - 3 - 2*
		29-33B1	230.00		1	8	A	TRF - 3 - 2*
		29-33B2	237.00	C	1	8	A	TRF - 3 - 2*
		30			1	8	A	TRF - 3 - 2*
		38	115.00	T	1	8	A	TRF - 3 - 2*
		38A	175.00	C	1	8	A	TRF - 3 - 2*
		38C	200.00	C	1	8	A	TRF - 3 - 2*
		38-25	175.00	C	1	8	A	TRF - 3 - 2*
		38-33B4	192.00	C	1	8	A	TRF - 3 - 2*

MANUFACTURER	YEAR	MODEL NO. & NAME	PRICE	STYLE	D	T	P	CIR. & STAGES
AMERICAN BOSCH MAGNETO CO. (cont)	1929	38-7D	217.00	C	1	8	A	TRF	- 3 - 2*
		387E	182.00	C	1	8	A	TRF	- 3 - 2*
		48	119.00	T	1	7	A	SG	- 3 - 2*
		48A	168.00	C	1	7	A	SG	- 3 - 2*
		48C	155.00	C	1	7	A	SG	- 3 - 2*
		48H	198.00	C	1	7	A	SG	- 3 - 2*
		48J	240.00	C	1	7	A	SG	- 3 - 2*
		48L	230.00	C	1	7	A	SG	- 3 - 2*
		48R	280.00	C	1	7	A	SG	- 3 - 2*
		48-16	198.00	C	1	7	A	SG	- 3 - 2*
		48-17	230.00	C	1	7	A	SG	- 3 - 2*
		48-18	240.00	C	1	7	A	SG	- 3 - 2*
		48-19	280.00	T	1	7	A	SG	- 3 - 2*
		49	119.00	T	1	5	A	SG	- 3 - 2*
		52 (Export)		C	1	7	D		
		53 (Phillips Tubes)		T	1	7	S		
	1930	54	168.00	C	1	7	S	SG	- 3 - 2*
		56	95.00	T	1	7	A	SG	- 3 - 2*
		56AB	133.00	C	1	8	A	SG	- 3 - 2*
		58A	144.00		1	9	A	SG	- 3 - 2*
		58B	159.00		1	9	A	SG	- 3 - 2*
		60D, 61	195.00		1	9	A	SG	- 3 - 2*
		60E	250.00		1	7	D	SG	- 3 - 2*
		62C	159.00						
AMERICAN ETHERPHONE CORP.	1924	Reflex	45.00	T	2	2	S	Rfx	- 1 - 2
	1925	RXS	60.00	T	2	5	S	Rfx	- 1 - 2
		TR-5	60.00	T	2	2	B	Rfx	
		RX-4						Rfx	
AMERICAN INTERSTATE RADIO SER.		Air Service		T	3	5	S	TRF	- 2 - 2
AMERICAN PIANO CO	SEE	Ware Mfg. Co.						
AMERICAN RADIO & RESEARCH	SEE	Amrad						
AMERICAN RADIO CORP.	1924	Super 5 Arc						Rfx	
	1925	#4 Lininger Arc	70.00	T	2		S		
		3A Arc-Lininger	95.00	T	2		S		
		4 Arc-Lininger	120.00	T	2		S		
		Super 5 Arc-Lininger							

MANUFACTURER	YEAR	MODEL NO. & NAME	PRICE	STYLE	D	T	P	CIR. & STAGES
AMERICAN RADIO MFG. CO	1926	American Beauty	55.00		3	5		TRF - 2 - 2
		"			3			TRF - 2 - 2
AMERICAN SALES CO.	1925	Indian	14.90	Por	2			
AMERICAN SPECIALTY CO.	1924	Electrola	125.00		3	5	S	TRF
	1925	24 Electrola	59.50		3	5	S	TRF
		60 "	60.00		3	5	S	TRF
		18 "	80.00		3	5	S	TRF
		40 "	85.00		3	5	S	TRF
		Electrola Standard	100.00	T	3	5	S	TRF - 2 - 2
		Grand		C	3	5	S	TRF - 2 - 2
	1926	30 Republic	59.50		3	5	S	TRF - 2 - 2
AMERICAN STANDARD ELEC. CO.	1924	Amerex						
AMERICAN WIRELESS CORP.	1925		165.00		3	5	S	TRF - 2 - 2
AMPLEX INSTRUMENT LABS.	1925	DX-5	75.00					TRF
		DE-EXER	39.50					TRF
	1926	DE-EXER	65.00					TRF
		Harmosonic						
AMRAD CORP.	1921	Regenerative	57.50	Box	4	3		RegDAA - - - 2
(American Radio & Research Corp.)	1922	"	30.00	T	2	1		Reg
		Shortwave	120.00	2T	3	3		DAA - - 2
		DT Det-Amp		2 Box	1	3		DAA - - 2
	1923		10.00	T				C
			21.50	T				C
			107.00					RF
		35	20.00		2	4	S	TRF - 1 - 2
		2771	40.00					C
		3366	125.00					Rfx
		3380		2 Box	2	4	S	TRF
		3500-1		2 Box	2	4	S	TRF - 1 - 2
		3500-2	25.00					TRF - 1 - 2
		3670-1	47.50		2	4	B	TRF - 1 - 2
		3670-2						
	1924	Inductrole						
		Neut.		3 Box	1	3	B	PT - - - 2
		3590						

25

MANUFACTURER	YEAR	MODEL NO. & NAME	PRICE	STYLE	D	T	P	CIR. & STAGES
AMRAD CORP. (cont)								
	1925	3500-3 Inductrole	100.00	T	2	4	S	TRF - 1 - 2
		3500-4 Cabinette	180.00	C	2	4	S	TRF - 1 - 2
		3500-6 Jewel	285.00	C	2	4	S	TRF - 1 - 3
	1926	T5	85.00	T	2	5	S	Neut. - 1 - 3
		S522	60.00	T	3	5	S	Neut. - 2 - 2
		S522C	90.00	C	3	5	S	Neut. - 2 - 2
		AC5	110.00	T	3	7	A	Neut. - 2 - 2
		AC5C	150.00	C	2	7	A	Neut. - 2 - 2
		AC9	110.00	T	2	9	A	Neut. - 3 - 3
		AC9C	150.00	C	2	9	A	Neut. - 3 - 3
		S733	65.00	T	2	7	S	Neut. - 3 - 3
		S733C	90.00	C	2	7	S	Neut. - 3 - 3
	1927	DC6 Warwick	138.00	T	1	6	S	Neut. - 3 - 2
		DC6C Berwick	195.00	C	1	6	S	Neut. - 3 - 2
		DC7 Windsor	195.00	T	1	7	S	Neut. - 4 - 2
		DC7C Hastings	238.00	C	1	7	S	Neut. - 3 - 2
		AC6 Warwick	295.00	T	1	7	A	Neut. - 3 - 2
		AC6C Berwick	295.00	C	1	8	A	Neut. - 4 - 2
		AC7 Windsor	395.00	T	1	8	A	Neut. - 3 - 2
		AC7C Hastings	295.00	C	1	8	A	Neut. - 3 - 2
	1928	70 Nocturn	295.00	C	1	8	A	Neut. - 3 - 2
		70 Concerto	320.00	C	1	8	A	Neut. - 3 - 2
		70 Sonata	475.00	C	1	8	A	Neut. - 3 - 2
		70 Opera	875.00	**RP**	1	8	A	**SG** - 3 - 2*
	1929	81 Duet	495.00	**RP**	1	8	A	**SG** - 3 - 2*
		81 Aria	198.00	**RP**	1	8	A	**SG** - 3 - 2*
		81 Serenata	245.00	C	1	8	A	**SG** - 3 - 2*
		81 Symphony	295.00	C	1	8	A	**SG** - 3 - 2*
		81 Minuet	158.00	C	1	8	A	**SG** - 3 - 2*
	1930	(See Crosley Radio Corp.)						
AMSCO PRODUCTS INC.	1923	Melco Supreme	140.00	T	3	5	S	TRF - 2 - 2
	1924	Acmedyne	125.00	T	3	4	S	TRF
	1925	MS-24 Melco Supreme	140.00	T	3	5	S	TRF - 2 - 2
		MS-25 " "	150.00	T	3	5	S	TRF - 2 - 2
		MS-5 " "	165.00	T	3	5	S	TRF - 2 - 2
ANDREA, F.A.D. INC.	SEE	F A D ANDREA INC.						
ANDREWS RADIO CO. "DERESNADYNE"	1924	A Deresnadyne		T	3	5	S	TRF - 2 - 2

MANUFACTURER	YEAR	MODEL NO. & NAME	PRICE	STYLE	D	T	P	CIR. & STAGES
ANDREWS RADIO CO. (cont.) "DERESNADYNE"	1925	M Deresnadyne	125.00		3	5	E	TRF - 2 - 2
		Standard Deresnadyne	150.00		3	5	E	TRF - 2 - 2
		DeLuxe "	165.00		3	5	E	TRF - 2 - 2
	1926	AC "	365.00					TRF
		11 "	125.00		3	5	S	TRF - 2 - 2
		DeLuxe "	165.00		3	5	S	TRF - 2 - 2
		111 "	285.00		3	5	A	TRF - 2 - 2
ANGELUS DIV. ELEC. RESEARCH LABS.	SEE	Elec. Research Lab.						
ANYLITE ELEC. CO.	1925	King Cole	80.00		2			TRF - 1 - 3
	1926	4 King Cole	65.00		2			TRF - 1 - 3
		5 " "	80.00		2			TRF - 1 - 4
		6 " "	100.00		1			TRF - 3 - 3
		7 " "	150.00		6	4		TRF - 3 - 4
	1927	6 King Cole	75.00	T	7	5		TRF - 3 - 3
		7 " "	92.50	T	8	6		TRF - 3 - 3
		8 " "	115.00	T	7	7		TRF - 4 - 3
		7 " "	175.00	C	8			TRF - 3 - 3
		8 " "	200.00	C				TRF - 4 - 3
APEX ELEC. MFG. CO.	1925	Super 5	95.00	T	3	5	S	TRF - 2 - 2
		DeLuxe	135.00	CT	3	5	S	TRF - 2 - 2
		Baby Grand	225.00	C	3	5	S	TRF - 2 - 2
	1926	Super 5	80.00		3			TRF
		DeLuxe	135.00		3			TRF
		Baby Grand	225.00		3			TRF
		Apartment Grand	300.00	T	1	8	A	Neut. - 2 - 3
	1927	Lyric	80.00	C	1	9	A	Neut. - 3 - 2
		Milan	135.00	T	1	7	A	Neut. - 4 - 2
		Corsair	170.00	C	1	7	A	Neut. - 4 - 2 *
		Minstrel	225.00	MT	1	7	A	Neut. - 3 - 2
		Troubadour	295.00	C	1	7	A	Neut. - 3 - 2
	1928	36	85.00	C	1	7	A	Neut. - 3 - 2
		136	130.00	C		7	A	Neut. - 3 - 2
		236	165.00	C				Neut. - 3 - 2
		50	75.95	C				Neut. - 3 - 2
		60	89.95	C				Neut. - 3 - 2
		70	129.95	C				Neut. - 3 - 2
	1929	75	129.95	C				Neut. - 3 - 2

MANUFACTURER	YEAR	MODEL NO. & NAME	PRICE	STYLE	D	T	P	CIR.	& STAGES
APPLEBY RADIO CO.	1925	V	135.00	T	2	5	S	TRF	- 2 - 2
		XV	135.00	B	2	5	S	TRF	- 2 - 2
		X	230.00		2	5	S	TRF	- 2 - 2
ARBORPHONE	SEE	Consolidated Radio Corp.							
ARCO ELEC. CORP.	1929	A	69.95	Ch				TRF	- 3 - 2
		B	75.00	Ch				TRF	- 3 - 2
ARGENTITE RADIO CORP.	1926	Argentite							
ARGUS RADIO CORP.	1925	Phono Panel	145.00	T	2	6		TRF	1 2 - 2
		Standard URR	160.00	C	2	6	AD	TRF	1 2 - 2
		235	235.00	C	2	6		TRF	1 2 - 2
		300	300.00		2			TRF	1 2 - 2
	1926	Standard	160.00		2			TRF	1 2 - 2
		235	235.00		2			TRF	1 2 - 2
		300	300.00					TRF	- 3 - 2
	1927	B-125	125.00	T		7	A		- 3 - 2
		B-195	195.00	T		8	A		- 3 - 2
		B-295	295.00	C		8	A		- 3 - 3
		B-395	395.00	C		8	A		- 3 - 3
		A-25	195.00	T					- 3 - 3
		375	295.00						
ARMAC RADIO CO.	1925	V3 Echophone	50.00	T	1	3	S	DAA	- - 2
		F5 "	110.00	T	2	5	S	RF	- 2 - 2
		4	75.00			4		TRF	
ARMLEY RADIO CORP.	1924	Karryadio	60.00	Por	3	6	B	TRF	- 3 - 2
	1925	Karr Yadio	75.00	Por	3	6	B	TRF	- 3 - 2
		Karryadio	75.00	Por	3	6	B	TRF	- 3 - 2
		Carryadio	125.00	Por	3	6	B	TRF	- 3 - 2
		Karr Yadio	195.00	Por	3	6	B	TRF	- 3 - 2
ARROW RADIO LABS. INC.	1926	D-14	60.00	C	2	4		TRF	- 1 - 2
		D-15	70.00	T	2	4		TRF	- 1 - 2
		C-15	110.00		2	4		TRF	- 1 - 2
		F-16	150.00		1	6		TRF	- 2 - 3

MANUFACTURER	YEAR	MODEL NO. & NAME	PRICE	STYLE MT	D 1	T 8	P A	CIR. & STAGES
ARTEE RADIO SALES & MFG. CORP.	1929	Melorad	62.50	T			A	TRF - 2 - 2
ARTHORA				T				
ASTRAL RADIO CORP.	1925	A	67.50	T	3	5	S	TRF - 2 - 2
		B	90.00	T	3	5	S	TRF - 2 - 2
		C	175.00	C	3	5	S	TRF - 2 - 2
		P	215.00	C	3	5	S	TRF - 2 - 2
ATCHISON RADIO MFG. CO.	1930	Mantel	52.00	M	1	7	A	SG - 2 - 2
		Midget 12	64.50	M	1	7	A	SG - 3 - 1
ATLANTIC & PACIFIC RADIO CO.	1924	Neutrodyne	97.50	T	3	5	S	TRF - 2 - 2
	1925	Standard Neutrodyne	65.00	T	3	5	S	TRF - 2 - 2
		Special	29.95	Kit	3	5	S	TRF - 2 - 2
				Kit	3			TRF - 2 - 2
ATLANTIC-PACIFIC RADIO SUPPLY	SEE	Oard						
ATLAS COLONIAL CORP.	1926							
A. AND T. RADIO CO.	1925	Babydyne	10.00	T	1	1	S	D - - - -
ATWATER KENT MFG. CO. (Model 5 was a promotional model. Model 10 was the first pre-wired A-K set sold, in late 1923. Early console cabinets were made by Pooley. There were numerous circuit variations of each model number.)	1921	5	60.00	B	1	5	S	DAAAA - 4
	1922	4052	72.00	B		4	S	
		4066	16.00	B		5	S	
		TA	14.00	Unit		2	S	- 2
		Coupled Cir. Tuner	32.00	Unit	1		S	
	1923	Variometer	10.00	B	1	2	S	DA - 1
		TA	32.00	Unit	1	2	S	DA - 1
		8 Duplex	35.50	B	1	3	S	DAA - 2
		11	23.50	B	1	1	S	D - 1
		Radiodyne	37.50	B	1	3	S	DAA - 2
		10	16.50	Unit	-	3	S	DAA - 2
		15	100.00	B	1	4	S	RF - 1 - 2
	1924	9 (Variometer)	70.00	C	3	5	S	TRF - 2 - 2
		10A	104.00	B	2	3	S	DAA - 2 - 2
		10B	104.00	B	3	5	S	TRF - 1 - 2
		9C (Var. Condenser)	65.00	B	2	4	S	TRF - 1 - 2

```
Model        Part No.
8            4325
9            4445, 4480, 4535, 4660
10           4340, 4490, 4540, 4550,
             4560, 4590, 4600, 4950
10 B         4610, 4650
10 C         4700
12           4620, 4910, 4375
15           4220, (4066)
```

At

MANUFACTURER	YEAR	MODEL NO. & NAME	PRICE	STYLE	D	T	P	CIR. & STAGES
ATWATER KENT MFG. CO. (cont.) Most table models also available in Pooley Cabinets. Some (e.g. 57) available built into tables.		10C	85.00	B	3	5	S	TRF	- 2 - 2
		12	105.00	B	3	6	S	TRF	- 2 - 3
		19	90.00	T	2	4	S	TRF	- 1 - 2
		20	100.00	T	3	5	S	TRF	- 2 - 2
	1925	DeLuxe	120.00	T	3	5	S	TRF	- 2 - 2
		21	80.00	T		5	B	TRF	- 2 - 2
		20C 7960 Compact	80.00	T	3	5	S	TRF	- 2 - 2
		20C 7570 Compact	100.00	T	3	5	S	TRF	- 2 - 2
		24 DeLuxe	70.00	MT	1	6	S	TRF	1 2 - 2
	1926	35, 35A	85.00	T	1	6	S	TRF	1 2 - 2
		30, 30A	140.00	T	1	7	S	TRF	1 3 - 2
	1927	32	90.00	T	1	6	S	TRF	- 3 - 2
		33	125.00	T	1	7	A	TRF	1 2 - 2
		36	88.00	T	1	7	A	TRF	1 3 - 2
		37	125.00	T	1	8	A	TRF	1 2 - 2*
	1928	38	77.00	MT	1	7	D	TRF	1 2 - 2
		40	87.00	MT	1	7	A	TRF	1 2 - 2*
		41	86.00	MT	1	7	A	TRF	1 2 - 2
		42	83.00	T	1	8	A	TRF	1 3 - 2
		43	106.00	MT	1	8	A	TRF	- 3 - 2
		44	49.00	T	1	6	S	TRF	1 3 - 2
		48	68.00	T	1	6	S	TRF	1 3 - 2
		49	150.00	C	1	7	S	PT	1 3 - 2
		50	117.00	MT	1	8	A	TRF	1 2 - 2*
	1929	52	94.00	MT	1	8	A	TRF	1 3 - 2
		45	83.00	MT	1	9	A	TRF	1 2 - 2*
		46	100.00	C	1	8	A	TRF	1 2 - 2
		47	117.00	MT	1	8	A	SG	- 2 - 2*
		53	68.00	T	1	7	A	TRF	1 2 - 2
		55	97.00	T	1	7	A	TRF	1 2 - 2
		56	105.00	C	1	8	D	SG	- 3 - 2*
		57	80.00	C	1	7	B	SG	- 2 - 2
		60	80.00	T	1	7	A	SG	- 3 - 2*
		61	62.00	C	1	9	A	SG	- 3 - 2*
		67	155.00	C	1	7	A	SG	- 3 - 2*
	1930	66	109.00	C	1	8	D	SG	- 3 - 2*
		1055C	121.00	C	1	7	D	SG	- 3 - 2*
		1060C	121.00	C	1	7	S	SG	- 3 - 2*
		1061C	103.00	C	1			SG	
		1067C							

MANUFACTURER	YEAR	MODEL NO. & NAME	PRICE	STYLE	D	T	P	CIR. & STAGES
ATWATER KENT MFG. CO. (cont.)		70, 72	119.00		1	7/8	D/A	SG	- 3 - 2*
		74	125.00		1	7/8	D/A	SG - 3 - 2*
		75 Comb.	195.00		1			SG - 3 - 2
		76	145.00		1	7/8	D/A	SG - 3 - 2*
		67	62.00	T	1	7	S	SG - 3 - 2*
AUDIOLA RADIO CO.	1921	Audiola	10.00	T	1	1	-	C - - - -
	1922	VT	22.50	T		1	B	D - - -
	1923	Audiola	19.00	T		1	B	D
		VT	22.50	T		1	B	D
	1924	Grand	45.00	Por	1	3	S	Rfx - 1 - 2
		Audiodyne	75.00	Por	2	4	E	TRF
		Super	100.00	Por	2	5	E	TRF
		Midget	10.00	Por		1	S	D - - -
	1925	Sealed Five	60.00	T	3	5	E	TRF - 2 - 2
		Big Six	90.00	T	3	6	E	TRF - 3 - 2
	1926	527	70.00	T	2	5	S	TRF - 2 - 2
		627	100.00	T	3	6	S	TRF - 2 - 3
		527C	120.00	C	2	5	S	TRF - 2 - 2
		627C	185.00	C	2	6	S	TRF - 2 - 3
	1927	6T	75.00	T	2	6	S	TRF - 3 - 2*
		8T	125.00	T	1	8	S	TRF - 4 - 2*
		6C	175.00	C	1	6	S	TRF - 3 - 2
		8C	225.00	C	1	8	S	TRF - 4 - 3
		6B	275.00		1	6	S	TRF - 3 - 2
		8B	137.00		1	8	S	TRF - 4 - 3
		6T	95.00	T	1	7	A	TRF - 3 - 2
	1928	829	147.50	MT	1	8	A	TRF - 4 - 2*
		929	85.00	T	1	9	A	SG - 2 - 2*
	1929	7330	95.00	Ch	1	7	A	SG - 3 - 2*
		8430	97.00	Ch	1	8	A	TRF - 3 - 1
	1930	60	107.00		1			SG - 3 - 1
		70	119.00		1	7	A	SG - 3 - 1
		80			1	8	A	SG - 3 - 1
		30			1		A	SG - 2 - 2*
		889			1		A	TRF 1 2 - 2*
AUTOMATIC RADIO MFG. CO.	1925	Bluebird	13.50	Por		1	B	D - - -
	1926	Arc	42.50	T		5		TRF - 2 - 2
		Arc	35.75	T		5	B	TRF - 2 - 2

31

MANUFACTURER	YEAR	MODEL NO. & NAME	PRICE	STYLE	D	T	P	CIR. & STAGES
AUTOMATIC RADIO MFG. (cont)		Arc	37.50	T		6	B	TRF -3-2
		Bluebird	42.50	T		5	B	TRF -2-2
		"	45.00	T		5	B	TRF -2-2
		"	50.00	T		5	B	TRF -2-2
	1927	Hudson	57.50	Ch		6	B	TRF -3-2
	1928	Liberty Bell	35.00	Ch		6	B	TRF -3-2
	1929	B Tom Thumb	57.50	Por	1	4	B	SG -1-2
		B DeLuxe	65.00	Por	1	4	B	SG -1-2
		DC	85.00	Por	1	4	D	SG -1-2
		AC	95.00	Por	1	5	A	SG -2-2
	1930	C Tom Thumb	69.50	M	1	5	s	SG -2-2
		224 Senior	95.00	A	1	6	s	SG -3-2
		Junior	49.50	A	1	6	s	SG -3-2
AUTO INDICATOR CO.	1924	Pocket Radio	27.50	Por	1	1	B	D - - -
	1925	Standard B	23.50	Por	1	3	B	DAA - - 2
		Adaunit	87.50	Por	2			
AUTO METAL PRO.	1926							
AUTOMOBILE RADIO CORP.	1930	109-A Transitone	140.00	Auto			s	TRF - 3 - 2
AUTOPHONE MFG. CO.	1926	Pritchard-Roever	325.00	C	3	6	s	TRF - 3 - 2
BABY GRAND MFG. CO.	1925	Baby Grand	175.00	T	3	5	s	TRF - 2 - 2
B. & H. RADIO PROD.	1926							
BAILEY ENG. CO.	1923	Milo Bailey	130.00					RF
		"	160.00					RF
		"	180.00					RF
	1924	Milo Battery	220.00					RF
								RF
BAILEY & CO.	1927	Musi King		T	2	6	s	TRF - 2 - 3
BAIRD RADIO & MFG. CO	1926							

MANUFACTURER	YEAR	MODEL NO. & NAME	PRICE	STYLE	D	T	P	CIR. & STAGES
BAKER-SMITH CO. INC.	1925	Sylfan	100.00	T	3	5	S	TRF
		"	130.00	T	3	5	S	TRF
		"	60.00	T		2	S	Reg.
		"	80.00	T		3	S	Reg.
	1926	565 Sylfan	90.00	T	3	4	S	TRF
		Slyfan	65.00	T	3	5	S	TRF
BALDWIN INC., NATHANIEL	1929	25	298.00	RP	1	8	A	SG - 3 - 2*
		35	219.00	HB	1	8	A	SG - 3 - 2*
		37	198.00	LB	1	8	A	SG - 3 - 2*
	1930	40	65.00	Por	1	6	AD	SG - 2 - 2
		50 Baldwinette	75.50	M	1	6	A	SG - 2 - 2
		51 "	105.50	M	1	6	A	SG - 2 - 2
		70 Consolette	111.00	LB	1	6	A	SG - 2 - 2
		71 Baldwinette	141.00	LB	1	6	A	SG - 2 - 2
		75 Hydaway	121.00	Por	1	8	A	SG - 3 - 2*
		80						
BALKEIT RADIO CO. (Formerly Pfanstiehl)	1928	A3	197.50	MT	1	8	A	Neut. - 3 - 2*
		A5	230.00	T	1	8	A	Neut. - 3 - 2*
		A7	487.50	C	1	8	A	Neut. - 3 - 2
		B7	475.00	C	1	9	A	Neut. - 3 - 2
		B9	950.00	C	1	9	A	Neut. - 4 - 2*
	1929	C	175.00	C	1	9	A	Neut. - 3 - 2
		F	75.00	Ch	1	8	A	SG - 3 - 2
	1930	Balkeit	125.00	LB	1	7	A	SG - 3 - 1
		SG8 Balkeit	71.00	Ch	1	6	A	SG - 3 - 1
		Midget Balkeit	54.50	M	1	5	A	SG - 2 - 1
BALL SQ. RADIO CO.	1926	BD-5 Baird	80.00	T	2	5	S	TRF - 1 - 3
BALTIMORE HUB-WHEEL & MFG. CO.	1925	Hubco Baby Grand	60.00	Por	3	5	S	TRF - 2 - 2
		Baby Grand DeLuxe	70.00	Por	3	5	S	TRF - 2 - 2
		Hubco Baby Grand	100.00	C	3	5	S	TRF - 2 - 2
		Hubco Super Five	150.00	Por	3	5	S	TRF - 2 - 2
	1926	Baby Grand 100	50.00	T	3	5	E	TRF - 2 - 2
		" 101	60.00	T	3	5	E	TRF - 2 - 2
		" 102 Del	65.00	T	3	5	E	TRF - 2 - 2

MANUFACTURER	YEAR	MODEL NO. & NAME	PRICE	STYLE	D	T	P	CIR. & STAGES
BALTIMORE HUB-WHEEL & MFG. CO. (cont.)		Baby Grand 103	75.00	T	3	5	E	TRF - 2-2
		" 104	100.00	T	3	5	E	TRF - 2-2
		" 105	100.00	C	3	5	E	TRF - 2-2
BANFER PROD. CORP.	1926	Pertone Five						
BARBLEY RADIO CO.	1926							
BARNETT LLOYD CO.	1925	R3	80.00		3	3	S	Rfx
		RX-5	125.00			5	S	TRF
		R-3 (Pooley)	200.00	C	3	3	S	Rfx
		DX-5 (Pooley)	245.00	C		5	S	TRF
BARTY RADIO CO.	1926	Standard	35.00	T	3	5	E	TRF - 2-2
		DeLuxe	37.50	T	3	5	E	TRF - 2-2
		Semi Console	75.00	C	3	5	E	TRF - 2-2
		Standard	100.00	C	3	5	E	TRF - 2-2
	1929	Chelsea	56.00	C	1	7	A	SG - 2-2
BATTERYLESS RADIO CORP.	1925		200.00	T	3	5	A	TRF - 2-2
		NB5 No-Bat-Ry	120.00	T	3	5	D	TRF - 2-2
		NB6 Bat-Ry-Les	140.00	T	3	5	A	TRF - 2-2
	1926		200.00	T	3	5	D	TRF - 2-2
			350.00	C	3	5	AD	TRF - 2-2
BAUGHMAN RADIO ENGINEERING CO.	1924	King Tut		C			-	C - - 1
		2 Tube		Por		2	E	DA - - 1
		Airline		Por		3	E	DAA - - 2
BEACON RADIO MFG. CO.	1925	Trinity Six	50.00	T	3	6	S	TRF - 2-3
	1926	2-T-5	50.00	T	2	5	S	TRF - 2-2
		2-5-61	75.00	T	2	6	S	TRF - 2-3
		2-T-61C	150.00	C	2	6	S	TRF - 2-3
BEAVER ELEC. CORP.	1925	Beavertone	75.00	T	2	5	S	TRF - 2-2
BEAVER MACHINE & TOOL CO.	1925	Baby Grand Crystal	3.00	Box	2	-	-	C - - -
BECHAUD RADIO LABS.	1926	Big Five	120.00	T	2	5	S	Reg.TRF - 1-3
BEN RADIO CORP.	1926	Ben A3	59.00	T	3	5	S	TRF - 2-2

MANUFACTURER	YEAR	MODEL NO. & NAME	PRICE	STYLE	D	T	P	CIR. & STAGES		
BEN RADIO CORP. (cont)										
	1924	Petite	50.00	T	3	5	S	TRF	- 2 - 2	
BENSON ENGINEERING CO.										
	1924	Superflex	65.00	Por	2	1	B	D	- - -	
		"	49.50			2	B	Rfx	- 1 - 1	
	1925	Neuway	63.50	KD		5	B	TRF	- 2 - 2	
		3X Superflex	75.00	Por	2	3	B	Rfx	- 1 - 2	
		4X " Loop	90.00	T	1	4	B	Rfx	- 2 - 2	
		6C	220.00	C	3	6	B	TRF	- 3 - 2	
BERSTAN RADIO PRODUCTS CO.										
	1924	Mysto C	3.00	Box	1	0	-	C	- - -	
BETTA-TONE RADIO CO.										
	1924			Box	2	0	-	C	- - -	
BETTER RADIO PRODUCTS										
	1925	Melody	135.00	C	2	4	S	TRF	- 1 - 2	
		"	39.00	Ch	2	4	S	TRF	- 1 - 2	
		"	51.00	T	2	4	S	TRF	- 1 - 2	
	1926	"	149.00	C	2	4	S	TRF	- 1 - 2	
			125.00			6		TRF		
			145.00			7		TRF		
BETTS & BETTS CORP.										
	1925	T-8 Transcontinental	225.00	T	2	7	E	RF	- 4 - 2	
BILTMORE RADIO CO.										
	1925	IV Master Reflex	100.00	T	3	4	E	Cry.Rfx	- 2 - 2	
		V "	125.00	T	3	5	E	Cry.Rfx	- 4 - 3	
		VC "	185.00	C	3	5	E	Cry.Rfx	- 4 - 3	
		VI "	115.00	T	3	6	E	TRF Rfx	- 3 - 3	
		VIC "	200.00	C	3	6	E	TRF Rfx	- 3 - 3	
		T5 Biltmore Master	68.00	T	3	5	E	TRF	- 2 - 2	
		T5C	160.00	C	3	5	E	TRF	- 2 - 2	
BIRD RADIO CORP.										
	1925	F-1	6.00	Box	2	0	-	C	- - -	
BLAIR RADIO LABS.										
	1925		75.00	T	3	6	S	TRF	- 2 - 3	
			125.00	C	3	6	S	TRF	- 2 - 3	
	1926	Standish	150.00	C	3	6	S	TRF	- 2 - 3	
		11	50.00	C	3	6	S	TRF	- 2 - 3	
		L'Elegante	75.00	T	3	6	S	TRF	- 2 - 3	
			75.00	C	3	6	S	TRF	- 2 - 3	
BLUE SEAL MFG. CO										
	1924 1925	4	70.00	T	2	4	S	TRF	- 1 - 2	

MANUFACTURER	YEAR	MODEL NO. & NAME	PRICE	STYLE	D	T	P	CIR. & STAGES
BLUE SEAL MFG. CO. (cont.)								
	1926	Cincodyne	135.00	T	3	5	S	TRF - 2 - 2
		5	140.00	T	4	5	S	TRF - 2 - 2
		Blue Seal	63.00	T	3	5	S	TRF - 2 - 2
		" "	135.00	T	3	5	S	TRF - 2 - 2
BOISSONNAULT CO. INC., G	1925	Whitestone Big 5	60.00	T	3	5	S	TRF - 2 - 2
	1926	Whitestone	35.00	T	3	5	S	TRF - 2 - 2
		"	35.00	T	3	5	S	TRF - 2 - 2
		" DeLuxe	37.50	T	3	5	S	TRF - 2 - 2
BOLDO RADIO & ELEC. CO.	1923		1.50				-	C - - -
			6.00					C - - -
			10.00			1	B	D - - -
			45.00			1	B	D - - -
	1924					1	B	D & C - - -
	1925	Boldo	10.00			1		D - - -
	1926	"	2.00					C - - -
BOONTON RADIO CORP.	1924	Portable	75.00	Por	1	4	B	DAAA - - 3
BOSCH MAGNETO CORP.	SEE	Am. Bosch Mag. Corp.						
BOSELLI	1926	Boselli Broadcast		C		6		
BOSSERMAN RADIO LAB.	1924	Super Flex	87.50					
		Junior	69.50					
	1925	Super Flex	89.50	CL	2	3		Rfx
		Super-Heterodyne	149.00	T	2	8	B	SH
BOSTON RADIO MFG. CO.	1926	Mastertone	37.50					
		Supertone	39.50					
		Trutone	35.00					
BOSWORTH ELEC. MFG. CO.	1925	B-1 Air Set	155.00	T	3	5	E	TRF - 2 - 2
	1926	B-2	115.00	T	2	5	S	TRF - 2 - 2
		B-1	155.00	T	3	5	S	TRF - 2 - 2
		B-3	155.00	T	2	6	S	TRF - 3 - 2
	1927	B-6	75.00	T	1	5	S	TRF - 2 - 2
		B-3	100.00	T	1	6	S	TRF - 3 - 2

MANUFACTURER	YEAR	MODEL NO. & NAME	PRICE	STYLE	D	T	P	CIR. & STAGES
BOSWORTH ELEC. MFG. CO. (cont.)		B-5	165.00	T	1	6	A	TRF - 2 - 2
		B-7	250.00	C	1	7	A	TRF - 3 - 2
BOWMAN & CO., A.W.	1923	Airphone	20.00			1	S	D - - - -
			25.00			1	S	D - - - -
BRANDEIS ELEC. MFG. CO.	1925		100.00	T	1	5		
			150.00	C	1	5		
			200.00	Grand	1	5		
BRANDEIS CORP., J.F.	1925	Brandola	85.00	T	3	5	S	TRF - 2 - 3
		"	125.00	T	1	6	S	TRF - 2 - 3
BRANDES INC., C.	SEE	Kolster Radio Inc.						
BRANDES PRODUCTS CORP.	SEE	Kolster Radio Inc.						
BRANDOLA	1924	Brandola	125.00	T	1			
BRANSTON INC., CHAS. A.	1924	R310 DeLuxe	92.50			4		RF
		R-95 Superhet		KD				SH - - - 1
		R304 " Wired		Ch				SH
		R306				1		D
		R-55				2		DA - - - -
		Crystal				0		C - - - -
	1925	R45 Hetrola V	55.00	Ch	2	5	S	TRF - 2 - 2
		R46 Hetrola V	75.00	T	2	5	S	TRF - 2 - 2
		R47 Hetrola V	120.00	CT	2	5	S	TRF - 2 - 2
	1926	R45	55.00	Ch	2	5	S	TRF - 2 - 2
		R46	75.00	T	2	5	S	TRF - 2 - 2
		R47	120.00	T	2	5	S	TRF - 2 - 2
BREMER TULLY MFG. CO.	1925	Nameless Parts Only		Kit	3	5		
		6 Counterphase	38.00	Kit	2	6	S	TRF - 2 - 2
		5 "	28.50	Kit	2	6	S	TRF - 3 - 2
	1926	6 "	155.00	T	1	6	S	TRF - 2 - 2
		8 " Power	225.00	T	1	8	S	TRF - 3 - 2
	1927	6-22 Counterphase	41.50	Kit	2	6	S	TRF - 4 - 3
		6-35	140.00	T	1	6	S	TRF - 3 - 2
		6-35	110.00	T	1	6	S	TRF - 3 - 2

MANUFACTURER	YEAR	MODEL NO. & NAME	PRICE	STYLE	D	T	P	CIR. & STAGES
BREMER TULLY MFG. CO. (cont.)		6-37 Counterphase	165.00	C	1	6	S	TRF	- 3 - 2
		8-12 "	215.00	T	1	8	S	TRF	- 4 - 3
		8-16 "	295.00	C	1	8	S	TRF	- 4 - 3
		6-37 "	80.00	C	1	7	A	TRF	- 3 - 2
		8-13 "	285.00	T	1	9	A	TRF	- 4 - 3
		8-16 "	365.00	C	1	9	A	TRF	- 4 - 3
		8-17 "	230.00	C	1	9	A	TRF	- 4 - 3
	1928	6-38 "	130.00	T	1	7	A	TRF	- 3 - 2
		6-40	190.00	C	1	7	A	TRF	- 3 - 2
		6-41	150.00	T	1	7	A	TRF	- 3 - 2*
		7-70	245.00	C	1	8	A	TRF	- 3 - 2*
		7-714	280.00	C	1	8	A	TRF	- 3 - 2*
		7-71D	130.00	T	1	8	A	TRF	- 3 - 2*
		8-20	375.00	C	1	9	A	TRF	- 4 - 2
		8-21	490.00	RP	1	9	A	TRF	- 4 - 2*
		8-22	60.00	C	1	6	S	Neut.	- 3 - 2*
	1929	80	164.00	C	1	8	A	Neut.	- 3 - 2*
		81	195.00	C	1	8	A	Neut.	- 3 - 2*
		82			1	8	A	SG	- 3 - 2*
		81A			1	8	A	SG	- 3 - 2*
		S81	164.00	C	1	9	A	SG	- 3 - 2*
		S82	195.00	C	1	9	A	SG	- 3 - 2*
		83			1	8	A		
BRENDONNE CORP.	1924	DeLuxe						
		Radio Fountain						
BRIGGS & STRATTON	1923	Crystal	12.00	Box		0	-	C	- - - -
BRILLIANTONE RADIO PRODUCTS INC.	1925	Naturelle	85.00		3	6	S	TRF	- 2 - 3
BRISTOL CO., THE	1923	Grimes Inverse Duplex		Box	1	4	S	Rfx	- 2 - 3
	1924	" "	190.00	Box	1	4	S	Rfx	- 2 - 3
BROADCAST MFRS. INC.	1923	Neutrodyne						
BRONX RADIO EQUIP. CO.	1923	Breco	50.00	T		3	S	DAA	- - - 2
	1924	D & 2A	50.00	T	2	3	S	DAA	- - - 2
	1925	BSC-3 Breco	110.00	T	3	4	S	DAAA	- - - 3
		BS-3 "	80.00		3	3	S	DAA	- - - 3
	1926	BR-5	100.00		3	5	S	RF	- 2 - 2

MANUFACTURER	YEAR	MODEL NO. & NAME	PRICE	STYLE	D	T	P	CIR. & STAGES
BRONX RADIO EQUIPMENT CO. (cont.)	1927	12 Breco	120.00	HB		5	S	- 2 - 2
BROOKLYN METAL STAMPING	1923	Pandora	5.00	Box		0		C	- - -
	1924	"		Box		0		C	- - -
	1925	Parts Only						- - -
	1926	Pandora	1.75	Box		0		C	- - -
BROOKLYN RADIO LAB.	1927	B.R.L.Royal 6	62.00	T	1	6	S	TRF	- 2 - 3
		B.R.L.Miniature	65.00	Por		7	B	TRF	- 3 - 3
		B.R.L.Royal 6E	650.00	C		7	A	TRF	- 2 - 3
		B.R.L.Grand 8C	800.00	C		10	A	TRF	- 4 - 4
BROWN & MANHART	1930	44	69.50	M	1	6	A	SG	- 2 - 2
		45	69.50	Por	1	6	A	SG	- 2 - 2
		48	89.50	C	1	6	A	SG	- 2 - 2
		60 Comb.	149.50	Comb.	1	6	A	SG	- 2 - 2
BROWN RADIO CORP.	1925	C-15 Ray-o-dyne	75.00	T	3	5	S	TRF	- 2 - 2
BROWN RADIO MFG. CO.	1925	B-77 Thorobred	110.00	T	3	5	E	TRF	- 2 - 2
		B-88 "	130.00	T	3	5	E	TRF	- 2 - 3
		B-66 "	225.00	C	3	5	E	TRF	- 2 - 3
	1926	B-77 "	115.00	T	3	5	S	TRF	- 2 - 2
		B-88 "	130.00	T	3	6	S	TRF	- 2 - 3
		B-66 "	225.00	C	3	6	S	TRF	- 2 - 3
BROWNING-DRAKE CORP.	1925	B-D	22.00	Kit	2	3	E	Reg.	- - 2
		B-D Standard	130.00	T	2	5	E	Reg.TRF	- 1 - 3
		B-D Junior	95.00	T	2	5	E	Reg.TRF	- 1 - 3
		B-D Senior	185.00	CT	2	5	E	Reg.TRF	- 1 - 3
	1926	5R	95.00	T	2	5	E	Reg.TRF	- 1 - 3
	1927	Official Kit		Kit		5	E		
		5R	95.00	T	2	5	E	Reg.TRF	- 1 - 3
		6A	105.00	T	1	6	S		- 1 - 3
		7A	145.00	T	1	7	S		- 2 - 3
	1928			Kit	1	2		Reg.TRF	
				Kit	1	5		Reg.TRF	
		34 Eight in Line	135.00	T	1	8	A	TRF	12 - 3
		36			1	8	A	TRF	12 - 3
		38			1	8	A	TRF	12 - 3

MANUFACTURER	YEAR	MODEL NO. & NAME	PRICE	STYLE	D	T	P	CIR. & STAGES
BROWNING-DRAKE CORP. (cont.)	1929	53	59.45	Kit	1	9	A	SG - 4 - 2*
		54	102.50	T	1	9	A	SG - 4 - 2*
		56	142.50	C	1	9	A	SG - 4 - 2*
		57	154.50	C	1	9	A	SG - 4 - 2*
		63	188.50	C	1	9	A	SG - 4 - 2*
		64	98.00	T	1	9	A	Reg.TRF - 4 - 2*
		66	137.50	C	1	9	A	Reg.TRF - 4 - 2*
		67	149.50	C	1	9	A	Reg.TRF - 4 - 2*
		83	183.50	C	1	7	A	Reg.TRF - 4 - 2*
		84	75.00	T	1	7	S	SG - 3 - 2*
	1930	68	119.00	C	1	9	S	SG - 3 - 2*
		69	95.00	LB	1	9	A	SG - 4 - 2*
		70	129.00	LB	1	9	A	SG - 3 - 2*
		71	150.00	HB	1	9	A	SG - 3 - 2*
		70R	192.00	LB	1	9	A	SG - 3 - 2*
		71R	229.00	HB	1	9	A	SG - 3 - 2*
		72	262.00	RP	1	9	A	SG - 3 - 2*
BRUNO RADIO CORP.	1923	3	30.00					
		8	25.00					
		10	65.00					
	1924	Powertone	39.50		1	3	S	DAA
	1925	Kit	29.50		1	3	S	DAA
		999	35.00	T	2	3	S	Reg.
	1926	Diamond	60.00	T	2	5	S	Reg.
		Oriole	150.00	T	2	5	S	Reg.
		Nightingale	175.00	T				
BRUNSWICK-BALKE-COLLENDER CO. (Brunswick Radio Corp.-1930)	1924	Radiola III 30		RP	2	2	B	Reg.DA - - 1
		Radiola 3A 35		RP	2	4	B	Reg.DAA - - 2*
		Regenoflex 100		RP	2	4	B	Reg.RDAA 1 - 2*
		Superheterodyne 160		RP	2	6	B	Rfx SH 1 3 2
		" 260		RP	2	6	B	Rfx SH 1 3 2
		" 360		RP	2	6	B	Rfx SH 1 3 2
	1925	60		RP	2	6	B	Rfx SH 1 3 2
		460		RP	2	6	B	Rfx SH 1 3 2
	1926	PR148C		RP	2	8	B	SH 1 2 2
	1927	PR138CPanatrope-Radiola		RP	2	8	B	SH 1 2 2
		Cordova		RP	2	6	B	Rfx SH 1 3 2

BRUNSWICK:
This name first used in 1924 or 1925 on a 5 tube 3 dial TRF receiver with RF transformers and condensers built by King Quality Products Inc. See Schwab Inc., Harold M.

Used RCA Radiola chasses extensively.

MANUFACTURER	YEAR	MODEL NO. & NAME	PRICE	STYLE	D	T	P	CIR. & STAGES
BRUNSWICK-BALKE-COLLENDER CO. (cont.)	1928	Cordova	550.00	RP	2	8	B	SH - 1 2 2
		PR17-8 Radiola 17	115.00	RP	1	7	A	TRF - 3 - 2
		5KR Radiola 18	215.00	T	1	7	A	TRF 1 2 - 2
		5KRO Radiola 18	175.00	LB	2	7	A	TRF 1 2 - 2
		5NO	375.00	T	2	9	A	SH 1 1 2 2
		5NC8	395.00	HB	1	9	A	SH 1 1 2 2
		3KRO Radiola 18	395.00	PR	2	7	A	TRF 1 2 - 2
		3NC8	700.00	HB	2	9	A	SH 1 1 2 2
		148	995.00	RP	1	8	B	SH - 1 2 2
		2KRO Radiola 18	250.00	RP	1	7	A	TRF 1 2 - 2
	1929	3NW8	995.00	RP	1	7	A	TRF 1 2 - 2
		3KR6	345.00	LB	1	7	A	TRF 1 2 - 2
		5KR6	175.00	RP	1	7	A	TRF 1 2 - 2
		2KRO	195.00	RP	1	7	A	TRF 1 2 - 2
		3KRO	295.00	HB	1	7	A	TRF 1 2 - 2
		3KR8	495.00	HB	2	7	A	SH - 1 2
		3NC8	595.00	LB	1	8	A	TRF 1 2 - 2
		R1	107.50	HB	1	8	A	TRF - 3 - 2
		14	148.00	RP	1	8	A	Neut. - 3 - 2
		21	174.00	LB	1	8	A	Neut. - 3 - 2
		31	272.00	HB	1	8	A	Neut. - 3 - 2
		S14	129.00	RP	1	8	A	SG - 3 - 2
		S21	154.00		1	8	A	SG - 3 - 2
		S31	249.00		1	8	A	SG - 3 - 2
		81			1	8	A	Neut. - 3 - 2
		82			1	7	A	SG - 3 - 2
		S81			1	7	A	SG - 3 - 2
		S82			1	8	A	SG - 3 - 2
	1930	15	139.50	LB	1	7	A	SG - 3 - 2
		22	170.00	HB	1	7	A	SG - 3 - 2
		S31	185.00		1	7	A	SG - 3 - 2
		42	480.00	C	1	9	A	SG - 3 - 2
		DC14			1	9	D	Neut. - 3 - 2#
		DC21			1	9	D	Neut. - 3 - 2#
		DC31			1	6	D	Neut. - 3 - 2#
		15B			1	9	B	SG - 3 - 2*
		DC15			1	9	D	SG - 3 - 2#
		DC22			1	9	D	SG - 3 - 2#

MANUFACTURER	YEAR	MODEL NO. & NAME	PRICE	STYLE	D	T	P	CIR. & STAGES
BRUNSWICK-BALKE-COLLENDER CO. (cont.)		DC32		RP			D	SG - 3 - 2#
BRYANT	1922			T	3	3		DAA - - 2
BUCKEYE ELEC. CO.	1925	Reflex Aristocrat	75.00		3	5	E	Rfx - 2 - 2
		DeLuxe "	100.00		3	6	E	Rfx - 2 - 2
	1926	200 Aristocrat	100.00	T	3	5	S	TRF - 2 - 2
		300 "	125.00	T	3	6	S	TRF - 2 - 3
		400 "	150.00	T	3	7	S	TRF - 2 - 4
BUCKINGHAM RADIO CORP.	1925	I	350.00		3	5	S	TRF - 2 - 2
		II			3	5	S	TRF - 2 - 2
		III			3	5	S	TRF - 2 - 2
		IV			3	5	S	TRF - 2 - 2
		V			3	5	S	TRF - 2 - 2
		VI		C	3	5	S	TRF - 2 - 2
		VII		Ch	3	5	S	TRF - 2 - 2
		Jr		T	2	6	A	TRF - 2 - 2
		1		C	1	7	A	TRF - 3 - 2
	1926	2		C	1	7	A	TRF - 3 - 2
	1927	5 Orthophonic		C	1	7	A	TRF - 3 - 2
		18		Ch	1	7	A	TRF - 3 - 2
		20 Orthophonic		C	1	7	A	TRF - 3 - 2
	1928	6950		RP	1	8	A	TRF - 3 - 2*
	1929	1			1	8	A	TRF - 3 - 2*
		2			1	8	A	TRF - 3 - 2*
		3			1	8	A	TRF - 3 - 2*
BUCKWALTER RADIO CORP.	1925	Supertone	150.00	RP	2		S	- - - -
	1926	Burad Supertone	90.00					
		"	150.00					
BUELL MFG. CO.	1925		37.50	Por	1	3	S	Reg. - - - 2
BURT BROS. INC.	1925	2400 (cabinet only)	112.00					
BUSH & LANE PIANO CO.	1926	1	80.00	T	1	6	S	Neut. - 2 - 3
	1927	1-C	102.50	Ch	1	6	S	Neut. - 2 - 3

Bu

MANUFACTURER	YEAR	MODEL NO. & NAME	PRICE	STYLE	D	I	P	CIR. & STAGES
BUSH & LANE PIANO CO. (cont.)		3-C	205.00	C	1	6	S	Neut. - 2 - 3
		4	130.00	T	1	7	S	Neut. - 4 - 2
		4-C	195.00	C	1	7	S	Neut. - 4 - 2
		6	175.00	T	1		A	Neut.
		6-0 Grand	275.00	C	1		A	Neut.
		7	170.00	T	1		A	Neut.
	1928	2	110.00	MT	1		A	Neut.
		4B	149.50	LB	1		A	Neut.
		9C	225.00	HB	1	8	A	Neut. 3 - 3 - 2*
		12C	375.00	RP	1	8	A	Neut. 3 - 3 - 2*
		11C	335.00	LB	1	8	A	Neut. 3 - 3 - 2*
		7C	235.00	HB	1	8	A	Neut. 3 - 3 - 2*
		10C	250.00	C	1	8	A	Neut. 3 - 3 - 2*
		11C	290.00	C	1	8	A	Neut. 3 - 3 - 2*
		12C	297.00	T	1	8	A	Neut. 3 - 3 - 2*
		20	125.00	CL	1	8	A	Neut. 3 - 3 - 2*
	1929	21	169.00	C	1	8	A	Neut. 3 - 3 - 2*
		30	169.00	C	1	8	A	Neut. 3 - 3 - 2*
		32	179.00	C	1	8	A	Neut. 3 - 3 - 2*
		34	189.00	C	1	8	A	Neut. 3 - 3 - 2*
		40	179.00	C	1	8	A	Neut. 3 - 3 - 2*
		50	197.00	C	1	8	A	Neut. 3 - 3 - 2*
		60	199.00	C	1	8	A	Neut. 3 - 3 - 2*
		70	207.00	C	1	8	A	Neut. 3 - 3 - 2*
		90	217.00	C	1	8	A	Neut. 3 - 3 - 2*
		10-C	250.00	C	1	8	A	SG 3 - 3 - 2*
		11-C	290.00	C	1	8	A	SG 3 - 3 - 2*
		12-C	297.00	T	1	8	A	SG 3 - 3 - 2*
		20	125.00	CL	1	8	A	SG 3 - 3 - 2*
		21	169.50	C	1	8	A	SG 3 - 3 - 2*
		30	169.50	C	1	8	A	SG 3 - 3 - 2*
		32	179.50	C	1	8	A	SG 3 - 3 - 2*
		34	187.50	C	1	8	A	SG 3 - 3 - 2*
		40	179.50	C	1	8	A	SG 3 - 3 - 2*
		50	197.50	C	1	8	A	SG 3 - 3 - 2*
		60	199.50	C	1	8	A	SG 3 - 3 - 2*
		70	207.50	C	1	8	A	SG 3 - 3 - 2*
		90	217.50	C	1	8	A	SG 3 - 3 - 2*
	1930	9K DeLuxe	179.50	C	1	8	A	Neut. 3 - 3 - 2*
		10K "	207.50	C	1	8	A	Neut. 3 - 3 - 2*

MANUFACTURER	YEAR	MODEL NO. & NAME	PRICE	STYLE	D	T	P	CIR. & STAGES
BUSH & LANE PIANO CO. (cont.)		11K DeLuxe	227.50	C	1	8	A	Neut. - 3 - 2*
		12K	297.50	C	1	8	A	Neut. - 3 - 2*
		9K	179.50	C	1	8	A	SG - 3 - 2*
		10K	207.50	C	1	8	A	SG - 3 - 2*
		11K	227.50	C	1	8	A	SG - 3 - 2*
		12K	297.50	RP	1	8	A	SG - 3 - 2*
BUTTON, P. H.	1925 1926	D100 Duodyne VT	100.00	T	2	4	E	TRF - 1 - 2
CADILLAC RADIO MFG. CO.	1926	Ampiola						
CALADYNE RADIO CO.	1926	Junior	50.00	T	3	5	S	TRF - 2 - 1
CALIFORNIA RADIO CORP.	1926	Aztec	75.00	T	3	5	S	TRF - 3 - 2
CAMFIELD RADIO MFG. CO.	1926	Duodyne Kit	10.00	T	3	5	S	TRF - 2 - 2
CAPITOL DISTRIBUTING CO.	1924	Songbird ''	95.00 80.00	Panel		5 5	S S	RF RF
CARDINAL RADIO MFG. CO.	1930	70 Comb. 80	99.50 69.50	M-RP M	1 1	6 6	A A	SG - 2 - 2 SG - 2 - 2
CARDINOLA RADIO CORP.	1925 1926	2N 1N 2N	135.00 60.00 90.00	T T CL	1 1 1	5 5 5	S S S	TRF - 2 - 2 TRF - 2 - 2 TRF - 2 - 2
CARDON-PHONOCRAFT CORP., THE	1930	103	520.00	RP	1	11	A	SG - 4 - 2
CARDWELL MFG. CORP., THE ALLEN D.	1922 1924	125A RF	125.00	T	2	3		DAA - - - 2 RF
CARLOYD ELECTRIC & RADIO CO.	1923 1924 1925	Malone Lemon Neut. 11	175.00 95.00	T T	3 3	5 5	S S	Neut. - 2 - 2 Neut. - 2 - 2
		Power Six ML400 Marine	104.00	T T P	2 3 2	5 6 4	S S S	TRF - 1 - 3 TRF - 2 - 3 Neut.
	1926	See "Malone Lemon Products Inc"		T	2	6	B	TRF - 3 - 2

MANUFACTURER	YEAR	MODEL NO. & NAME	PRICE	STYLE B	D	T	P E	D	CIR. & STAGES
CARTER MFG. CO.		Carco							
CARTERET RADIO LAB.	1930	AC	85.00	Ch	1	6	A	SG	- 4 - 1*
		DC	85.00	Ch	1	7	D	SG	- 4 - 2*
		Moto Radio	113.00	A	1	5	S	SG	- 2 - 2
		"	121.00	A	1	5	S	SG	- 2 - 2
		AC-7	59.00	M	1	5	A	SG	- 2 - 1*
		AC-8	65.00	M	1	6	A	SG	- 2 - 2
		DC-8	59.00	M	1	6	D	TRF	- 3 - 2
		DC-HW	65.00	M	1	6	D	SG	- 3 - 1*
CHAMPION RADIO CO.	1926	C-5 Monarch	38.00	T	2	5	S	TRF	- 1 - 2
		B-5 Champion	39.50	T	3	5	S	TRF	- 2 - 2
		B-6	49.50	T	3	5	S	TRF	- 2 - 2
CHAMPION RADIO MFG. CORP.	1930	S-2	59.50	M	1	6	A	SG	- 2 - 2
CHAMPION RADIO PRODUCTS CO.	1924	C		Box			-	C	- - -
CHAPIN CO., CHAS. E.	1927			T	3	5	S	TRF	- 2 - 2
CHELSEA RADIO CORP.	1923	102	40.00	Box	2	1	E	Reg.	- - -
			95.00	T	2	3	E	Reg.	- - 2
		102	225.00						
	1924	102	95.00	T	2	3	E	Reg.	- - 2
	1925	107 Regenodyne	75.00	T	3	5	E	Reg.	- - 2
		Super 5	50.00	T	2	3	E	TRF	- - 2
		122	26.00	T	3	3	S	Reg.	- - 3
		Super 6	60.00	C	3	6	E	TRF	- - 2
		130 Super 5	125.00	T	3	5	S	TRF	- - 2
	1926	Super 5	50.00	T	2	5	E	Reg.	- - 2
		140 Bearcat	26.00	T	3	6	S	TRF	- - 3
		Super 6	60.00	T	3	6	S	TRF	- - 3
		Truphonic Six	125.00	T	2	7	S	Reg.TRF	- 3 - 3
		DeLuxe	95.00	T	3	6	S	TRF	- 2 - 3
	1927	122		T	2	7	S	Reg.TRF	- 3 - 3
		Super Six	60.00	T	3	6	S	TRF	- 2 - 3
CHERINGTON RADIO LABS.	1925	Crystal	2.50				-	C	- - -
CHICAGO NIPPLE MFG. CO.	1926	Blue Ribbon							

MANUFACTURER	YEAR	MODEL NO. & NAME	PRICE	STYLE	D	T	P	CIR. & STAGES
CHICAGO RADIO LAB.	SEE	Zenith						
CHIEFTAIN RADIO CORP.	1925		135.00	T	1	5	B	TRF - 2 - 2
CHISHOLM BARFIELD CORP.	1925	The Radio Knight	55.00	T	3	5	S	TRF - 2 - 2
CHRISTENSEN PHONO CO. INC.	1923	Ech-O-Nola						
	1924	Console Grand						
CLAPP-EASTHAM CO.	1920	ZRF-ZRD-ZRA	68.00	Ch	3	2		D - - 1
	1921	ZRV	38.00	Ch	3	1		Reg. - - 1
	1922	RZ Radak		T	3	2		Reg. - - 2
		HR Radak	40.00	T	2	1	B	D - - 2
	1923	HR and HZ (Radak)	80.00	2T	2	3	B	DAA - 1 - 1
		R23 and A23	100.00	2T	3	3	B	DA - 1 - 2
		C3	100.00	T	3	3	B	DAA - 1 - 2
		C23	125.00	T	3	4	B	RDAA - 1 - 2
		R4 Radak	25.00	Box	1	1	B	D - - -
		R4 and A4	50.00	Boxes	3	3	B	DAA - - 2
		C64	220.00	T	3	5	E	TRF - 2 - 2
		R43 Radak		T	2	1	B	Reg. - - ,
	1924	R4	25.00	Box	1	1	B	D - - -
		R4 and A4	50.00	Boxes	3	3	B	DAA - - 2
		C64	220.00	T	2	5	E	TRF - 2 - 2
	1925	DD	34.00	T	2	3	E	Reg. - - 2
		DD	38.00	T	2	3	E	Reg. - - 2
		Gold Seal	75.00	T	2	5	E	Reg.RF - 1 - 3
CLEARTONE RADIO DIVISION	1923	2 Goldcrest (20)	40.00			2		Rfx - 1 - 2
		3 " (30)	55.00			3		Rfx - 1 - 2
		RFAA 60 Goldcrest	60.00		1	4		TRF - 1 - 2
		31 Goldcrest	70.00			3		Rfx - 1 - 2
		4 " (40)	75.00	T		4		Rfx - 3 - 2
		41	90.00			3		Rfx - 1 - 2
		32	115.00			4		TRF - 1 - 2
		62	120.00	C	1	4	E	Rfx - 3 - 2
		42	135.00	C		4		Rfx - 1 - 2
	1924	60	60.00		1	4	E	TRF - 1 - 2
		61	75.00		1	4	E	TRF - 1 - 2

MANUFACTURER	YEAR	MODEL NO. & NAME	PRICE	STYLE	D	T	P	CIR. & STAGES
CLEARTONE RADIO DIVISION (cont.)		70 Clearodyne	75.00	C	1	4	S	TRF - 1 - 2
		71 "	90.00	Por	1	4	S	TRF - 1 - 2
	1925	72 "	135.00	C	1	4	S	TRF - 1 - 2
		80 Super Clearodyne	120.00	T	2	5	S	TRF - 2 - 2
		82	190.00	T	2	5	S	TRF - 2 - 2
		90	185.00	C	2	7	D	TRF 3 1 - 2
		91	200.00	T	2	7	D	TRF - 2 - 2
		Console	275.00	C	2	7	D	TRF 3 1 - 2
		Series 100	200.00	T	3	5	E	TRF - 2 - 2
	1926	Standard 110	145.00	T	1	6	A	TRF - 2 - 2
	1927	Standard 110	165.00	T	1	6	A	TRF - 2 - 2
		Compact 110	180.00	T	1	6	A	TRF - 2 - 2
		Standard 110T	200.00	T	1	6	A	TRF - 2 - 2
		Mayflower Compact	270.00	C	1	6	A	TRF - 2 - 2
		Standard 110C	295.00	C	1	6	A	TRF - 2 - 2
		Senator Console	345.00	C	1	6	A	TRF - 2 - 2
		Congressional	325.00	C	1	6	A	TRF - 2 - 2
		Senator	325.00	C	1	6	A	TRF - 2 - 2
	1928	"	85.00	T	1	7	A	TRF - 3 - 2
	1929	112	135.00	HB	1	7	A	TRF - 3 - 2
	1930	112	162.50	HB	1	7	A	TRF - 3 - 2
CLEARTONE RADIO SUPPLY CO.	1925	Perfect	7.50	Box	1			C - - - -
CLEMENTS & SON, G. E.	1926							
CLEVELAND AUTO ACCESSORIES CO.	1925	Supertone Five	100.00	T	3	5	S	TRF - 2 - 2
CLEVELAND PRODUCTS CO.	1924 / 1925	A-5	120.00	T	3	5	E	TRF - 2 - 2
CLOVER-LEAF MFG. CO.	1926	Wow						C - - - -
COCKADAY	SEE	Silver-Marshall Inc.						
COLBURN RADIO LABORATORIES	1924	Baby Grnad		C				
COLONIAL RADIO CORP.	1925	16	200.00		3	5	B	TRF - 2 - 2
		16-5	125.00		3	5	S	TRF - 2 - 2

MANUFACTURER	YEAR	MODEL NO. & NAME	PRICE	STYLE	D	T	P	CIR. & STAGES
COLONIAL RADIO CORP. (cont.)		16-6	175.00	T	3	6	B	TRF - 3 - 2 2
		17	85.00		3	4	B	TRF - 1 - 2 2
		17-5	58.00	T	2	5	B	TRF - 2 - 2 2
		20-6	175.00		3	6	B	TRF - 3 - 2 2
		21-5	87.50	C	5	3	S	TRF - 2 - 2 2
		23-5	85.00					
	1926	24-5	85.00	Por				
	1927	25				6	S	TRF - 2 - 3
	1928	26				6	D	TRF - 2 - 2
	1929	28 AC	147.50	T	1	6	A	TRF - 2 - 2
		28 DC	167.50	T	1	5	D	TRF - 2 - 2*
		31 AC	268.00	C	1	7	A	TRF - 2 - 2*
		31 DC	268.00	C	1	7	D	TRF 1 2 - 2*
		32 Cavalier AC	268.00	C	1	8	A	SG - 4 - 1
		32 Picadilly AC	268.00	C	1	8	A	SG - 4 - 1
		32 Moderne AC	270.00	C	1	8	A	SG - 4 - 1
		32 Cavalier DC	268.00	C	1	7	D	SG - 4 - 1
		32 Picadilly DC	268.00	C	1	7	D	SG - 4 - 1
	1930	32 Moderne DC	270.00	C	1	7	D	SG - 4 - 1
		33 Princess AC	129.50	LB	1	7	A	SG - 2 - 2*
		33 Mayflower AC	139.50	HB	1	7	A	SG - 2 - 2*
		33 Windsor AC	149.50	LB	1	6	D	SG - 2 - 2*
		33 Princess AC	129.50	HB	1	6	D	SG - 2 - 2*
		33 Mayflower DC	139.50	HB	1	6	A	SG - 2 - 2*
		33 Windsor DC	149.50	HB	1	7	D	SG - 2 - 2*
		34 Lafayette AC	225.00	HB	1	6	A	SG - 2 - 2*
		34 Lafayette DC	225.00	HB	1	7	D	SG - 2 - 2*
COLUMBIA PHONOGRAPH CO.	1927	900 Amp	475.00	LB	-	5	A	AA
	1928	960	600.00	RP	1	7	A	TRF - 3 - 2
		C1, C9	140.00	T	1	8	A	TRF - 4 - 2
		C2	160.00	T	1	7	A	TRF - 3 - 2
		C3	200.00	HB	1	8	A	TRF - 4 - 2
		C4	285.00	HB	1	9	A	TRF - 4 - 2
		C5	350.00	HB	1	6	D	TRF - 3 - 2
		C6	140.00	T	1	6	D	TRF - 3 - 2
		C7	200.00	HB	1	7	A	TRF - 3 - 2
	1929	950	450.00	Desk	1	8	A	TRF - 3 - 2
		961	600.00	RP	1	8	A	TRF - 4 - 2
		940	297.50	RP	1	8	A	TRF - 4 - *

MANUFACTURER	YEAR	MODEL NO. & NAME	PRICE	STYLE	D	T	P	CIR. & STAGES
COLUMBIA PHONOGRAPH CO. (cont.)	1930	C111	155.00	HB	1		A	TRF - 4 - *
		C11	145.00	HB	1		A	TRF
		C20 Telefocal	185.00	LB	1		A	TRF
		C21 "	235.00	HB	1		A	SG
		939 "	325.00	RP	1	8	A	TRF
		991	900.00	RP	1		A	TRF
		981			1	12	A	TRF
COLUMBIA PRINT, THE (Radio Div.)	1926	BST-6	40.00	T	3	6	E	TRF - 2 - 3
		BST-5	40.00	T	3	5	E	TRF - 2 - 2
COLUMBIA RADIO CO.	1921	Columbia	55.00	T	0	3		DAA - - - 2
COMMERCE CO.	1919	Radiophone		B	0	0		C - - - -
COMO APPARATUS CO.	1924	Como	125.00	Kit	2	9	E	SH - - 3 3
CONCERT RADIO PHONE CO.	1925	Jr. Concert	3.50	Box	1		-	C - - -
		Sr. "	75.00	Por	2	3	B	NonReg. - - - 2
		Grand "	120.00	T	3	5	S	TRF - 2 - 2
		Concert Monotube	12.50	T	3	1	E	Reg. - - -
		" Tritube	35.00	T	3	3	E	Reg. - - - 2
		DeLuxe	75.00	T	3	5	S	TRF - 2 - 2
		Concert Grand	50.00	T	3	5	S	TRF - 2 - 2
		" Supreme	190.00	T	2	5	S	TRF - 2 - 2
CONNECTICUT TEL. & ELEC. CO.	1923	Connecticut		Box	1	3		DAA - - - 2
CONSCO ELECTRIC CO.	1925	5-60 Gold Medal	60.00	T	3	5	S	TRF - 2 - 2
CONSOLIDATED BATTERY CO.	1926	Consol	95.00	T	2	7	S	TRF - 3 - 2
CONSOLIDATED RADIO CORP. (Machine Specialty Co.) "Precision Products"	1923	Arborphone	90.00	T	3	5	S	TRF - 2 - 2
	1925	26-5 Arborphone	55.00	T	3	5	S	TRF - 2 - 2
	1926	Arborphone	165.00	HB	3	5	S	TRF - 2 - 2
		"	55.00	T	3	5	S	TRF - 2 - 2
	1927	27 Arborphone	60.00	T	2	5		TRF - 2 - 2
		271	65.00	C	1	5	B	TRF - 2 - 2
		272	99.50	C	1	5	B	TRF - 2 - 2
			125.00		1	5	B	TRF - 2 - 2

MANUFACTURER	YEAR	MODEL NO. & NAME	PRICE	STYLE	D	T	P	CIR.	STAGES
CONSOLIDATED RADIO CORP. (cont.)		25	125.00	T	1	6	B	TRF	- 3 - 2
		252	185.00	T	1	6	B	TRF	- 3 - 2
		253	250.00	T	1	6	B	TRF	- 3 - 2
		255	600.00	T	1	6	B	TRF	- 3 - 2
	1928	45	75.00	T	1	7		TRF	- 3 - 3
		55	185.00	T	1			TRF	- 4 - 3
		45	75.00	T	1		B		
CONSUMERS RADIO CO.	1927	Con-Rad	34.75	T	1	6	S	TRF	- 2 - 3
	1928	Super Six	66.66	T	1	6	S	TRF	- 2 - 3
		Con-Rad	34.75	T	1	6	S	TRF	- 2 - 3
		Super Six	66.66	T	1	6	S	TRF	- 2 - 3
CONTINENTAL RADIO & MFG. CO.	1923	BR	55.00						
	1924	BRA	90.00						
		BRA	90.00						
		Cell	100.00						
		C-22	65.00						
		C-One-Thirty-Three	150.00						
	1925	Continental Five	100.00	T	3	5	E	TRF	- 2 - 2
CONTINENTAL RADIO CORP.	1929	R-20 Star-Raider	435.00	C	1	11	A	TRF	3 3 - 1*
		R-25 "	475.00	C	1	11	A	TRF	3 3 - 1*
		R-30 "	525.00	C	1	11	A	TRF	3 3 - 1*
		R-105 "	1600.00	C	1	11	A	TRF	3 3 - 1*
		RP40				11	A	TRF	3 3 - 1*
CO-OPERATIVE SALES CO.	1924	Voisometer	55.00			2			
		"	75.00			3			
COSMOPOLITAN PHUSIFORMER CO.	1924				3			RF	
	1925	Five	59.00		3	5	E	TRF	- 2 - 2
			66.00				E	TRF	- 2 - 2
COSRADIO INC.	1920	Short Wave	45.00		4	1		Reg.	- - -
CRAIN BROS. RADIO SHOPPE	1925	X Aeriola	12.00					C	- - - -
	1926	Crain Craft Jr.	12.00					C	- - - -
CRESCENT RADIO MFG. CO.	1926	C-5 Crescentyne	75.00	T	2	5	E	TRF	- 2 - 2

MANUFACTURER	YEAR	MODEL NO. & NAME	PRICE	STYLE	D	T	P	CIR. & STAGES
CRESCENT RADIO MFG. CO. (cont.)	1927	C-6 Crescentyne	80.00	T	2	6	E	TRF - 2 - 3
		E-5 "	90.00	T	2	5	E	TRF - 2 - 2
		E-6 "	95.00	T	2	6	E	TRF - 2 - 3
		M-6	65.00	T	1	5	S	TRF - 2 - 3
		C-6	80.00	T	1	5	S	TRF - 2 - 3
		K-6	90.00	C	1	5	S	TRF - 2 - 3
		K-16	150.00	C	1	5	S	TRF - 2 - 3
		M-28	190.00	C	1	5	S	TRF - 2 - 3
		K-28	200.00	C	1	5	S	TRF - 2 - 3
CROSLEY MFG. CO.	SEE	Crosley Radio Corp.						
CROSLEY RADIO CORP. Precision Equipment Co. (ACE) was controlled by Powell Crosley and was brought into Crosley Radio Corp. in 1924. AMRAD was brought into the Crosley line by 1930.	1921	Harko	7.00	T	0	0	-	C - - -
	1922	Ace AVC	56.00	Box 2	3	1	-	Reg. - - -
		C.R.No-1	25.00	Box	1	0	-	C - - -
		RFTA Amp.	15.00	Box	1	1	B	RFA - - -
		Audion Det	7.50	Box	0	2	B	D - - -
		Two-Step Amp	25.00	Box	0	2	B	AA - - -
		Harko Sr.	14.00	T	1	1	B	D - - -
		Harko Sr. Audio	20.00	T	1	1	E	D - 1 -
		Harko Sr. V	30.00	T	2	2	E	TRF - 1 -
		Crosley VI	50.00	T	2	2	B	Reg. - 1 -
		AceTru Concert Receptor	14.00	T	1	1	S	Reg. - 1 -
		Ace	18.00	T	2	2	S	TRF - 1 - 2
		IV	55.00	T	2	4	S	TRF - 1 - 2
		X	70.00	T	2	4	S	TRF - 1 - 2
		XV (X with speaker)	100.00	C	2	4		TRF - 1 - 2
	1923	XX (Console X)	35.00	T	1	1	S	Reg. - 1 -
		Ace TRU	50.00	T	3	3	E	Reg. - 1 -
		3B Ace	125.00	T	1	1	E	Reg. - 1 -
		3C "	20.00	T	1	1	E	Reg. - 1 -
		V "	25.00	T	1	1	E	Reg. - 1 -
		V Special	20.00	T	1	2	E	Reg. - 1 -
		VC	38.00	T	2	2	S	Reg. - 1 - 2
		VC and 2A Ace	28.00	Por	2	2	B	TRF - 1 -
		VI	40.00	T	2	3	S	TRF - 1 - 1
		VI Portable	48.00	Por	3	3	B	TRF - 1 - 1
		VIII	60.00	T	2	4	E	TRF - 1 - 2
		VIII Portable	65.00	T	2	3	S	TRF - 1 - 1
		XJ Super, XL						
		XII	65.00					

MANUFACTURER	YEAR	MODEL NO. & NAME	PRICE	STYLE	D	T	P	CIR. & STAGES
CROSLEY RADIO CORP. (cont.)	1924	XXV	150.00	C	2	4	S	TRF - 1 - 2
		Ace 3C	125.00	T	1	3	E	Reg. - - -
		Super VI	30.00	T	2	2	S	TRF - 1 - -
		Super XJ, XL	65.00	T	2	4	E	TRF - 1 - 2
		XL	140.00	T	2	4	E	TRF - 1 - 2
		50	14.50	T	1	1	E	Reg. - - -
		50 and 50A amp.	32.50	Boxes	1	3	E	Reg. - - 2
		50P	18.50	Por	1	1	E	Reg. - - -
		51	18.50	T	1	2	E	Reg. - - 1
		51 and 51A amp.	32.50	Boxes	1	3	E	Reg. - - 2
		51P	25.00	Por	1	2	E	Reg. - - 1
		51S	23.50	T	1	2	E	Reg. - - 1
		51SD Special DeLuxe	23.50	T	1	2	E	Reg. - - 1
		52	30.00	T	1	2	E	Reg. - - 2
		52P	35.00	Por	1	3	E	Reg. - - 2
		52S	35.00	T	1	3	E	Reg. - - 2
		52SD Special DeLuxe	37.50	T	1	3	E	Reg. - - 2
		Trirdyn 3R3 Panel	50.00	T	2	3	E	Rfx Reg. - 1 - 2
		" " Stand,	65.00	T	2	3	E	Rfx Reg. - 1 - 2
		" " Special	75.00	T	2	3	E	Rfx Reg. - 1 - 2
		" " Panel	75.00	T	2	3	E	Rfx Reg. - 1 - 2
		" " Newport	110.00	T	2	3	E	Rfx Reg. - 1 - 2
		" " Biltmore	110.00	T	2	3	E	Rfx Reg. - 1 - 2
		" " Super	50.00	T	2	3	E	Rfx Reg. - 1 - 2
	1925	Pup	9.75	M Box	1	1	B	Reg. - - , 2
		Super-Trirdyn Regular	50.00	T	2	3		Rfx Reg. - 1 - 2
		" " Special	60.00	T	2	3		Rfx Reg. - 1 - 2
		" " DeLuxe	112.50	C	2	4		Rfx Reg. - 1 - 2
	1926	4-29	29.00	Por	2	4	S	Reg.TRF - 1 - 2
		4-29P	32.00	T	3	5	S	Reg.TRF - 2 - 2
		5-38	38.00	T	1	5	S	Reg.TRF - 2 - 2
		5-50	50.00	C	1	5	S	Reg.TRF - 2 - 2
		5-75	75.00	C	1	5	S	Reg.TRF - 2 - 2
		5-90	90.00	C	3	5	S	RFL - 2 - 2
		RFL60	60.00	T	3	5	S	RFL - 2 - 2
		RFL75	75.00	C	2	6	S	RFL - 3 - 2
	1927	RFL90	90.00	C	1	6	S	Reg.TRF 12 - 2
		6-60	60.00	C	1	6	S	Reg.TRF 12 - 2
		6-85	85.00	C	1	6	S	Reg.TRF 12 - 2

MANUFACTURER	YEAR	MODEL NO. & NAME	PRICE	STYLE	D	T	P	CIR. & STAGES
CROSLEY RADIO CORP. (cont.)								
	1928	AC7 (Balanced Input)	120.00	T	1	7	A	Reg.TRF - 2 - 2
		AC7C (" ")	145.00	T	1	7	A	Reg.TRF - 2 - 2
		Bandbox 601	55.00	MT	1	6	S	Neut. - 3 - 2
		" 602	125.00	MT	1	7	A	Neut. - 3 - 2
		Bandbox Jr. 401	35.00	MT	1	4	B	Neut. - 1 - 2
		" 401A	35.00	MT	1	5	B	Neut. - 2 - 2
		Gembox 608	65.00	MT	1	6	A	Neut. - 2 - 2
		Gemchest 609	94.00	MC	1	7	A	Neut. - 2 - 2
		" 610	65.00	MT	1	7	A	Neut. 1 2 - 2
		Jewelbox 704	95.00	MT	1	7	A	Neut. 1 2 - 2
		" 704A	95.00	MT	1	8	A	Neut. 1 2 - 2
		" 704B	95.00	MT	1	8	D	Neut. 1 2 - 2*
		Showbox 705	85.00	MT	1	8	A	Neut. 1 2 - 2*
		" 706	80.00	MT	1	8	A	Neut. 1 2 - 2*
	1929	708 Showchest	109.00	MC	1	8	A	Neut. 1 2 - 2*
		804 Jewelbox	105.00	MT	1	8	A	Neut. - 3 - 2
		20	44.00	Ch	1	6	S	SG - 3 - 2
		21	49.00	MT	1	6	S	SG - 3 - 2
		22	88.50	C	1	7	S	SG - 3 - 2
		30	50.00	Ch	1	7	A	Neut. - 3 - 2
		31	55.00	MT	1	7	S	Neut. - 3 - 2*
		32	95.50	C	1	8	A	Neut. - 3 - 2*
		40	65.00	Ch	1	8	A	Neut. - 3 - 2*
		41	70.00	MT	1	8	A	Neut. - 3 - 2*
		41A	70.00	MT	1	8	A	Neut. - 3 - 2*
		42	125.00	C	1	9	A	Neut. - 4 - 2
		60	80.00	Ch	1	8	D	Neut. - 4 - 2*
		61	85.00	MT	1	8	D	Neut. - 4 - 2*
		62	135.00	C	1	8	D	Neut. - 3 - 2*
		82	150.00	C	1	8	D	Neut. - 4 - 2*
		83	155.00	C	1	8	A	Neut. - 4 - 3
		30S Monotrad	62.00	Ch	1	7	A	SG - 2 - 2*
		31S	67.00	MT	1	7	A	SG - 2 - 2*
		33S	115.00	C	1	7	A	SG - 2 - 2*
		34S	125.00	C	1	8	A	SG - 2 - 2*
		40S Unitrad	80.00	Ch	1	8	A	SG - 3 - 2*
		41S	85.00	MT	1	8	A	SG - 3 - 2*
		42S	140.00	C	1	8	A	SG - 3 - 2*
		45S			1	8	A	SG - 3 - 2*
		82S	160.00	C	1	8	A	SG - 3 - 2*

MANUFACTURER	YEAR	MODEL NO. & NAME	PRICE	STYLE	D	T	P	CIR.	& STAGES
CROSLEY RADIO CORP. (cont.)		60S	80.00	Ch	1	8	D	SG	- 3 - 2*
		61S	85.00	MT	1	8	D	SG	- 3 - 2*
		62S	135.00	C	1	8	D	SG	- 3 - 2*
		63S		C	1	8	D	SG	- 3 - 2*
(including AMRAD)	1930	Chum	75.00	C	1	6	A	SG	- 2 - 1*
		Playmate	90.00	C	1	7	A	SG	- 2 - 2*
		Comrade	105.00	C	1	8	A	SG	- 2 - 2*
		Buddy	55.00	MT	1	6	A	SG	- 2 - 1*
		26H		MT	1	7	s	SG	- 3 - 2*
		Crony 26J	112.00	C	1	7	s	SG	- 3 - 2*
		Partner 26K	118.00	C	1	7	s	SG	- 3 - 2*
		Mate 53E		C	1	5	A	SG	- 2 - 1
		Pal 53F	69.50	C	1	5	A	SG	- 2 - 1
		Wood's Desk 53M		Desk C	1	5	D	SG	- 2 - 1
		New Buddy 54G	64.50	Mantle	1	6	A	SG	- 2 - 2*
		Director 76A	107.50		1	7	D	SG	- 2 - 2*
		" 77A	107.50	RP	1	7	A	SG	- 2 - 2*
		Arbiter 77B	137.50	C	1	8	A	SG	- 2 - 2*
		Rondeau 84C	150.00	RP C	1	8	A	SG	- 3 - 2*
		Sondo 84D	240.00	M. Case	1	5	s	SG	- 3 - 2
		Roamio 90	75.00	Mldd	1	5	s	SG	- 2 - 2
		Buddy Boy	59.50	C	1	5	A	SG	- 2 - 2
		Classmate	85.50	C	1	7	A	SG	- 2 - 2*
		Administrator	112.50		1	7	A	SG	- 2 - 2*
CROUCH WILSON CO.		K CLAR-A-DYNE	75.00		3		S		- 2 - 2
CRUVER MFG. CO	1923	Proudfoot	45.00						- - - 2
			45.00						
			35.00						- - - 1
CUMMINGS RADIO CORP.	1928	Solodyne	12.50		1	1	B	D	- - - -
CURRY & COUTILLIER LABS.	1923	Radio Argentite						C	- - - -
	1924	Rfx						Rfx	- - - -
CUTTING & WASHINGTON RADIO CORP.	1922	11A	85.00	T	3	3		Reg.	- - - 2
		12		T	2	1		Reg.	- - - -
	1923	C & W	55.00					Reg.	- - - -

MANUFACTURER	YEAR	MODEL NO. & NAME	PRICE	STYLE	D	T	P	CIR. & STAGES
CUTTING & WASHINGTON RADIO CORP. (cont.)		C & W	97.50					Reg.
		C & W	135.00					Reg.
		C & W	285.00					Reg.
	1924	C & W	325.00	C	2	4	S	Reg.
DANZIGER - JONES INC.	1924	Telos Kit		Kit	4	6	E	TRFRfx - 3 - 3
	1925	Telemonic Three		T	4	6	S	TRFRfx - 3 - 2
DAVEN RADIO CO.	1923		350.00					
	1924	Tubes etc. Only.						
	1925	" "						
	1926	" "						
	1927	Bass Note " "	150.00	T	2	6	S	TRF - 2 - 3
			68.50	Kit	2	6	S	TRF - 2 - 3
DAVIDSON RADIO CORP.	1923	2-R5	125.00					RF
	1924	2-R5	125.00					RF
DAVISON-HAYNES MFG. CO.	1930	69A	69.50	M				- 2 - 1
DAVIS PHONOGRAPH & RADIO CORP.	1926							
DAVIS RADIO CO.	1923		160.00					
	1924							
DAY FAN ELECTRIC CO.	SEE	Gen. Motors Radio Corp.						
DAYTON FAN & MOTOR CO., THE	SEE	Gen. Motors Radio Corp.						
DEEM RADIO PROD. CORP.	1926							
DeFOREST RADIO CO. (also Radio-Craft Co. Inc.)	1919	Fifteen Panel	160.00	T	2	3		DAA - - 2
	1920	T200-P300	160.00	2T	2	2		DA - - 1
		Radio-Craft SW-LW	1450.00	T	4			Reg.
	1921	" " SW	65.00	T				Reg.
		Interpanel	125.00	T	2	3		DAA - - 2
		MS-1 Interpanel (Incl Transmitter)	189.25	T	2	3	E	DA - - 1
	1922	Radiohome (DT700)	36.00	Box	2	1	B	D - - -
		D6 Radiocraft Radio-phone		T	2	3	S	Reg.
		DT600 Everyman Radio-phone	25.00	Box			-	C - - -
		MC 1,2, MR 4,5,6 MP 400						
		DT800						

De

MANUFACTURER	YEAR	MODEL NO. & NAME	PRICE	STYLE	D	T	P	CIR. & STAGES
DeFOREST RADIO CO. (cont.)	1923	D7 Reflex Radiophone	175.00	T	2	3	S	Rfx.C - 3 - 2
		Everyman	31.50	Box	2	-	.	C - . - .
		MR6	112.00			3		
		D4 Radiophone			2	1	S	D - . - 2
		D4 and D5 Radiophone	150.00	Boxes	2	3	S	DAA - . - 2
		D10	20.00	T	1	4	S	Rfx TRF - 3 - 3
		DT600	169.50	T		4		C - . - .
	1924	D12	184.50	T	2	4	S	Rfx TRF - 3 - 2
		D12	371.50	T	2	4	S	Rfx TRF - 3 - 2
	1925	D14	190.00	T	2	5	E	Rfx TRF - 3 - 2
		D17	200.00	T	2	5	E	Rfx TRF - 3 - 3
		D17	125.00	T	2	5	E	Rfx TRF - 3 - 2
		D17A	130.00	Por	3	5	E	TRF - 2 - 2
		F5	90.00	T	3	5	E	TRF - 2 - 2
		F5AW	110.00	T	3	5	E	TRF - 2 - 2
		F5M	450.00	C	1	6	S	
		W6F Renaissance	385.00	T	1	6	S	
		W6T	235.00	C				
		W5F	85.00	T	3	5	E	TRF - 2 - 2
		F5	90.00	T	3	5	E	TRF - 2 - 2
		F5						
	1926	Tubes only.						
	1927	"						
	1928	"						
	1929	"						
	1930	Short Wave CS5	75.00	T	1	4	S	SG TRF - 1 - 2
DEITRICKSON RADIO CO. INC.	1923	Simplex	8.50					C - . - .
		DeLuxe	15.00					C - . - .
	1924		10.00			1		
			16.00			2		
			60.00			5		
	1925	2-R-3	12.00	Box	2	1	B	Reg.
		2-R-4	16.00	Box	2	2	B	Reg.
		5-RF	40.00	T	2	5	S	TRF - 2 - 2
		Duo 5	85.00	T	2	5	S	TRF - 2 - 2
DELANCEY, FELCH & CO.	1923	Delfelco	20.00					
DELCO RADIO CORP. (later part of General Motors)	1930	3003 "Automotive"	175.00	A	1	5	S	SG - 2 - 2
DELCO-REMY DIVISION, GEN'L MOTORS CORP	1929	Cadillac LaSalle	165.00	A	1	5	S	SG - 2 - 2

MANUFACTURER	YEAR	MODEL NO. & NAME	PRICE	STYLE	D	T	P	CIR. & STAGES
DERESNADYNE	SEE	Andrews Radio Co.						
De ROY RADIO CORP.	1924	Phusiformer						
DETROIT RADIO CO.	1923	Air Muse	6.00	Box	2	-	-	C - - - -
DeWITT-La FRANCE CO.	1923	Superadio	54.00				S	DA - - - 1
			89.00				S	TRF - 1 - 2
	1924	"	50.00	T	2	5	S	TRF - 1 - 3
	1925	" Reactodyne 5	60.00	T	2	5	S	TRF - 1 - 3
		" 6	56.00	T	2	5	S	TRF - 1 - 3
		Superadio	17.50	Kit	2	7	S	SH - 1 2 2
		" Superheterodyne						
DIAL LESS RADIO CORP.	1925	Dial Less	150.00	T	1	6	S	TRF - 2 - 3
DIAMOND RADIO CO.	1928		79.85	C	1	7	A	
DIAMOND T. RADIO MANUFACTURERS	1925	Special S-10	49.50	T	3	5	S	TRF - 2 - 2
		DeLuxe D 15	80.00	T	1	5	S	TRF - 2 - 2
		C 20	160.00	C	3	5	S	TRF - 2 - 2
	1926	S-10	49.50	T	3	5	S	TRF - 2 - 2
		Super Special	49.50	T	3	5	S	TRF - 2 - 2
		Baby Grand	89.50	C	3	6	S	TRF - 3 - 2
	1927	Super Special	65.00	T	1	7	S	TRF - 3 - 2
		Diamond Special	75.00	T	1	6	S	TRF - 3 - 2
		Baby Grand	110.00	C	1	6	S	TRF - 3 - 2
		"	195.00	C	1	8	S	TRF - 3 - 3
		Chief	150.00	C	1	7	A	TRF - 3 - 3
		"	250.00	C	1	8	A	TRF - 3 - 3
	1928	American Beauty	48.00	T	1	6	A	TRF - 3 - 2
		Baby Grand	80.00	C	1	6	A	TRF - 3 - 2
		S.D.	120.00	SRP	1	6	A	TRF - 3 - 2
		Chief	175.00	C	1	6	A	TRF - 3 - 2
DICTOGRAPH PRODUCTS CO.	1925		225.00	T	1	6	A	TRF - 2 - 3
	1926			T			A	TRF - - 3
DIMMOCK BOGART RADIO CO.	1925	Arionola M4	50.00		2		S	TRF
		" M4L	50.00		2		S	TRF

MANUFACTURER	YEAR	MODEL NO. & NAME	PRICE	STYLE	D	T	P	CIR. & STAGES
DIMMOCK BOGART RADIO CO. (cont.)		Arionola M6	79.75		3		S	TRF
DISTANTONE RADIOS INC.	1925	A	37.50	T	3	5	S	TRF - 2 - 2
		B	47.50	T	3	5	S	TRF - 2 - 2
	1926	A	37.50		3	5	S	TRF - 2 - 2
		B	47.50	T	3	5	S	TRF - 2 - 2
		E	60.00	T	2	5	S	TRF - 2 - 2
		C	75.00		1	5	S	TRF - 2 - 2
		F	115.00		1	6	S	TRF - 2 - 2
		D	150.00		1	6	S	TRF - 2 - 3
	1927	Batteryless	275.00	C	2	6	A	TRF - 2 - 2
		E with Power Unit	165.00	C	2	6	A	TRF - 2 - 2
		E without Power Unit	325.00	C	2	5	A	TRF - 2 - 2
		E with Power Unit	165.00	C	2	6	A	TRF - 2 - 2
		E without Power Unit	60.00	T	2	5	S	TRF - 2 - 2
		E	75.00	T	2	5	S	TRF - 2 - 2
		C			1	5	S	TRF - 2 - 2
DIVA RADIO CORP.	1924	599			3	1		D - 1 - -
		600				6	S	TRF - 3 - 2
		603				3		DAA - - 2
		604 Superdyne	22.00		3	5	S	TRF - 2 - 2
		605						SH
		606						Rfx
		701				1		Rfx
		702				2		
	1925	Kardonstrip	35.00		3	5	S	TRF - 2 - 2
	1926	Kardonstrip Diva 3	35.00	T	3	5	S	TRF - 2 - 2
		Diva 2	45.00	T	2	5	S	TRF - 3 - 2
		Diva DeLuxe 1	65.00	T	1	6	S	TRF - 2 - 2
		Diva		Ch	3	5	S	TRF - 3 - 2
		" 5	23.50	T	3	5	S	TRF - 2 - 2
		" 5	37.50	T	2	5	S	TRF - 2 - 2
		DeLuxe	47.50	T	1	6	S	TRF - 3 - 2
DIXIE RADIO CORP.	1926	11	250.00	T	3	5	A	TRF - 2 - 2
		7	285.00	T	3	5	A	TRF - 2 - 2
DORON BROS. ELEC. CO.	1925	R5 Super Equidyne	125.00	T	3	5	S	TRF - 2 - 2

MANUFACTURER	YEAR	MODEL NO. & NAME	PRICE	STYLE	D	T	P	CIR. & STAGES
DOTSON HIEBERT CO.	1926	B-6	90.00	T	3	6	S	TRF - 2 - 3
		C-6	115.00	T	3	6	S	TRF - 2 - 3
DRAY RADIO LAB.	1925	599	125.00	T	3	6	B	TRF - 3 - 2
DREXEL RADIO MFG. CO.	1925	DR-4	95.00	T	2	4	E	TRF - 1 - 2
	1926	DR-5	125.00	T	3	5	E	TRF - 2 - 2
DU BOIS-LEACH RADIO SERVICE	1927	6	60.00	T	1	6	S	TRF - 2 - 3
		Unitrola	75.00	T	1	6	S	TRF - 3 - 2
DUCK CO., WM. B.	1923	CQ	59.50	T	3	3	S	DAA - - 2
		CQA	49.00	T	3	3	S	RF - 3 - -
		RFQ	39.00	T	2	2	S	RF - 2 - -
	1924	A884	125.00	T	3	5	E	TRF - 2 - 2
	1925	A884 DeLuxe Balanced	100.00	T	3	5	E	TRF - 2 - 2
	1926	A884 "	95.00	T	3	5	E	TRF - 2 - 2
		A885	150.00	C	3	6	E	TRF - 3 - 2
		A886	200.00	C	3	6	E	TRF - 3 - 2
DUKE RADIO CO.	1926		28.00	Ch	3	5	S	TRF - 2 - 2
	1927		21.00	Ch	3	5	S	TRF - 2 - 2
DUNGAN-STERNFIELD RADIO SALES	1926	Red Band	60.00	T	3	5	S	TRF - 2 - 2
DUNN MFG. CO.	1926	Dunsonola	50.00	T	1	5	S	TRF - 2 - 2
DYNAMOTIVE RADIO CORP.	1925	Dynamotive RC250	185.00	T	3	5	D	TRF - 2 - 2
		" RC250	235.00	T	3	5	A	TRF - 2 - 2
		Dynergy A	185.00	C	3	5	D	TRF - 2 - 2
		" A	235.00	C	3	5	A	TRF - 2 - 2
DYNA RADIO CO.	1923	235VT	65.00	T	2	3	S	DAA - - 2
EAGLE RADIO CO.	1923	Eagle Neutrodyne	175.00	T	3	5	S	Neut. - 2 - 2
	1924	"	175.00	T	3	5	S	Neut. - 2 - 2
		Eaglet	75.00	T	2	3	B	Neut. - 1 - 2
		Eagle Bal. Neut. B	175.00	T	3	5	S	Neut. - 2 - 2
		BS	100.00	C	3			
	1925	C	275.00	C	3	5	S	Neut. - 2 - 2

MANUFACTURER	YEAR	MODEL NO. & NAME	PRICE	STYLE	D	T	P	CIR. & STAGES
EAGLE RADIO CO. (cont.)			125.00	C	3	5	S	Neut. - 2 - 2
			150.00	C	3	5	S	Neut. - 2 - 2
			235.00	C	3	5	S	Neut. - 2 - 2
			250.00	C	3	5	S	Neut. - 2 - 2
			275.00	C	3	5	S	Neut. - 2 - 2
	1926			T Desk	2	5	S	Neut. - 2 - 2
EARL	SEE	Freshman Co.						
EASTERN SPECIALTY CO., THE	1923	Tesco A	1.25		1	-	-	C - - - -
EATON EDWARDS RADIO CO.	1926							
ECHOPHONE RADIO INC. (Echophone Radio Mfg. Co.) Common sales agency for a group of 3 manufacturers all under the name Radio Shop. Confused, overlapping model numbers. See also Armac Radio Co.	1924	F5 "5"	110.00	T	2	5	S	TRF Reg. - - 2
		V3 "3"	50.00	T	2	3	S	Reg. - - -
		"4"	125.00	T	2	4	B	TRF Reg. - 1 - 2
	1925	Echophone 3	75.00	Por.	2	3		DAA - - -
		" 4	50.00	T	2	3	B	DAA - - 2
		R-3	75.00	T	2	4	B	TRF - 1 - 2
		R-5	48.00	T	1	3	S	NonReg. - - 2
		R-5	85.00	T	2	5	S	TRF - 2 - 2
		V4	200.00	C	2	5	S	TRF - 2 - 2
	1926	4AC	125.00	T		5		
		6ACX	135.00	T		6		
		27AC	178.00	C		6		
	1927	40AC	256.00	C		6		
		41AC	125.00	T		6		
	1928	46	130.00	T		6		
		46	174.00	LB		6		
	1929	56	189.00	HB		7		
		56	206.00	LB		7		
	1930	Midget	225.00	HB		6		
			59.50	M	1	6	A	SG - 2 - 1
ECODYNE RADIO CO.	1924	RF, RT13	115.00	T	4	5	S	TRF - 2 - 2
		R.S.,	150.00	T	4	5	S	TRF - 2 - 2
	1925	R1-13	115.00	T	4	5	S	TRF - 2 - 2
		R-5	150.00	T	4	5	S	TRF - 2 - 2
ECONOMIC APPLIANCE CO.	1923	Eaco Duplex	90.00					

MANUFACTURER	YEAR	MODEL NO. & NAME	PRICE	STYLE	D	T	P	CIR. & STAGES
ECONOMIC APPLIANCE CO. (cont.)	1924	Eaco Duplex	100.00					
		" "	115.00					
EDISON, THOMAS A. INC. (Used Splitdorf chasses also)	1928	R1	315.00	HB	1	7	A	TRF - 3 - 2
		R2	260.00	HB	1	7	A	TRF - 3 - 2
		C1 (Splitdorf M-6)	1100.00	RP	1	9	A	TRF - 3 - 2
		C2	495.00	RP	1	7	A	TRF - 3 - 2*
	1929	R4	215.00	C	1	8	A	Neut. - 3 - 2*
		R5	175.00	C	1	8	A	Neut. - 3 - 2*
		C4		RP	1	8	A	Neut. - 3 - 3*
	1930	R6	297.00	C	1	9	A	SG - 3 - 3*
		R7	268.00	HB	1	9	A	SG - 3 - 3*
E. D. MFG. CO., THE	1923			Box	1	1		D - - -
EISEMANN MAGNETO CORP.	1924	8-D	125.00	T	2	5	S	TRF - 2 - 2
		RF2	110.00	T	2	5	S	TRF - 2 - 2
		6-D	125.00	T	3	5	E	TRF - 2 - 2
ELECTRAD CORPORATION OF AMERICA	1923		10.00					C
ELECTRAD INC.	1924							
ELECTRICAL RESEARCH LABS. "ERLA"	1923	Quad Six	27.35	T		4	S	Rfx - 4 - 2
	1924	One Tube Kit	36.95	Kit		1		D - - -
		Two Tube Kit	49.36	Kit		2	S	DA - - 1
		Three Tube Kit		Kit		3	S	DAA - - 2
		Duo-Reflex	75.00	Kit		4	S	Rfx - 4 - 2
		Erla		T		5	S	TRF - 2 - 2
	1925	Angelus		Por	3	5		
		"		P		5		
		Nestor 5		P	3	5	S	TRF - 2 - 2
		Pearson 5		T	3	5	S	TRF - 2 - 2
		Town & Country	150.00	Por	2	6		TRF - 1 - 1
		Superflex	85.00	T	2	3	S	TRF - 2 - 1
		"	95.00	T	2	4	S	TRF - 2 - 2
		"	105.00	Por	2	5	B	TRF - 2 - 2
		Console	145.00	C	2	5	S	TRF - 2 - 2
			270.00					

MANUFACTURER	YEAR	MODEL NO. & NAME	PRICE	STYLE	D	T	P	CIR. & STAGES
ELECTRICAL RESEARCH LABS. (cont.)	1925	Cirkit Superflex		Kit	3	5	S	TRF	- 2 - 2
		Standard 5	69.50	CT	2	3	S	TRF - 1 - 1
		DeLuxe 5	77.50	T	3	5	S	TRF - 2 - 2
		Standard Console	113.50	T	3	5	S	TRF - 2 - 2
		DeLuxe Console	142.50	C	2	5	S	TRF - 2 - 2
		Superflex Cirkit K7	49.50	Kit	3	5	S	Rfx - 2 - 2
		Circloid Kit	49.50	Kit	2	5	S	TRF - 2 - 2
	1926	Monodic S5	89.50		2	5	S	RFL - 2 - 2
		" S5	95.50		2	5	S	RFL - 2 - 2
		" S50	129.50		2	5	S	RFL - 2 - 2
		" S50	146.50		2	5	S	RFL - 2 - 2
	1927	Sextet	210.00	T	1	6	S	RFL - 3 - 2
		DeLuxe Sextet	285.00	LB	1	5	S	RFL - 3 - 2
		Monodic C12	65.00	T	2	6	S	RFL - 3 - 2
		" S51, C12	75.00	T	1	6	S	RFL - 3 - 2
		Single Six S52, C53	90.00	T	1	5	S	RFL - 3 - 2
		Monodic S50, C50	115.00	C	2	6	S	RFL - 3 - 2
		" S51, C22	125.00	C	1	6	S	RFL - 3 - 2
		" S51, C51	135.00	C	1	6	S	RFL - 3 - 2
		Single Six S52, C52	170.00	C	1	7	S	RFL 1 - 3 - 2
		Super 7 S61, C60	175.00	T	1	7	S	RFL 1 - 3 - 2
		" " S61, C61	255.00	C	1	7	S	RFL - 3 - 2
		" " S61, C62	295.00	C	1	7	S	RFL - 3 - 2
	1928	75	95.00	T	1	7	A	RFL - 3 - 2
		75	150.00	C	1	7	A	RFL - 3 - 2
		75	175.00	C	1	7	A	RFL - 3 - 2
		75	265.00	RP	1	9	A	RFL - 4 - 2
		85	265.00	T	1	9	A	RFL - 4 - 2
		85	350.00	C	1	9	A	RFL - 4 - 2
		85	325.00	C	1	8	A	RFL - 4 - 2
	1929	30	169.50	HB	1	8	A	SG - 3 - 2*
		31	147.00	HB	1	8	A	SG - 3 - 2*
		32	139.50	HB	1	8	A	SG - 3 - 2*
		C4F Duo Concerto	189.50	RP	1	8	A	SG - 3 - 2*
		C5F " "	119.50	HB	1	8	A	SG - 3 - 2*
		R2-A2			1	8	A	TRF - 3 - 2*
	1930	71	69.50	T	1	7	A	SG - 2 - 2
		72	77.50	T	1	7	A	SG - 3 - 2

MANUFACTURER	YEAR	MODEL NO. & NAME	PRICE	STYLE	D	T	P	CIR. & STAGES
ELECTRICAL RESEARCH LABS. (cont.)		73	99.50	LB	1	7	A	SG	- 3 - 2
		35	104.00	LB	1	9	A	SG	- 3 - 2*
		37	170.00	HB	1	8	A	SG	- 3 - 2*
		38	240.00	HB	1	8	A	SG	- 3 - 2*
		39	310.00	HB	1	8	S	SG	- 3 - 2*
		77	59.50	T	1	7	A	SG	- 2 - 2*
			69.50	M	1	7	A	SG	- 2 - 2
ELECTRICAL PRODUCTS MFG. CO.	1925	Dymac Selecto 5	75.00	T	3	5	S	TRF	- 2 - 2
	1926	" Somerlog	175.00	T	2	6	S	TRF	- 3 - 2
ELECTRICAL RESEARCH & MFG. CO.	1924	Superheterodyne	125.00	Por	1	3	E	Rfx	- 2 - 2
	1925	Superiorflex P3	100.00	T	1	3	E	Rfx	- 2 - 2
		" S-3	250.00	C	1	3	E	Rfx	- 2 - 2
		" 419-3	145.00		1	3	E	Rfx	- 2 - 2
	1926	" PS3	85.00		1	3	E	Rfx	- 2 - 2
		" S3							
ELECTRICAL SPECIALTY CO.	1921	Esco Regen. Set	50.00	T	3	1		Reg	- · -
ELECTRIC APPARATUS CO.	1924								
ELECTRIC CITY NOVELTY & MFG. CO.	1923	Radio	3.50					C	: -
	1923	Radio	7.50					C	: -
	1924	C	3.50					C	: -
	1924	C	7.50					C	: -
ELECTRIC MACHINE CORP.	1923	Elmco	65.00					RF	
	1924	"	100.00					RF	
ELECTRIC SERVICE CO.	1926	Escodyne Star	60.00						
ELECTRIC SERVICE ENGINEERING CORP.	1924	Dyneodyne	240.00					RF	
ELECTRIC SERVICE SHOP	1925	Simpli-dyne	75.00			2	E	TRF	- 2 - 2
ELECTRO IMPORTING CO.	1919	Regen. Rec.	50.00	T	2	-	-	PT	
ELECTROPHONE CORP.	1926	Hyatt		Por		6			
ELGIN RADIO CO.	1929	"AC"	24.00	Ch	1	6	A	SG	- 2 - 2

MANUFACTURER	YEAR	MODEL NO. & NAME	PRICE	STYLE	D	T	P	CIR. & STAGES
ELGIN RADIO SUPPLY CO.	1925	Super Reinartz 2LO	32.05	T	1	1	E	Reg. - - - 1
		" " 2LO	41.80	T	1	2	E	Reg. - - - 1
		"1926" 2LO	51.60	T	1	3	E	Reg. - - - 2
		Super Reinartz	75.00	T	1	2	E	Reg. - - - 2
			57.60	T	2	3	E	Reg. - - - 2
ELING CO., R. W.	1926	Raymond R-18	45.00	T	3	5	S	TRF - 2 - 2
ELITE RADIO STORES	1925	Tzigan Superhet.	125.00		1		D	Rfx - 4 - 2
ELKAY	1925	Elkay			2			
ELL ESS RADIO EXCHANGE INC.	1923	Gem	7.50					C - - -
	1924	Gem-C	7.50		1			
		Journal	9.00					
ELMORE-LAMBLING RADIO CO.	1930	Gem	69.50	M	1	6	A	SG - 3 - 2
EL-PAIGE RADIO CO.	1926	Paige	17.50					C - - -
		Crystal	5.00					
EMERSON RADIO & PHONOGRAPH CO.	1924	"Combinations" Distributing; Amrad Neutrodyne Federal 135 Panel						
	1925	125 Cabinet $67.50 No Radio Products						
	1926	" " "						
	1927	" " "						
	1928	C	100.00	HB	1	8	A	TRF - 3 - 2*
	1929	D	100.00	HB	1	8	A	TRF - 3 - 2*
		F				8	A	TRF - 3 - 2*
		Series 65			2	8	A	SG - 3 - 2*
		C2	100.00		1	8	A	SG - 3 - 2*
		D2	100.00		1	8	A	SG - 3 - 2*
EMPIRE ELECTRIC MANUFACTURING CO.	1926	Empire 5	57.50	T	3	5	S	TRF - 2 - 2
		5S	75.00	T	3	5	S	TRF - 2 - 2
		5C	90.00	C	3	5	S	TRF - 2 - 2
EMPIRE RADIO CORP.	1922	"Unit Panels"	59.00	4 Ch	2	3	E	TRF - 1 - 2

MANUFACTURER	YEAR	MODEL NO. & NAME	PRICE	STYLE	D	T	P	CIR. & STAGES	
E. & N. PRODUCTS CO.	1926	163	125.00	T	2	5	A	TRF	- 2 - 2
		169	160.00	C	2	5	A	TRF	- 2 - 2
		214	160.00	T	2	7	A	TRF	- 3 - 3
		238	225.00	C	2	7	A	TRF	- 3 - 3
EQUITABLE RADIO CORP.	1925	Claratone	50.00	T	3	5	E	TRF	- 2 - 2
		" 124	39.00	T	3	5	S	TRF	- 2 - 2
		" 124LS	60.00					TRF	
		Professional 124P	45.00					TRF	
ERLA	SEE	Elec. Research Labs.							
ESCHER CO.	1926								
ESSEX MANUFACTURING CO.	1923	Pall Mall	14.75	Box			-	C	- - - -
	1924								
	1925	Pall Mall	65.00	T	2		S	TRF	- 1 - 2
	1926	Knight Super Six	100.00	T	2	6	S	TRF	- 2 - 3
EVEREADY	SEE	National Carbon Co.							
EVOLUTION PHONE CO	1926	Tyrolian							
EXCELL RADIO MFG.	1926		85.00						
			135.00						
EXLNTONE CORP.	1925	S-24		Period	1	4	S	RF	- 1 - 2
		C-24		Period	1	4	S	RF	- 1 - 2
		W-25		Period	1	4	S	RF	- 1 - 2
		Midget		M	1	5	S	RF	- 1 - 3
EXPERIMENTERS INFO. SERVICE INC. Charles R. Leutz used this company to pub-licize his Superhet designs. See also Norden-Hauck.	1923	Superhet		B/P	2	7	S		- 2 2
	1924	" C	2.00	B/P	2	7	E		2
		J (RF Amplifier)	2.00	B/P	2	7	S		- 2 2
	1925	Superhet C7	1.00	B/P	2	7	S		- 2 2
		" C7	1.00	T	2	10	S		- 3 2 2
		" C10							
F. A. D. ANDREA, INC. (FADA) (FADA Radio & Electric Corp.)	1922	Hazeltine Kit		Kit	2	1		Rfx	- - - 1
		Fada		T		1	E	D	- - - -

65

MANUFACTURER	YEAR	MODEL NO. & NAME	PRICE	STYLE	D	T	P	CIR. & STAGES
F. A. D. ANDREA, INC. (FADA) (cont.)		Fada						
	1923	Receiver-Amp	80.00	T	2	3	E	- - 2
			65.00	T	2	3	E	- - 2
		One Sixty	65.00	T	2	4	S	- - 2
			120.00	T	3	4	S	- 1 - ½
			25.00	Kit	3	4/5	S	- - 2
	1924		25.00	Kit	3	5	S	- - 2
		175A Neutroceiver	160.00	T	3	5	S	Neut. - 2 - 2
		175/90A " Grand	235.00	T	3	5	S	Neut. - 2 - 2
		185A Neutrola	270.00	C	3	5	S	Neut. - 2 - 2
		185/90A " Grand	295.00	C	3	5	S	Neut. - 2 - 2
		195 Neutro Jr.	75.00	T	2		B	Neut.
		195A Neutro Jr.	40.00	T	3		S	Neut. - 2 - 2
	1925	160A	120.00	T	3		S	Neut. - 2 - 2
		165A	25.00	Kit	3		S	Neut. - 2 - 2
	1924	166A	64.00	Kit	3		S	Neut. - 2 - 2
		167A	67.60	Kit	3		S	Neut. - 2 - 2
		169A	72.00	Kit	3		E	Neut. - 2 - 2
		170A	125.00	Ch	3	5	S	Neut. - 2 - 2
		192A Neutrolette	85.00	T	3	5	S	Neut. - 2 - 2
		192BS	110.00	P	3	5	S	Neut. - 2 - 2
		192S	110.00	P	2	5	S	Neut. - 1 - 2
		195A Neutro Jr.	75.00	T	3	5	S	Neut. - 2 - 2
		196A	110.00	P	3	5	S	Neut. - 2 - 2
		197A	110.00	P	3	5	E	Neut. - 2 - 2
		SF10-70 Davenport	225.00	C	3	5	E	Neut. - 2 - 2
		SF20-70 Beethoven	250.00	C	3	5	E	Neut. - 2 - 2
		SF30-70 Queen Anne	300.00	Desk	3	5	E	Neut. - 2 - 2
		SF40-70	275.00	C	3	5	E	Neut. - 2 - 2
	1926	175AL Neutroceiver	175.00	T	2	6	E	Neut. - 3 - 2
		460A	160.00	T	3	6	A	Neut. - 3 - 2
		R60	100.00	P	3	6	S	Neut. - 3 - 2
	1927	262CA or UA	95.00		3	6	A	Neut. - 3 - 2
		265A			2	6	S	Neut. - 3 - 2
		265 CA or UA			2	6	A	Neut. - 3 - 2
		Special	250.00	T	2	8	A	Neut. - 4 - 3
		Fada 8	400.00	C	2	8	A	Neut. - 4 - 2
		472			2	8	S	Neut. - 4 - 2
		475UA	185.00		2	7	S	Neut. - 4 - 2
		475A						

MANUFACTURER	YEAR	MODEL NO. & NAME	PRICE	STYLE	D	T	P	CIR. & STAGES
F. A. D. ANDREA INC. (FADA) (cont.)	1927	475C	250.00		2	8	A	Neut. - 4 - 2
		480A	300.00		2	8	S	Neut. - 4 - 3
		480B	300.00		2	8	S	Neut. - 4 - 2
		L65C	160.00	T	2	7	A	Neut. - 3 - 2
		CA45/72 CA or UA			2	8	A	Neut. - 4 - 2
		SF45/75	285.00	C	2	7	S	Neut. - 4 - 2
		CA45/75 CA or UA			2	8	A	Neut. - 4 - 3
		SF45/75C	385.00		2	8	E	Neut. - 4 - 3
		SF50/80	400.00	C	1	8	S	Neut. - 4 - 3
		SF50/80B	400.00	C	1	8	A	Neut. - 3 - 2
		RP62 CA or UA			1	6	S	Neut. - 3 - 2
		RP65 CA or UA			1	6	S	Neut. - 4 - 3
		RP80A			1	8	A	Neut. - 3 - 2
	1928	10	110.00	T	1	7	A	Neut. - 4 - 3
		11	135.00	T	1	7	A	Neut. - 3 - 2
		12	120.00	T	1	6	D	Neut. - 3 - 2*
		16	110.00	T	1	8	A	Neut. - 3 - 2*
		17	135.00	T	1	8	A	Neut. - 3 - 2
		30	187.50	C	1	7	A	Neut. - 4 - 2*
		31	235.00	C	1	7	A	Neut. - 4 - 2*
		50		C	1	9	A	Neut. - 4 - 2*
		70		C	1	9	A	Neut. - 4 - 2*
		71		RP	1	9	A	Neut. - 4 - 2*
		72		T	1	9	A	Neut. - 4 - 2*
		50E180	225.00	T	1	9	A	Neut. - 4 - 2*
		50E420	95.00	C	1	9	A	Neut. - 4 - 2*
		70E180	340.00	C	1	9	A	Neut. - 4 - 2*
		70E420	360.00		1	9	A	Neut. - 4 - 2*
		72E180			1	9	A	Neut. - 4 - 2*
		72E420			1	9	D	Neut. - 3 - 2*
	1929	18	120.00	T	1	7	A	Neut. - 3 - 2
		20	137.00	T	1	8	S	Neut. - 3 - 2*
		22			1	6	A	Neut. - 3 - 2*
		25	165.00	C	1	8	A	Neut. - 3 - 2*
		32	225.00	C	1	8	A	Neut.SG - 3 - 2*
		35	245.00	C	1	9	D	Neut. - 3 - 2*
		35B	255.00	C	1	7	A	SG - 2 - 2*
		36	175.00	C	1	8	A	SG - 3 - 2*
		40	260.00	C	1	7	D	SG - 3 - 2*
		48A	300.00	T	1	8	E	Neut. - 3 - 3

MANUFACTURER	YEAR	MODEL NO. & NAME	PRICE	STYLE	D	T	P	CIR. & STAGES	
F. A. D. ANDREA, INC. (FADA) (cont.)	1929	75	360.00	C	1	8	A	SG	- 3 - 2*
		77	675.00	RP	1	8	A	SG	- 3 - 2*
	1930	41	218.00	HB	1	8	A	SG	- 3 - 2*
		42	159.00	LB	1	8	A	SG	- 3 - 2*
		44	188.00	LB	1	8	A	SG	- 3 - 1*
		45			1	8	A	SH	- 1 - 1*
		46	228.00	HB	1	8	A	SG	- 3 - 2*
		47	328.00	RP	1	8	A	SG	- 3 - 2*
		48			1	10	A	SH	- 1 2 2*
		49			1	10	A	SH	- 1 2 2*
		51			1	7	A	SH	- 1 1 1
		53			1	7	A	SH	- 1 1 1
		57			1	7	A	SH	- 1 1 1
		81	231.00	HB	1	12	D	SG	- 3 - 2#
		82	172.00	LB	1	12	D	SG	- 3 - 2#
		84	201.00	LB	1	12	D	SG	- 3 - 2#
		86	241.00	HB	1	12	D	SG	- 3 - 2#
FALCK (Advance Electric Co. in 1930)	1925	Reflex	150.00	T	1	4	S	Rfx	
	1927	No-Battery	99.50	C	1	5	A	Rfx	
	1928	Climax	178.50	C		5			
		9A	198.50	C		9			
		9D	99.50	C		7			
		11	120.00	C		7			
		52	99.50	C		7			
		61	99.50	C		7			
	1929	26 Jr.	109.50	C		7			
		23 Sr.	99.50	M		7			
FANSTEEL PRODUCTS CO. INC.	SEE	Balkeit Radio Co. and Pfanstiehl							
FARAWAY RADIO CO., THE	1924	F	59.50	T	3	4	E	TRF	- 1 - 2
		R	29.50	T	3	2	E	DA	- : 1
	1926	55	63.59	T	3	5	E	TRF	- 2 - 2
		R	22.50	T		2	E	DA	- : 1
FARMERS WIRELESS TELEPHONE CO.	1926	Aurodyne	50.00	T	3	5	E	TRF	- 2 - 2
		"	70.00	T	3	5	E	TRF	- 2 - 2

MANUFACTURER	YEAR	MODEL NO. & NAME	PRICE	STYLE	D	T	P	CIR. & STAGES
FARMERS WIRELESS TELEPHONE CO. (cont.)		Aurodyne	95.00	C	3	5	E	TRF - 2 - 2
		"	110.00	C	3	5	E	TRF - 2 - 2
		"	55.00	P	3	5	E	TRF - 2 - 2
		"	75.00	P	3	5	E	TRF - 2 - 2
		"	40.00	P	3	5	S	TRF - 2 - 3
		"	55.00	T	3	6	S	TRF - 2 - 3
		"	75.00	C	3	6	S	TRF - 2 - 3
		"	115.00	C	3	6	S	TRF - 2 - 3
FARRAND MANUFACTURING CO. "Farrand Godley"	1925	Godley Single 9	195.00	T	1	9	S	TRF - 5 - 3
		" "	235.00	T	1	9	S	TRF - 5 - 3
		" DeLuxe	375.00	T	1	9	S	TRF - 5 - 3
FEDDERS MFG. CO.	1923	Radio Ranger JRH		T		6	S	RF - 3 - 2
FEDERAL BRANDES INC.	SEE	Kolster Radio Inc.						
FEDERAL RADIO CORP.	1922	Federal Jr. (Cry & Amp)	52.00	2 Box	1	2	B	C & AA - - 2
		8	58.00	T	-	2	E	DA - - 1
		9 Amplifier	58.00	T	1	1	E	A - - -
		55 R. F. Amp.	52.00	MT	1	2	E	PT+ - - -
		56	98.00	MT	1	2	E	PT-O - 2 -
		57	116.00	MT	1	4	S	"TRF" - 1 - 2
		DX58	177.00	MT	1	4	S	"TRF" - 1 - 2
	1923	59	223.00	MT	1	6	E	RF - 3 - 2
	1924	61	140.00	Por	1	4	B	RF - 1 - 2
		102	105.00	MT	3	3	E	RF - 1 - 1
		110	123.00	MT	1	4	E	RF - 1 - 1
	1925	DX58	98.20	P	2	3	E	RF - 1 - 2
		135	120.00	P	2	3	E	RF - - -
		200	150.00	T	2	5	E	RF - 2 - 2
		141	120.00	C	2	5	E	RF - 2 - 2
		142	230.00	C	2	5	E	RF - 2 - 2
		143	330.00	HB	2	5	E	RF - 2 - 2
		144	464.00	HB	3	6	E	RF - 3 - 2
		161	106.00	P		4	E	RF - - -
		Orthosonic A10	75.00	T	3	5	S	TRF - 2 - 2
		" B20	100.00	T	3	5	S	TRF - 2 - 2

MANUFACTURER	YEAR	MODEL NO. & NAME	PRICE	STYLE	D	T	P	CIR. & STAGES
FEDERAL RADIO CORP. (cont.)	1925	Orthosonic B30	130.00	T	3	5	S	TRF - 2 - 2
		" B35	250.00	C	3	5	S	TRF - 2 - 2
		" B36	250.00	C	3	5	E	TRF - 2 - 2
		C20	165.00	T	2	7	E	TRF - 4 - 2
		C30	200.00	T	2	7	E	TRF - 4 - 2
		C34	300.00	C	2	7	E	TRF - 4 - 2
		C40	350.00	C	1	7	S	TRF - 4 - 2
	1926	D10	100.00	T	1	5	S	TRF - 2 - 2
		E10	150.00	T	1	6	S	TRF - 3 - 2
		F10	250.00	T	1	7	S	TRF - 2 - 2
		D40	200.00	C	1	5	S	TRF - 2 - 2
		E40	300.00	C	1	6	A	TRF - 3 - 2
	1927	F40	400.00	T	1	7	A	TRF - 4 - 2
		F10-60	360.00	C	1	6	A	TRF - 3 - 2
		E45-60	460.00	C	1	7	A	TRF - 4 - 2
		F45-60	600.00	C	1	7	A	TRF - 4 - 2
		Oxford	775.00	C	1	7	A	TRF - 4 - 2
		Louvain	900.00	C	1	7	A	TRF - 4 - 2
		Mandarin	1125.00	C	1	7	A	TRF - 4 - 2
		Milan	1225.00	T	1	5	A	TRF - 2 - 2
		D10-60	185.00	T	1	6	A	TRF - 3 - 2
		E10-60	275.00	C	1	6	A	TRF - 2 - 2
		D40-60	285.00	C	1	6	A	TRF - 3 - 2
		E40-60	460.00	C	1	7	A	TRF - 4 - 2
	1928	E41-60	495.00	C	1	7	A	TRF - 4 - 2
		F-11	250.00	T	1	7	S	TRF - 4 - 2
		F40-60	560.00	C	1	7	A	TRF - 4 - 2
		F41-60	595.00	C	1	7	A	TRF - 4 - 2
		F11-60	360.00	C	1	7	S	TRF - 4 - 2
		F50	650.00	C	1	7	A	TRF - 4 - 2
		F50-60	775.00	C	1	7	A	TRF - 4 - 2
		F51-60	810.00	C	1	7	S	TRF - 4 - 2
		F60	775.00	C	1	7	A	TRF - 4 - 2
		F60-60	900.00	C	1	7	A	TRF - 4 - 2
		F61-60	935.00	C	1	7	S	TRF - 4 - 2
		F70	110.00	C	1	7	A	TRF - 4 - 2
		F70-60	1125.00	C	1	7	A	TRF - 4 - 2
		F71-60	1160.00	C	1	7	A	TRF - 4 - 2
		F80	110.00	C	1	7	S	TRF - 4 - 2

MANUFACTURER	YEAR	MODEL NO. & NAME	PRICE	STYLE	D	T	P	CIR. & STAGES
FEDERAL RADIO CORP. (cont.)	1929	F80-60	1250.00	C	1	7	A	TRF - 4 - 2
		F81-60	1260.00	C	1	7	A	TRF - 4 - 2
		G10-60	130.00	T	1	7	A	TRF - 2 - 2*
		G41-60	220.00	C	1	7	A	TRF - 2 - 2*
		K10	114.50	T	1	7	A	SG - 2 - 2*
		K40	154.50	C	1	7	A	SG - 2 - 2*
		K41	164.50	C	1	7	A	SG - 2 - 2*
		L36	149.50	LB	1	8	A	SG - 3 - 2*
		L46	179.50	C	1	8	A	SG - 3 - 2*
		M36	245.00	CL	1	8	A	TRF - 3 - 2*
		M41	295.00	C	1	8	A	TRF - 3 - 2*
		M46	295.00	C	1	8	A	TRF - 3 - 2*
		M10	175.00	T	1	8	A	TRF - 3 - 2*
FEDERAL TELEGRAPH CO.	SEE	Kolster Radio Inc.						
FEDERAL TELEGRAPH CO.	1924	Commercial						
FERGUSON CO., J.B.	1924	"TRF"	110.00	Por	2	4	B	TRF - 1 - 2
	1925	"TRF"	120.00	Phono	2	4	E	RF - 1 - 2
		" 3V	130.00		2	4	E	RF - 1 - 2
		" 3	120.00	Por	2	4	B	RF - 2 - 3
	1926	8	226.00	T	1	6	S	TRF - 2 - 3
		10	110.00	T	2	6	S	TRF - 2 - 3
		6	180.00	T	2	6	S	TRF - 2 - 3
		6	290.00	C	1	6	S	TRF - 2 - 3
		8	348.00	C	2	6	S	TRF - 2 - 3
		10 with table	147.50	Stand	1	6	S	TRF - 2 - 3
	1927	12	75.00	T	2	6	S	TRF - 2 - 3
		12	75.00	T	1	6	S	TRF - 2 - 3
		10	110.00	T	2	6	S	TRF - 2 - 3
		12	145.00	CL	1	7	A	TRF - 3 - 2
		18	195.00	T		7	A	TRF - 6 - 3
		14	235.00	T	1	6	S	TRF - 2 - 3
		10 with table	147.50	Stand				TRF
FERRIS RADIO SUPPLY CO.	1925	3TR	50.00	T	2	3	E	DAA - - - 2

MANUFACTURER	YEAR	MODEL NO. & NAME	PRICE	STYLE	D	T	P	CIR. & STAGES
FILTER-FLEX RADIO CORP.	1927		98.50	T	1	5	A	TRF - 1 - 2
			125.00	DC	1	5	A	TRF - 1 - 2
			150.00	HB	1	5	A	TRF - 1 - 2
FIND ALL RADIO CO.	1930	SG4	35.00	T	1	4	B	SG - 1 - 2
		AG.SG4	46.95	T	1	5	A	SG - 1 - 2
FIRTH, JOHN	1921	Firth		Box	2	3		DAA - - 2
FISCHER, C. C.	1927	599 Viking	25.00	T	1	5	B	TRF - 2 - 2
FLASH RADIO CORP.	1926	Flash Vest Pocket						
FLINT RADIO CO. INC.	1928	Little Chief	49.50			7		
		AX	160.00	C		7		
		CX	135.00	C		7		
		C	99.50	C		7		
	1929	Chief	49.50	M		5		
		Standard	59.50	M		5	A	SG
		79	98.00	C		5	A	SG
		113	136.00	C		7	A	SG - 2 - 2*
		129	152.00	C		7	A	SG - 2 - 2*
	1930	Dolores	69.50	M	1	5	A	SG - 2 - 1
		San Gabriel	69.50	M	1	5	A	SG - 2 - 1
		Del Rey	69.50	M	1	5	A	SG - 2 - 1
		Fantasy	69.50	M	1	5	A	SG - 2 - 1
		Spanish Mission	69.50	M	1	5	A	SG - 2 - 1
FORDHAM RADIO EXCHANGE	1923 1924							
FOREIGN & DOM. ELEC. COM.	1925	Electradyne	110.00	T	2	2	A	Rfx TRF - 1 - 2
FORMAN & CO.	1923 1924	Novelty Set	1.25					C - - - -
								C - - - -
FRANCRONE INC.	1926	Electric F1	150.00	T	2	5	S	- 2 - 2
FRANKLIN RADIO CO.	1926	Big Five	125.00	T	3	5	S	RF - 2 - 2
		Cheltenham	150.00	C	3	5	B	RF - 2 - 2

MANUFACTURER	YEAR	MODEL NO. & NAME	PRICE	STYLE	D	T	P	CIR. & STAGES		
FRANKLIN RADIO CO. (cont.)	1923	Portable	180.00	Por	3	5	B	RF	- 2 - 2	
		Consolette	180.00	T	1	6	B	RF	- 2 - 3	
FREED-EISEMANN RADIO CORP. (Freed Radio and Television Corp.)	1923	105 Marvel	10.00	Box	3	5	.	C	-	-
	1924	350	24.00	Kit	3	5	S	TRF	- 2 - 2	
		370	24.00	Kit	3	5	S	TRF	- 2 - 2	
		NR5	150.00	T	3	5	S	Neut.	- 2 - 2	
		NR6	150.00	T	2	4	S	Neut.	- 1 - 2	
		NR12	100.00	T	3	5	S	Neut.	- 2 - 2	
		NR20	175.00	P	2	4	S	Neut.	- 1 - 2	
		NR215	95.00	P	2	4	S	Neut.	- 1 - 2	
		NR400	95.00	P	3	5	S	TRF	- 2 - 2	
		KD-50	80.00	Kit	3	5	S	Neut.	- 2 - 2	
	1925	Aristona LaSalle								
		NR7	110.00	T	3	6	S	Neut.	- 2 - 2	
		NR 35	195.00	C	3	6	S	Neut.	- 2 - 3	
		NR45	160.00	T	3	6	S	Neut.	- 2 - 3	
		NR405	120.00	T	3	5	S	Neut.	- 2 - 2	
		FE15	75.00	T	3	5	S	TRF	- 2 - 2	
		FE18	90.00	T	3	5	B	TRF	1 2 - 2	
		FE30	185.00	T	3	6	S	TRF	- 3 - 2	
	1926	NR15	75.00	T	2	6	S	Neut.	1 2 - 2	
		NR30	85.00	T	1	6		Neut.	- 4 - 2	
		NR40	95.00	T	1	6		Neut.	- 4 - 2	
		NR48	135.00		1	8		Neut.	- 2 - 2	
		NR70	110.00		1	8		Neut.	- 3 - 2	
		NR800	385.00	T	3	6	S	TRF	- 3 - 2	
		NR850	650.00	HB	2	6	S	TRF	1 3 - 2	
		10	60.00	T	1	6	S	TRF	- 3 - 2	
		30	75.00	T	1	7	S	TRF	- 3 - 2	
		40	85.00	T	1	6	S	TRF	1 3 - 2	
		48	125.00	T	2	6	S	Neut.	- 3 - 2	
		50	175.00	T	1	6	S	Neut.	- 3 - 2	
	1927	NR8	90.00	T	1	6	S	Neut.	- 3 - 2	
		NR9	100.00	T	1	6	S	Neut.	- 3 - 2	
		NR11	125.00	T	1	7	A	Neut.	- 3 - 2	
		NR11 AC	225.00	T	1	7	A	Neut.	- 3 - 2	
		NR57	145.00	T	1	7	A	Neut.	- 3 - 2	
		NR60 AC	160.00	T	1	7	D	Neut.	- 3 - 2	
		NR60 DC	160.00	T				Neut.		

MANUFACTURER	YEAR	MODEL NO. & NAME	PRICE	STYLE	D	T	P	CIR. & STAGES
FREED-EISEMANN RADIO CORP. (cont.)		NR66	125.00	T	1	6	S	Neut.	- 3 - 2
		NR67	175.00			7	S	Neut.	- 4 - 2
		NR77	175.00	T	1	6	A	Neut.	- 3 - 2
		411	100.00	T	1	6	S	TRF	- 2 - 2
		130						TRF	- 2 - 2
	1928	NR50 Great Eighty	125.00	MT	1	8	A	Neut.	1 3 - 2
		NR80W DC	125.00	T	1	8	A	Neut.	1 3 - 2
		NR80 Hand Decorated	135.00	MT	1	8	D	Neut.	1 3 - 2*
		NR80	125.00	MT	1	8	D	Neut.	1 3 - 2*
		NR80W	135.00	T	1	8	D	Neut.	1 3 - 2*
		NR80 Hand Decorated	160.00	MT	1	8	A	Neut.	1 3 - 2
		NR85	160.00	MT	1	8	A	Neut.	1 3 - 2
		NR85W		T	1	8	A	Neut.	1 3 - 2
		NR85-F9 Adler Royal	282.50	HB	1	8	A	Neut.	- 3 - 2
		NR85 Hamilton	290.00	HB	1	8		Neut.	- 3 - 2
	1929	NR10	55.00	MT	1	7	s	Neut.	- 3 - 2*
		NR53	99.50	C	1	8	A	Neut.	- 3 - 2*
		NR55	99.50	C	1	7	D	Neut.	- 3 - 2*
		NR55 DC	75.00	MT	1	8	A	Neut.	- 3 - 2*
		NR56	75.00	MT	1	7	D	Neut.	- 3 - 2*
		NR56 DC	145.00	C	1	8	A	Neut.	- 3 - 2*
		NR78	145.00	C	1	9	D	Neut.	- 3 - 2*
		NR78 DC	172.50	C	1	8	A	Neut.	- 3 - 2*
		NR79	172.50	C	1	9	D	Neut.	- 3 - 2*
		NR79 DC	225.00	C	1	9	A	Neut.	- 3 - 2*
		NR95	182.50	C	1	8		Neut.	- 4 - 2*
		NR90							
FREEPORT RADIO CORP.	1925	ABC-A	85.00	T	2	3	S	DAA	- - 2
		ABC-B	85.00	T	2	3	S	DAA	- - 2
FRENCH JESSE & SONS PIANO CO.	1930	Junior	69.50	M	1	5	A	SG	- 2 - 1
		Louis XVI	136.00		1	8	A	SG	- 3 - 2*
		Elizabethan	146.00		1	8	A	SG	- 3 - 2*
		Hepplewhite	152.00		1	8	A	SG	- 3 - 2*
		Florentine	156.00		1	8	A	SG	- 3 - 2*
FRESHMAN CO. INC., CHAS.	1924	Masterpiece	17.50	Kit	3	5	S	TRF	- 2 - 2
		"	60.00	T	3	5	S	TRF	- 2 - 2

MANUFACTURER	YEAR	MODEL NO. & NAME	PRICE	STYLE	D	I	P	CIR. & STAGES
FRESHMAN CO. INC., CHAS. (cont.)	1925	Masterpiece	60.00	T	3	5	E	TRF - 2 - 2
		"	39.50	Kit	3	5	E	TRF - 2 - 2
		5F2	39.50	T	3	5	E	TRF - 2 - 2
		5F4	49.50	T	3	5	E	TRF - 2 - 2
		5F5	60.00	T	3	5	E	TRF - 2 - 2
		5F6	82.50	C	3	5	E	TRF - 2 - 2
		5F7	89.50	T	3	5	E	TRF - 2 - 2
		Concert	75.00	T	3	5	E	TRF - 2 - 2
		Master Unit	75.00	C/T	3	5	E	TRF - 2 - 2
		Franklin	115/70	C	3	5	S	TRF - 2 - 2
	1926	6F1	99.50	C	3	5	S	TRF - 2 - 2
		6F2	106.50	C	3	5	S	TRF - 2 - 2
		6F3	69.50	T	3	5	S	TRF - 2 - 2
		6F4	71.50	T	3	5	S	TRF - 2 - 2
		6F5	57.50	T	3	5	S	TRF - 2 - 2
		6F6	38.50	T	3	5	S	TRF - 2 - 2
		6F7	42.50	C	3	5	S	TRF - 2 - 2
		6F9	99.50	C	3	5	S	TRF - 2 - 2
		6F10	106.50	C	3	5	S	TRF - 2 - 2
		6F11, 6F12	119.50	T	3	5	S	TRF - 2 - 2
		Master Unit	69.50	C	3	5	S	TRF - 2 - 2
		6F16	79.50	C	3	5	A	TRF - 2 - 2
	1927	G1	156.00	T	1	7	A	TRF - 3 - 2
		G2	175.00	C	1	7	A	TRF - 3 - 2
		G3	200.00	C	1	7	A	TRF - 3 - 2
		G4	225.00	C	1	7	A	TRF - 3 - 2
		G5	250.00	C	1	7	A	TRF - 3 - 2
		G6	350.00	RP	1	7	A	TRF - 3 - 2
		G7 Equaphase	185.00	C	1	7	A	TRF - 3 - 2
		G10	195.00	C	1	6	S	TRF - 3 - 2
		F1	70.00	T	1	6	S	TRF - 3 - 2
		F2	110.00	C	1	6	S	TRF - 3 - 2
		F4	160.00	C	1	6	S	TRF - 3 - 2
		F5	185.00	C	1	6	S	TRF 1 2 - 2
		7F1	70.00	T	1	6	S	TRF 1 2 - 2
		7F2	54.50	T	1	6	S	TRF 1 2 - 2
		7F3	87.50	C	1	6	S	TRF 1 2 - 2
		7F4	120.00	C	1	6	S	TRF 1 2 - 2
		7F5	109.50	C	1	6	S	TRF 1 2 - 2
		7AC2	54.50	T	1	7	A	TRF 1 2 - 2

MANUFACTURER: FRESHMAN CO. INC., CHAS. (cont.)

YEAR	MODEL NO. & NAME	PRICE	STYLE	D	T	P	CIR. & STAGES
1928	7AC3	153.00	C	1	7	A	TRF	1 2 - 2
	7AC4	185.00	C	1	7	A	TRF	1 2 - 2
	7AC5	175.00	C	1	7	A	TRF	1 2 - 2
	H9	500.00	RP	1	8	A	TRF	1 2 - 2
	K	500.00		1	7	A	TRF	- 3 - 2
	L			1	6	D	TRF	- 3 - 2
	LS			1	6	D	TRF	- 3 - 2
	M11	85.00	T	1	7	A	TRF	1 2 - 2
	N11	115.00	T	1	7	A	TRF	1 2 - 2
	N12	195.00	C	1	7	A	TRF	1 2 - 2
	N14	195.00	C	1	7	A	TRF	1 2 - 2
	N17	195.00	C	1	7	A	TRF	1 2 - 2
	Q15	69.00	T	1	5	A	SG	- 1 - 2
	Q16	99.00	C	1	5	A	SG	- 1 - 2
	QD16	149.50	C	1	5	A	SG	- 1 - 2
	3Q15			1	5	A	SG	- 1 - 2
	3Q16			1	7	A	SG	- 1 - 2
1929	2N			1	8	A	TRF	1 2 - 2*
	21	75.00	MT	1	7	A	TRF	- 3 - 2*
	21 Earl	75.00	MT	1	8	D	TRF	- 3 - 2*
	21	80.00	MT	1	8	A	TRF	- 3 - 2*
	22	99.50	C	1	7	A	TRF	- 3 - 2*
	22	104.00	C	1	8	D	TRF	- 3 - 2*
	22 Earl			1	9	A	TRF	- 3 - 2*
	24 "			1	8	D	TRF	- 3 - 2*
	31	139.00	C	1	9	A	TRF	- 3 - 2*
	31 Earl	139.00	C	1	8	D	TRF	- 3 - 2*
	31	144.00	C	1	8	A	TRF	- 3 - 2*
	31S			1	8	A	SG	- 3 - 2*
	32	169.00	C	1	7	D	TRF	- 3 - 2*
	32	169.00	C	1	8	A	TRF	- 3 - 2
	32	174.00	C	1	8	A	TRF	- 3 - 2*
	32S			1	9	D	SG	- 3 - 2*
	33 Earl			1	8	A	TRF	- 3 - 2*
	33S "			1	9	A	SG	- 3 - 2*
	41	225.00	HB	1	9	D	TRF	1 3 - 2*
	41	235.00	HB	1	9	A	SG	1 3 - 2*
	41 Earl			1	9	A	TRF	1 3 - 2*
	121 "	55.00	MT	1	6	B	TRF	- 3 - 2

MANUFACTURER	YEAR	MODEL NO. & NAME	PRICE	STYLE	D	T	P	CIR.	& STAGES
F. R. S. RADIO CORP.									
	1923	FRS	17.50	Box	1	1	S	D	- - -
	1923	FRS	40.00	Box	3	3	S	DAA	- - 2
G. A. RADIO MANUFACTURING CORP.									
	1926	Voceleste							
		Pico							
GARDENHOUR, A. J.									
	1925	DX25 Gar-shear-dyne	100.00	T	3	4	S	TRF	- 1 - 2
		TRF25 " " "	110.00	T	3	5	S	TRF	- 2 - 2
GAROD CORP.									
	1923	RAF Neutrodyne	135.00	T	3	4	S	Neut.	- 2 - 1
	1924	"	135.00	T	3	4	S	Neut.	- 2 - 1
		V	195.00	T	3	5	S	Neut.	- 2 - 2
		Georgian	450.00	C	3	5	S	Neut.	- 2 - 2
	1925	RAF	135.00	T	3	4	S	Neut.	- 2 - 1
		V	195.00	T	3	5	S	Neut.	- 2 - 2
	1926	Georgian	400.00	C	3	5	A	Neut.	- 2 - 2
		EA	275.00	T	3	5	A	Neut.	- 2 - 2
		EA	310.00		3	5	A	Neut.	- 2 - 2
		EC			1	7	A	Neut.	- 4 - 2
GEARHEART-SCHLEUTER									
	1926	Super 5		T	3	5	S	TRF	- 2 - 2
GENERAL AMERICAN RADIO MFG. CO.									
	1924	Gar Products Cameo A	125.00	T	3	5	S	TRF	- 3 - 2
	1925	Jewel B	175.00	T	3	5	S	TRF	- 3 - 2
GENERAL ELECTRIC CO. All G. E. tube sets were sold under the RCA name until 1931									
	1921	ER-753		MT	1	-	-	C	- - - -
GENERAL INSTRUMENT CO.									
	1921	Six Seventy One		T	1	6	E	TRF	- 2 - 3
GENERAL MOTORS RADIO CORP. (See also Delco Radio Corp. and Delco-Remy.)									
	1924	5105 OEM 11	90.00	T	3	3	S	Rfx	- 2 - 2
		5106 OEM 7	98.00	T	3	4	S	Rfx	- 2 - 2
		5107 Day Radia	225.00	Desk	3	4	S	Rfx	- 2 - 2
	1925	5108 Dayola	125.00	T	3	4	S	Rfx	- 2 - 2
		5109 Daycraft	160.00	T	3	4	S	Rfx	- 2 - 2
		5110 Daytonia	285.00	C	3	4	S	Rfx	- 2 - 2
		5111 OEM 7	98.00	T	3	4	S	Rfx	- 2 - 2
		5112 Dayola	110.00	T	3	4	S	Rfx	- 2 - 2

MANUFACTURER	YEAR	MODEL NO. & NAME	PRICE	STYLE	D	T	P	CIR. & STAGES
GENERAL MOTORS RADIO CORP. (cont.)	1925	5113 Daytonia	300.00	C	1	5	s	Rfx 1 1 - 2
		5114 Dayfan 5	115.00	T	1	5	s	Rfx 1 1 - 2
		5115 OEM 12	75.00	T	4	4	s	Rfx - 2 - 2
		5116 Daycraft 5	165.00	C	1	5	s	Rfx 1 1 - 2
		5117 Day Royal	300.00	C	1	5	s	Rfx 1 1 - 2
		5118 Day Grand	195.00	P	1	5	s	Rfx 1 1 - 2
	1926	Dayphone 5	105.00	CT	1	5	s	Rfx 1 2 - 2
		5121 Dayfan 6	100.00	T	1	6	s	TRF 1 2 - 2
		5122 Daycraft 6	139.00	T	1	6	s	TRF 1 2 - 3
		5124 Dayfan 7	115.00	T	1	7	s	TRF 1 2 - 3
		5125 Daycraft 7	150.00	C	1	7	s	TRF 1 2 - 3
		5126 Day Grand 7	195.00	C	1	7	s	TRF 1 2 - 3
		5127 Day Royal 7	250.00	T	1	7	s	TRF 1 2 - 3
		5128 Dayfan 5	89.00	T	1	5	s	Rfx 1 1 - 2
		5129 Daymar 7	195.00	CT & C	1	7	s	TRF 1 2 - 3
	1927	5131 Daycraft 5	129.00	C	1	5	s	Rfx 1 1 - 2
		5133 Daytonia	295.00	T	1	5	s	TRF 1 1 - 2
		5140 Dayfan 6 Jr.	110.00	T	1	6	s	TRF 1 2 - 2
		5057 Dayfan 6 AC	65.00		1	6	s	TRF 1 2 - 2
		5143 Daycee 6	195.00	T	1	7	A	TRF 1 2 - 2
		5144 Day Royal	235.00	C	1	7	A	TRF 1 2 - 2
		5145 Day Console	115.00	T	1	7	A	TRF 1 2 - 2
		5146 Dayfan 6 AC	235.00	C	1	6	A	TRF 1 2 - 2
		5147 Day Console AC	155.00	T	1	6	A	Rfx - 3 - 2
		5148 Daycraft	160.00	T	1	5	D	TRF 1 2 - 2
		5152 Day Console	115.00	T	1	6	D	TRF 1 2 - 2
		5153 Day Console	150.00	C	1	6	D	TRF 1 2 - 2
		5154 Daycraft	220.00		1	6	A	TRF 1 2 - 2
		5158 Daymar		C	1		A	TRF 1 2 - 2
		Dayfan 6 Jr.			1		A	TRF 1 2 - 2
	1928	5163 Daycee	140.00	C	1	7	A	TRF 1 2 - 2
		5164 Daymar	280.00	C	1	7	A	TRF 1 2 - 2
		5165 Day Royal	195.00	C	1	7	A	TRF 1 2 - 2
		5166 Dayfan	115.00	T	1	7	A	TRF 1 2 - 2
		25 8AC (5069)	150.00	C	1	9	A	TRF 1 3 - 2*
		26 8AC (5069 & 80)	295.00	T	1	9	A	TRF 1 3 - 2*
		27 8AC (5069 & 80)	150.00	C	1	9	A	TRF 1 3 - 2
		28	295.00	C	1	9	A	TRF 1 3 - 2
		35	79.50	C	1	7	s	TRF 1 3 - 2

MANUFACTURER	YEAR	MODEL NO. & NAME	PRICE	STYLE	D	T	P	CIR. & STAGES
GENERAL MOTORS RADIO CORP. (cont.)	1929	43	295.00	C	1	9	A	TRF 1 - 3 - 2*
		48	150.00	T	1	9	A	TRF 1 - 3 - 2*
		54	295.00	C	1	9	A	TRF 1 - 3 - 2*
		56	150.00	T	1	9	A	TRF 1 - 3 - 2*
		66	115.00	T	1	9	A	TRF 1 - 3 - 2*
		67	45.00	T	1	7	S	TRF
		68 A 5003	169.50	C	1	9	A	TRF 1 - 3 - 2*
		69	225.00	C	1	9	A	TRF 1 - 3 - 2*
		72	175.00	C	1	9	A	TRF 1 - 3 - 2*
		73	65.00	T	1	7	S	TRF
		741	119.50	C	1	7	S	TRF
		80	169.50	C	1	9	A	TRF 1 - 3 - 2*
		81	175.00	C	1	9	A	TRF 1 - 3 - 2*
		82	225.00	C	1	9	A	TRF 1 - 3 - 2*
		83	115.00	T	1	9	A	TRF 1 - 3 - 1*
		90	189.50	C	1	7	A	SG - 3 - 1*
		91	240.00	C	1	7	A	SG - 3 - 1*
		93 A5005	189.50	C	1	7	A	SG - 3 - 1*
		94 A5005	240.00	C	1	8	A	SG - 3 - 2*
	1930	120	136.00	LB	1	8	A	SG - 3 - 2*
		130 Sheraton	152.00	C	1	8	A	SG - 3 - 2*
		140 Italian	172.00	C	1	8	A	SG - 3 - 2*
		150 Queen Anne	198.00	C	1	8	A	SG - 3 - 2*
		160 Georgia	272.00	C	1	8	A	SG - 3 - 2*
GENERAL RADIO	1926	Hudson Big 6		T	1	6	S	TRF
				T	3	6	S	TRF
GIBLIN CORP.	SEE	Standard R & Elec. Co.						
GIBSON & DUSTIN	1922	#3 Audion GD-1 Crystal						
GIBSON SEARS RADIO CORP.	1925	Sterling Five	60.00	T	2		E	TRF - 1 - 3
GILBERT, R. W.	1930	69	69.50	M	1	6	A	SF TRF - 3 - 1
GILFILLAN BROS. INC.	1923	R-475	5.00	Box	1	-		C - - -
		R550	15.00	Box	1	3	E	DAA - - - 2
	1924	R475	4.50	Box	1	1	E	DA. - - - 1
		R550		Box	1	2	E	
		GN-1	175.00	T	3	5	S	Neut. - 2 - 2
		GN-2	140.00	T	3	5	S	Neut. - 2 - 2

MANUFACTURER	YEAR	MODEL NO. & NAME	PRICE	STYLE	D	T	P	CIR. & STAGES
GILFILLAN BROS. INC. (cont.)	1925	GN-3	65.00	T	2	4	B	Neut. - 1 - 2
	1926	Portable	65.00	Por	1	6	B	Neut.
		GN-4	70.00	T	2	4	S	Neut. - 1 - 2
		GN-5	110.00	T		5	S	Neut. - 2 - 2
		GN-6	350.00	C	2	5	S	Neut. - 2 - 2
		10	90.00	T	2	5	S	Neut. - 2 - 2
		20	175.00	T	1	6	S	Neut. - 2 - 2
		30	350.00	C	2	6	A	Neut. - 3 - 2
		40	235.00	T	3	6	A	Neut. - 3 - 2
	1927	60	217.00	C	1	6	A	Neut. - 3 - 2
		70	350.00	T	1	8	A	Neut. - 3 - 2
		80	360.00	C	1	8	A	Neut. - 3 - 2
		90	685.00	C	1	6	A	Neut. - 3 - 2
		55	247.00	C	1	6	A	Neut. - 3 - 2
		65	287.50	CL	1	9	A	Neut. - 3 - 2*
	1928	33	247.50	HB	1	9	A	Neut. - 3 - 2*
		44	295.00	C	1	9	A	Neut. - 3 - 2*
		66	295.00	RP	1	9	A	Neut. - 3 - 2*
		77	395.00	LB	1	8	A	SG - 4 - 2
	1929	100	156.50	LB	1	8	A	SG - 4 - 2
		100	187.00	T	1	9	A	SG - 3 - 2*
		101	205.00	T	1	9	A	SG - 3 - 2*
		101	200.00	HB	1	9	A	SG - 3 - 2*
		102	266.00	HB	1	9	A	SG - 3 - 2*
	1930	103	99.50	LB	1	6	A	SG - 3 - 1
		105	132.00	HB	1	6	A	SG - 3 - 1
		106	165.00	RP	1	6	A	SG - 3 - 1
		107						SG
GLED RADIO CO.	1924		125.00			4		RF
			150.00			6		RF
	1925		150.00	Por	1	6	B	RF
GLOBE ELECTRIC CO.	1923	810	80.00			4		RF
	1924	770	55.00			4		RF
		775 Duodyne	80.00			5		RF
		815 "	110.00			5		RF
		900	135.00					RF
		815	280.00	C				RF
		900	300.00	C				RF
	1925	"Panel"	60.00	Ch	3	4	B	TRF - 1 - 2

MANUFACTURER	YEAR	MODEL NO. & NAME	PRICE	STYLE	D	T	P	CIR. & STAGES
GLOBE ELECTRIC CO. (cont.)		"Panel"	80.00	Ch	3	5	B	TRF - 2 - 2
		770	55.00	Por	2	4	S	TRF - 1 - 2
		775 Duodyne	80.00	T	3	4	S	TRF - 2 - 2
		880	100.00	T	3	5	S	TRF - 2 - 2
		815 "	110.00	T	3	5	S	TRF - 2 - 2
		900 "	135.00	C	3	5	S	TRF - 2 - 2
		772	140.00	C	2	4	S	TRF - 1 - 2
		902 "	310.00	T	3	5	S	TRF - 2 - 2
		900 "	120.00	T	3	5	S	TRF - 2 - 2
		700	50.00	T	2	4	S	TRF - 1 - 2
		830	65.00	T	3	5	S	TRF - 2 - 2
	1926	Duodyne						
GLOBE PHONE MANUFACTURING CO.	1923	Globe	6.50				C	- - - -
GLUCK RADIO MANUFACTURING CO.	1925	RF5 Gluckson	98.00	T	3		S	TRF - 2 - 2
GOERDES CO., FRED W.	1925	Dolores DeLuxe	125.00	Glass	3	6	S	TRF - 2 - 3
	1926	Dolores DeLuxe	125.00	Glass	3	6	S	TRF - 2 - 3
GOETZ CO., THE EDW. J.	1923	Edgco DeLuxe	75.00					
GOLDEN-LEUTZ CORP. (Became Leutz, Inc. in 1927) See also Experimenters Information Service and Norden-Hauck.	1924	Super Pliodyne 9	295.00	T	2	9	S	TRF - 5 - 3
		Pliodyne 6	95.00	T	2	6	S	TRF - 2 - 3
	1925	" "	60.00	T	2	6	S	TRF - 2 - 3
		Super Pliodyne 9	295.00	T	2	9	S	TRF - 5 - 3
		Universal Pliodyne	125.00		2	6	S	TRF - 2 - 3
		Admiralty Plio-6	125.00	T	2	6	S	TRF - 2 - 3
		Imperial Plio-6	185.00	T	2	6	S	TRF - 2 - 3
		Admiralty Plio-6 Jr.	210.00	T	2	6	S	TRF - 2 - 3
		Imperial Plio-6 Jr.	270.00	C	2	6	S	TRF - 2 - 3
		Imperial Plio-6	275.00	T	2	6	S	TRF - 2 - 3
		Admiralty Plio-6 Sr.	280.00	T	2	7	S	TRF - 2 - 4
		Admiralty Super 8	350.00	T	2	6	S	TRF - 2 - 3
	1926	9-SE	309.00	C	2	7	S	TRF - 2 - 3
		Imperial Plio-6 Jr.	400.00	T	2	6	S	TRF - 2 - 3
		Imperial Super 8	460.00	TC	2	7	S	TRF - 2 - 4
		Imperial Plio-6 Sr.	500.00	C	2	6	S	TRF - 2 - 3
		Imperial Plio-6 Sr.	520.00	T	2	6	S	TRF - 2 - 3
		Imperial Super 8	570.00	TC	2	7	S	TRF - 2 - 4

MANUFACTURER	YEAR	MODEL NO. & NAME	PRICE	STYLE	D	T	P	CIR. & STAGES
GOLDEN-LEUTZ CORP. (cont.)		Imperial Super 8	610.00	C	2	7	S	TRF	- 2 - 4
		Univ. Transoceanic	990.00	MT	1/5	9	S	TRF	- 4 - 4
		Universal Super 8	460.00	T	2	8	S	TRF	
		Super Plio 9	295.00		2		S	TRF	
		Plio 6	75.00		2		S	TRF	
	1927	Universal Plio 6	125.00			9	S	TRF	- 4 - 4
		Trans'ic Phantom	250.00	MT		9	S	TRF	- 4 - 4
		Univ. Transoceanic	150.00		5		B	TRF	- 2 - 3
		Universal Plio 6	59.00		2		B		- 4 - 4
		Transoceanic 7	150.00				B		- 4 - 4
	1928	Super Pliodyne	650.00			6	B	TRF	- 2 - 3
		P-6	80.00	MT	1	9	B	TRF	- 4 - 4
		AA	200.00	MT	1	9	B	SG	- 4 - 4
		SA	250.00	MT	1	9	S	SG	- 4 - 4
		SG	650.00	MT	5	9	S	SG	- 4 - 4
	1929	Univ. Transoceanic	250.00	C	1	9	A	SG	- 3 - 2*
		Seven Seas Console							
		Silver Ghost							
		Univ. Trans. Phantom							
	1930	Seven Seas Console	295.00	HB	1	9	A	SG	- 3 - 2*
		Seven Seas Console	195.00	LB	1	9	A	SG	- 3 - 2*
		" " Egyptian	610.00	C	1	9	A	SG	- 3 - 2*
		Silver Ghost	2400.00	RP	1	11	A	SG	- 4 - 3*
		7CS	375.00	RP	1	9	A	SG	- 3 - 2*
		SG	2000.00	4 MT	4	12	A	SG	- 4 - 3*
		C S-w		4 MT	4	6	S	TRF Reg.	- 2 - 3
		L S-w			4	6	S	TRF Reg.	- 2 - 3
C and L are in 4 joined metal boxes. Tuning dials can be ganged. L has vernier tuning.								
GOLD MEDAL (Trade Name)	SEE	Consco Elec. Co.						
GOLD MEDAL RADIO CORP.	1926	5-60	25.00	T	3	5	S	TRF	- 2 - 2
		DeLuxe	40.00	T	2	5	S	TRF	- 2 - 2
GOLLOS RADIO CORP.	1925			T	3	5	S	TRF	- 1 - 3
GORMAC ELECTRIC CO.	1926	G-2	40.00	T	3	5	E	TRF	- 2 - 2
		G	45.00	T	3	5	E	TRF	- 2 - 2
		Air Pilot	55.00	T	3	5	E	TRF	- 2 - 2
		Highboy	115.00	C	3	5	E	TRF	- 2 - 2
GOSSARD RADIO & WIRE CO.	1927	527	55.00	T	3	6	S	TRF	- 3 - 2
		627	65.00	T	4	7	S	TRF	- 4 - 2

MANUFACTURER	YEAR	MODEL NO. & NAME	PRICE	STYLE	D	T	P	CIR. & STAGES
GOSSARD RADIO & WIRE CO. (cont.)		527-S	70.00	T		6	S	TRF - 3 - 2
		627-S	80.00	T		7	S	TRF - 4 - 2
		527-C	125.00	C		6	S	TRF - 4 - 2
		627-C	175.00	C		7	S	TRF - 4 - 3
		727-C	275.00	C		8	S	TRF - 4 - 3
		727-C	275.00	C		8	S	TRF - 5 - 2
		727-E	400.00	C		8	S	TRF - 5 - 2
	1928	78B-7	350.00	T		7	S	TRF - 4 - 2
		78B-6	80.00	T		6	S	TRF - 3 - 2
		78B-5	55.00	T		5	S	TRF - 2 - 2
GOTHAM WIRELESS INC.	1924	Royal Knight						
GOULDING MANUFACTURING CO.	1925	5G Ultradyne	225.00	T	2	6	S	TRF - 3 - 2
		3G "	275.00	Por	2	6	S	TRF - 3 - 2
		7G "	300.00	C	2	6	S	TRF - 3 - 2
GOULD SUPPLY CO.	1926 1927	Serenader		T	3	6	S	Reg. TRF - 2 - 3
GRAY & DANIELSON MFG. CO.	1927 1928 1929 1930				1			SH - - - -
	1930	14	64.50	M	1	6	A	SG - 3 - 1
GRAYBAR ELECTRIC CO.	1929	330	147.00	T	1	9	A	SH 2
		340	375.00	C	1	9	A	SH 2
		311	77.50	C	1	7	A	TRF - 3 - 2
		500	110.00	T	1	5	A	SG TRF - 2 - 1
		550	179.00	C	1	5	A	SG TRF - 3 - 1
		310	95.00		1	7	A	TRF - 3 - 2
		320			1	7	A	TRF - 3 - 1
	1930	700	142.00	LB			A	SG - 3 - 1
		770	179.00	HB			A	SG - 3 - 1
		900		RP			A	SG - 3 - 1
GREAT EASTERN RADIO CORP.	1923		80.00	Box	1	5	S	TRF - 1 - 3
GREATER AT. & PACIFIC RADIO CORP.	SEE	At. & Pac. Radio Co.						

83

MANUFACTURER	YEAR	MODEL NO. & NAME	PRICE	STYLE	D	T	P	CIR. & STAGES		
GREAT WESTERN RADIO CORP.	1923	Radyne	130.00						-	-
	1924	"	130.00			3	B	TRF	- 1	- 2
		"	145.00			5	B	TRF	- 2	- 2
	1925	H Radyne	70.00			5	B	TRF	- 2	- 2
		A "	130.00			5	B	TRF	- 2	- 2
		F "								
		Radyne	275.00	CT						
GREBE, A. H. & CO.										
Grebe's first receiver was the CR-1 1 tube regen, 1919. Grebe sold a number of receiver stages in wooden table cabinets, including:	1920	CR-3A, CR-2, CR-4		T	2	1	E	Reg.	-	-
	1921	CR-5	80.00	T	2	1	E	Reg	-	-
		CR-6	180.00	T	2	3	E	Reg	-	2
		KT-1		Por						
	1922	CR-5 (Vernier)		T	2	1	E	Reg	-	-
		Radio Phono (CR-6)		RP	2	3	E	Reg	-	2
		RORB Det-Amp	75.00	T	0	3	E	DAA	-	2
		RORK Amp.	55.00	T	2	2	E	AA	-	
		RORN R. F. Amp		T	2	1	B	RFA	- 1	-
		CR-8 (SW), CR-7 (LW)	80.00	T	2	3	E	Reg.	-	
	1923	CR-9	130.00	T	2	4	E	TRF Reg.	- 1	- 2
		CR-12	175.00	T	2	2	E	TRF Reg.	- 1	-
	1924	CR-13	110.00	T	2	2	E	Reg.	-	
		CR14	155.00	T	3	5	S	TRF	-	2
	1925	Synchrophase	155.00	T	3	5	S	TRF	-	2
		MU1 Synchrophase	156.00	T	3	5	B	TRF	-	2
		MU2 "	320.00	C	1	5	S	TRF	-	2
		DeLuxe		C	1	5	B	TRF	-	2
	1926	Puritan	195.00	C	1	5	E	TRF	-	2
		Princess	220.00	LB	1	5	E	TRF	-	2
		Lancaster	260.00	LB	1	5	E	TRF	-	2
		Andalusia	340.00	C	1	5	E	TRF	-	2
		Renaissance	1400.00	LB	1	5	E	TRF	-	2
		CR18 (Short Wave)	100.00	T	1	2	S	DA	-	1
	1927	C7	145.00	T	1	7	S	TRF	-	2
		Synchrophase Seven	135.00	T	1	7	S	TRF	-	2
	1928	AC6	227.50	T	1	7	A	TRF	- 3	- 2
		AC7	195.00	T	1	8	A	TRF	- 3	- 2
		AC6	600.00	C	1	8	S	TRF	- 4	- 2*
		CR16	150.00	T	1	5	A	TRF	- 1	- 3
		2227 Table only	24.50	Table	1	7	A	TRF	- 3	- 2

RORB   DA
RORD   DAA
RORE   A
RORF   DAA
RORG   DA
RORH   D
RORJ   AA
RORK   AA
RORL   DA
RORN   RFA
RORO   AAA
RORQ   RFA

MANUFACTURER	YEAR	MODEL NO. & NAME	PRICE	STYLE	D	T	P	CIR. & STAGES
GREBE, A. H. & CO. (cont.)		2249 Speaker Stand		Stand				
		2250 Pwr. Amp. & Spkr						
		Power Amp. Table						
		DeLuxe	510.00	T	1	7	A	TRF - 3 - 2
		Buckeye	62.50	C	1	7	A	TRF - 3 - 2
		Buckeye (Cab. only)		C	1	9	A	TRF - 3 - 2
		820		C	1	7	A	TRF - 3 - 2*
		820		C	1	8	A	TRF - 4 - 2
	1929	21950A} Super	219.50	LB	1	7	A	SG - 3 - 1*
		21950B} Synchrophase	219.50	LB	1	7	D	SG - 3 - 1*
		270A	270.00	HB	1	7	A	SG - 3 - 1*
		270B	270.00	HB	1	7	D	SG - 3 - 1*
		270C	270.00	C	1	7	A	SG - 3 - 1*
		285A	285.00	HB	1	7	A	SG - 3 - 1*
		285B	285.00	HB	1	7	D	SG - 3 - 1*
		450A	450.00	RP	1	7	A	SG - 3 - 1*
		450B	450.00	RP	1	7	D	SG - 3 - 1*
	1930	CR18 Sp'l Short Wave	110.00	T	1	3	S	DAA Reg - - 2
		160 (AH-1 Chassis)	160.00	C	1	7	A	SG - 3 - 1*
		18950	189.50	C	1	7	A	SG - 3 - 1*
		225M	225.00	C	1	7	A	SG - 3 - 1*
		225W	225.00	C	1	7	A	SG - 3 - 1*
		265	265.00	C	1	7	A	SG - 3 - 1*
GRIFFIN SMITH MFG. LTD.	1930		69.50	M	1	5	A	SG - 2 - 1
GRIGSBY-GRUNOW CO. "MAJESTIC"	1928	61	85.00	T	1	8	A	SH - 1 - 1*
Even-decade chassis models were used in each series. For example, model 90 chassis was used in cabinet models 90, 91, 92 and 93.		62	99.50	T	1	8	A	SH - 1 - 1*
	1929	71	137.50	HB	1	8	A	RFL - 3 - 2*
		72	167.50	RP LB	1	9	A	RFL - 3 - 2*
		181	265.00	LB	1	8	A	RFL - 3 - 2*
		91	137.50	HB	1	8	A	RFL - 4 - 1*
		92	167.50	RP LB	1	8	A	RFL - 4 - 1*
		101	245.00	LB	1	8	A	RFL - 4 - 1*
	1930	90	95.00	HB	1	8	A	RFL - 4 - 1*
		91	116.00	LB	1	8	A	RFL - 4 - 1*
		92	146.00	LB	1	8	A	RFL - 4 - 1*
		93	146.00	LB	1	8	A	RFL - 4 - 1*
		102	184.00		1	8	A	RFL - 4 - 1*
		103	203.50		1	8	A	RFL - 1 - 1*
		50			1	8	A	SH - 1 - 1*
		31			1	6	A	TRF - 2 - 1*

MANUFACTURER	YEAR	MODEL NO. & NAME	PRICE	STYLE	D	T	P	CIR.	STAGES
GRIGSBY-GRUNOW CO. (cont.)		130	107.50	LB	1	7	A	SG (PT)	3 - 1*
		131	127.50	LB	1	7	A	SG (PT)	3 - 1*
		132	157.50	HB	1	7	A	SG (PT)	3 - 1*
		233	245.00	HB	1	7	A	SG (PT)	3 - 1*
GRIMES, DAVID INC.	1924	3XP	85.00	T	3	3	B	Rfx	2 - 3
	1925	4DL Inverse Duplex Reflex	125.00	T	3	4	B	Rfx	2 - 3
		Baby Grand	49.50	T	2	3	B	Rfx	2 - 3
		5B Baby Grand Duplex	59.50	T	3	5	B	TRF	1 - 3
		5D	85.00	T	3	5	B	TRF	2 - 2
		Empire	100.00	T	3	5	B	TRF	2 - 2
		Renaissance	100.00	T	3	1	B	D	- - -
		Monotube	12.50	T	2		E		
	1926	Tritube	35.00	T	2	3	E	DAA	- - 2
GUARANTY RADIO GOODS CO.	SEE	Columbia Print							
GULBRANSEN CO. Acquired Wells-Gardner line in 1930.	1928	200	235.00	RP	1	9	A	TRF	1 3 - 2*
	1929	290	149.50	HB	1	9	A	TRF	1 3 - 2*
		290A	144.00	HB	1	9	A	TRF	1 3 - 2*
		291	139.50	LB	1	9	A	TRF	1 3 - 2*
		292	149.50	HB	1	9	A	TRF	1 3 - 2*
		295	159.50	C	1	9	A	TRF	1 3 - 2*
		296	149.50	HB	1	9	A	TRF	1 3 - 2*
		297	149.50	LB	1	9	A	TRF	1 3 - 2*
		9950	130.00	HB	1	8	A	SG	- 3 - 2
	1930	161	99.50	HB	1	5	S	SG	- 2 - 2
		53							
GUNDLACH MANHATTAN OPTICAL CO.	1924		5.00	Board	1			C	- - -
	1925		6.00	Board	1			C	- - -
	1926	Korona Crystal		Board	1			C	- - -
				Board	1			C	- - -
GUTHRIE CO.	1924	Bob-o-link	25.00			2		Rfx	
		Nightingale	32.50			4		RF	
		Blue Bird	75.00			4			

MANUFACTURER	YEAR	MODEL NO. & NAME	PRICE	STYLE	D	T	F	CIR. & STAGES
GUTHRIE CO. (cont.)	1925	Mocking Bird	90.00	T	2	6	E	TRF - 2 - 2
		Goldfinch	75.00	C	3	5	E	TRF - 2 - 3
	1926	5 Nightingale	35.00	C	3	5	E	TRF - 2 - 2
		6	40.00	T	3	6	E	TRF - 2 - 3
		5-50	50.00	T	3	5	E	TRF - 2 - 3
		6-60	60.00	T		6	E	TRF - 2 - 3
	1927	E-6-2 Nightingale	40.00	Ch		6	E	TRF - 2 - 3
		S-6-1	60.00	Ch		7	E	TRF - 3 - 4
		A-8-1	75.00					
HADDAWAY MANUFACTURING CO.	1926	6R	85.00	C				TRF
		6R2	125.00	Panel				TRF
		6R	160.00	C				TRF
	1927	AC6	162.00				A	TRF - 2 - 3
HALES	1925	Californian	80.00	T	2	5	S	TRF
HALL, CHARLES	1924	Flexodyne	225.00					RF
	1925	27 Flexodyne	775.00					
	1926	11						
HALLDORSON CO., THE	1923		98.00		3	4	S	TRF - 1 - 2
	1924	RD400	120.00	T	3	4	S	TRF - 2 - 1
			67.50	T	3	4	S	TRF - 2 - 1
			98.00	T	2	4	S	TRF - 2 - 2
	1925	RF400	65.00		3	4	S	TRF - 2 - 2
		RF500	75.00		3	5	S	TRF - 2 - 2
		"	115.00					TRF - 2 - 2
	1926	"	75.00	T		5		TRF - 2 - 2
			75.00					
HALLER, W. B.	1923	III Hallerio	5.00					C
	1924	IV	3.00		2			C
		V	4.00		1			C
	1925	1½	5.00		1			C
		3½	1.50		1			C
		III	3.50					C
			3.00					

MANUFACTURER	YEAR	MODEL NO. & NAME	PRICE	STYLE	D	T	P	CIR. & STAGES
HALLER, W. B. (cont.)		IV Hallerio	4.00					C - - - -
		V "	5.00					C - - - -
	1926	Hallerio	2.50		2			C - - - -
		III Hallerio	3.00		1			C - - - -
		IV (4) "	4.00		1			C - - - -
		5	6.00					C - - - -
HALLOCK & WATSON	1923	RF12	100.00					RF
	1924	RF12	100.00					
		RF22	125.00		4			
		TR5-5	135.00		5			
	1925	TR-5 Halowat	90.00					RF
		TR-R "	90.00					
	1926	TR-5 "			3	5	E	TRF - 2 - 2
		AW-5 "	160.00					
HALVERSON CO., H. J.	1924							C - - -
HAMBURG BROS.	1924	No. 1 Pennsylvania	4.20					C - - -
		No. 2 "	3.00					C - - -
	1925	No. 1 "	4.50					C - - -
		No. 2 "	3.00					C - - -
	1926	No. 1 " Jr.	2.00					C - - -
		No. 2 " "	2.00					C - - -
HAMILTON RADIO INC	1925	Babe	125.00	Por	1	6	B	RF - 3 - 2
HAMMARLUND-ROBERTS, INC.	1925	Hammarlund-Roberts	60.85	Kit	2	5	S	Reg. TRF - 1 - 2
	1926	HI-Q		Kit	2	5	S	TRF - 2 - 2
	1927	HI-Q		Kit	2	6	S	TRF - 2 - 2
		HI-Q Six		Kit	1	6	S	TRF - 3 - 2
	1928	HI-Q-29 Junior	54.35	Ch	1	7	A	SG 1 - 1 - 3
		HI-Q-29 "	103.95	Ch	1	5	S	SG 1 - 1 - 3
		HI-Q-29 Master	99.50	Ch	2	5	S	SG - 2 - 2
		HI-Q-29 "	151.80	Ch	2	6	A	SG - 2 - 2
	1929	HI-Q-30, 31			1	7	S	SG (PT) - 3 - 2*
	1930	HI-Q-30, 31			1	8	A	SG (PT) - 3 - 2*
		HI-Q-30, 31			1	7	D	SG (PT) - 3 - 2*

MANUFACTURER	YEAR	MODEL NO. & NAME	PRICE	STYLE	D	T	P	CIR. & STAGES
HANSCOM RADIO DEVICES	1925	Superunit	37.50		-	4	S	SH
	1926	"	75.00		-	4	S	SH
		" A	37.50		-	4	B	TRF - 3 - 2
		" C	50.00		-	6	S	TRF - 3 - 2
		" 6	37.50		-	4	S	TRF - 3 - 2
		" Jr.			-		S	TRF - 1 - 2
HANSEN STORAGE CO.	1924	Nightingale	32.50	T	1	4	S	TRF - 1 - 2
	1925	"	57.50	T	2	4	S	TRF - 1 - 2
		Gold Finch	75.00	T	2	5	S	TRF - 2 - 2
		American Crest	150.00		2	5	S	TRF - 2 - 2
HARCO PRODUCTS CO.	1923	Radio						
	1924	Tektor						
HARCOURT RADIO CO.	1924	Reflex Erla	100.00		5			Rfx - - - -
	1925	Harco Crystal	3.00		1	3		Rfx
								C
HARDING MANUFACTURING CORP.	1925	RF5	125.00	T	3	5	S	TRF - 2 - 2
		RF6	175.00	T	3	6	S	TRF - 2 - 3
		" "	275.00	C	3	6	S	TRF - 2 - 3
HARGRAVES, C. E. & H. T.	1924	Mel-o-tone						C - - - -
	1925							
	1926	Mel-o-tone						C - - - -
HARKNESS RADIO CORP., KENNETH	1925	Counterflex	33.50	T	2	2	S	Rfx
		"	36.00	T	2	3	S	Rfx
	1926	Harkness	47.50	T	3	5	S	Rfx
HARMON & SONS, W. H.	1925	IVC Harmonson	185.00	T	2	4	E	TRF - 1 - 2
		IVC " Grand	205.00	T	2	4	E	TRF - 1 - 2
		IVA "	80.00		2	4	E	TRF - 1 - 2
		IVA "	110.00		2	4	E	TRF - 1 - 2
		IVC "	130.00		2	4	E	TRF - 2 - 2
		Harmonson Unitro	175.00		1	5	E	TRF - 2 - 2
		IVA-R Harmonson	50.00		2		E	TRF - 1 - 1

MANUFACTURER	YEAR	MODEL NO. & NAME	PRICE	STYLE	D	T	P	CIR.	& STAGES
HARMON & SONS, W. H. (cont.)		VC Harmonson Grand	135.00		3		E	Reg. RF	- 1 - -
		Unitrol Grand	175.00		1		E	TRF	- 2 - -
		Unitrol	150.00		1		E	TRF	- 2 - -
	1926	IVA Harmonson	75.00		2	4	E	TRF	- 1 - 2
	1927	VC	135.00	T	3		E	TRF	- 1 - 3
		5-C "	100.00	T			B		- 2 - 3
		Unitrol	150.00	T			B		
HARMONY MANUFACTURING CO.	1925	5	162.50	T	1	5	S	RF	- 2 - 2
HAROLD HERBERT INC.	1926	39	39.50	T	3	5	S	TRF	- 2 - 2
		59	59.50	T	3	5	S	TRF	- 2 - 2
	1927	Lectro	120.00	T	3		A	TRF	
		200	200.00	T	3		A	TRF	
		275	275.00	C	3		A	TRF	
HARRIS & BIRDSEYE	1924	Harco							
HARTMAN ELEC. MFG. CO.	1925	10A Adam P	225.00	C	2	4	B	TRF	- 1 - 2
		12A " "	245.00	C	3	5	B	TRF	- 1 - 2
		10A Italian Period	305.00	C	2	4	B	TRF	- 2 - 2
		12A " "	295.00	C	3	5	B	TRF	- 1 - 2
		10A Q. Anne P.	315.00	C	2	4	B	TRF	- 1 - 2
		12A " "	135.00	Por.	3	5	B	TRF-	- 1 - 2
		10B	155.00	Por.	2	4	B	TRF	- 2 - 2
		12B	100.00	Por.	3	5	B	TRF	- 1 - 2
		10C	120.00	Por	2	4	B	TRF	- 1 - 2
		12C	120.00	T	3	5	B	TRF	- 2 - 2
	1926	Compact	100.00	C	1	6	E	TRF	- 3 - 2
		Jr. Upright	135.00	C	1	6	E	TRF	- 3 - 2
		Sr. Upright	175.00	C	1	6	E	TRF	- 3 - 2
		Sheraton	180.00	C	1	6	E	TRF	- 3 - 2
	1927	Compact	65.00	T	1	6	S/B	TRF	- 3 - 2
		Jr. Upright	95.00	C	1	6	S/B	TRF	- 3 - 2
		Sr. Upright	120.00	C	1	6	S/B	TRF	- 3 - 2
		Sheraton	120.00	C	1	6	S/B	TRF	- 3 - 2
HARVEY MANUFACTURING CO.	1927	527	39.50	Ch	1	4	S	TRF	- 2 - 2
		627	49.50	Ch	1	5	S	TRF	- 3 - 2
		727	200.00	C	1	6	S	TRF	- 3 - 3
HATRY & YOUNG	1930	HY-7 S. W.	58.50	K	1	6	S	SH	- - 2 1

MANUFACTURER	YEAR	MODEL NO. & NAME	PRICE	STYLE	D	T	P	CIR. & STAGES	
HAYES & NEWTON	1923	Universal	110.00 90.00 85.00	Boxes	2	3	S	DAA	- - - 2
	1924	Universal				3			
HAYES PRODUCTS CO.									
HAYNES-GRIFFIN RADIO SERVICE INC.	1926			T	2	5	S/A	TRF	
	1925	Superhet.	100.00	Por	2	8	B		
HEARWELL ELECTRIC CO	1924	Variometer Lyric	10.00	Box	1	-	-	C	- - - -
	1925	Whole Wave Receiver	8.00	Box	1	-	-	C	- - - -
	1926	Forbes Short Wave	35.00	Box	1	-	B	C	- - - -
			3.75	Box	1	1	-	D	- - - -
			10.00	Por	2	-	B	C	- - - -
			10.00	Box	1	1	B	Reg.	- - - -
HEINEMANN ELECTRIC CO.	1923	3051 Sensory	10.00					C	- - - -
HENDERSON BROS.	1926	Compact	29.50	T	3	5	S	TRF	- 2 - 2
		Standard	45.00	T	3	5	S	TRF	- 2 - 2
HENNINGER CORP., A. P.	1926			T	2	6		TRF	- 2 - 3
HERALD RADIO CO.	1926	Dyne 6	50.00	C	2	6	S	TRF	- 2 - 3
HERKE RADIO PRODUCT CO.	1923	HRP	25.00						
	1924	"	98.50						
		"	25.00						
		"	98.50						
		Cry.	150.00						
		"	2.75						
		Neut.	10.00						
			250.00						
HERZOG RADIO CORP.	1924 1925	Automatic	310.00		1	6 7		RF	- 3 - 3
HESSON RADIO LABORATORIES	1926	Super Heturnat	185.00						

91

MANUFACTURER	YEAR	MODEL NO. & NAME	PRICE	STYLE	D	T	P	CIR. & STAGES
HETEROPLEX MANUFACTURING CO.	1924	Warner Heteroplex	100.00			3		
HETROLA RADIO CO. LTD.	1925	R-199P	165.00	Por	2	7	B	SH
HIGH FREQUENCY LABORATORIES	1928	Isotone	105.00	Ch	1	10	S	SG SH - - 3 3*
	1929	Special Nine	95.00	Ch	1	9	S	SG SH - - 4 2
		Mastertone		Ch	1	11	A	SG SH - - 4 2*
	1930	Mastertone		Ch	1	10	A	SG SH - 1 2 2*
HOAG MANUFACTURING CO.	1925	Blitzdyne	65.00	T	2	5	E	TRF - 2 - 2
HOLLYWOOD RADIO CO.	1925	Hollywood Five	45.00	T	3	5	S	TRF - 2 - 2
HOLLYWOOD YALE CORP.	1925	Masterpiece	110.00	T	3	6	B	TRF - 2 - 3
HOLT ENGLER CORP.	1925	Engler 5DV		P	2	5		
HOME ELECTRIC & MFG. CO.	1923	Mercury	50.00					TRF
		Baby Grand	36.00					Rfx
		Virginia	44.00					Rfx
		Neptune	78.00					Rfx
		Jupiter	90.00	Por				Rfx
		1 Porto	43.00					Rfx
		2 Porto	50.00					Rfx
		3 Porto	56.00			1		
	1924	Baby Grand	36.00			2		
		Virginia	44.00			2		TRF
		Mercury	50.00			3		
		Neptune	78.00			4		
		Jupiter	90.00					
HOMER PRODUCTS INC.	1927	Homer	80.00	Ch			B	
		Homer	95.00	T			B	
		Senior	150.00	T			B	
HONESDALE RADIO CO.	1925	1 Wayne 4	50.00	T	1	4	S	TRF - 1 - 2
		1 " 2	55.00	T	1	4	S	TRF - 1 - 2
		Wayne 5	65.00	T	3	5	S	TRF - 2 - 2
		Wayne Superior	100.00	T	2		S	Rfx
HORN, H. H.	1930	Tiffany Tone	59.50	M	1	7	A	TRF - 2 - 1*
HORNE	1922	Neptune, Jupiter, Mars, Venus						

MANUFACTURER	YEAR	MODEL NO. & NAME	PRICE	STYLE	D	T	P	CIR. & STAGES
HOWARD MANUFACTURING CO. Common chasses were used across model lines. "Green Diamond 8" chasses were used in Neutrodyne sets. "SG" chasses were used in 1929-30 with minor variations.	1924	Table	135.00	T	3	5	S	Neut. - 2 - 2
		Console	325.00	C	3	5	S	Neut. - 2 - 2
		Phonograph Panel	180.00	P	3	5	S	Neut. - 2 - 2
	1925	D4	135.00	T	3	4	B	Neut. - 2 - 1
		A5	200.00	T	3	5	S	Neut. - 2 - 2
	1926	S7	375.00	T	2	7	S/A	Neut. - 3 - 3
		S7	675.00	C	2	7	S/A	Neut. - 3 - 3
		A6	200.00	T	2	6	S	Neut. - 2 - 3
		A6	425.00	C	2	6	S	Neut. - 2 - 3
	1927	135	325.00	C	2	6	S	Neut. - 2 - 3
		135	135.00	Desk C	1	7	A	TRF - 3 - 2
		135	165.00	C	1	7	A	TRF - 3 - 2
		135	290.00	Desk C	1	7	A	TRF - 3 - 2
		135	325.00	C	1	7	A	TRF - 3 - 2
		135	245.00	Desk	1	7	A	TRF - 3 - 2
		135	395.00	C	1	7	A	TRF - 3 - 2
		445 (135 chassis)	445.00	C	1	7	A	TRF - 3 - 2
		495 (135 chassis)	495.00	C	1	7	A	TRF - 3 - 2
		S7	375.00	T	1	9	A	Neut. - 3 - 3
		S7	675.00	C	1	9	A	Neut. - 3 - 3
	1928	Consolette	175.00	C	1	9	A	Neut. - 4 - 2*
		Hepplewhite	235.00	C	1	9	A	Neut. - 4 - 2*
		Gothic	275.00	C	1	9	A	Neut. - 4 - 2*
		Florentine	275.00	C	1	9	A	Neut. - 4 - 2*
		High Boy	199.50	C	1	9	A	Neut. - 4 - 2*
	1929	Sheraton	235.00	HB	1	9	A	Neut. - 4 - 2*
		Louis XVI	255.00	HB	1	9	A	Neut. - 4 - 2*
		Consolette		C	1	8	A	SG - 3 - 2*
		Hepplewhite		C	1	8	A	SG - 3 - 2*
		Gothic		C	1	8	A	SG - 3 - 2*
		Florentine		C	1	8	A	SG - 3 - 2*
		High Boy		HB	1	8	A	SG - 3 - 2*
		Sheraton		HB	1	8	A	SG - 3 - 2*
		Louis XVI		LB	1	7	A	SG - 3 - 1*
	1930	Plymouth SG A	165.00	HB	1	7	A	SG - 3 - 1*
		Consolette SG A	185.00	HB	1	7	A	SG - 3 - 1*
		Puritan SG A	215.00	HB	1	7	A	SG - 3 - 1*
		Patrician SG A	215.00	HB	1	7	A	SG - 3 - 1*
		Combination SG C	325.00	LB RP	1	7	A	SG - 3 - 1*
		SG B	69.50	M	1	6	A	SG - 3 - 1

MANUFACTURER	YEAR	MODEL NO. & NAME	PRICE	STYLE	D	T	P	CIR. & STAGES
HOWE AUTO PRODUCTS CO.	1925		1.75				C	- - - -
	1926	No. 1	1.75				C	- - - -
		No. 2	5.00				C	- - - -
			7.50				C	- - - -
HUDSON TERMINAL RADIO & ELEC. CO.	1925	Sloped	40.00	T	3	6	S	TRF	- 2 - 1
		Console	125.00	C	3	6	E	TRF	
HUNT CO., W. D.	1926	Hexadyne	125.00	Por	1	5	B	RF	- 3 - 2
		"	300.00	C	1	6	A	RF	- 3 - 2
HUNTINGTON RADIO CO.	1925	5	115.00	T	2	5	E	TRF	- 2 - 2
		6	145.00	T	3	6	E	TRF	- 3 - 2
HYATT ELECTRIC CORP.	1927	A	95.00	Por		6	B	TRF	- 3 - 2
	1928	A	75.00	Por		6	B	TRF	- 3 - 2
		C	60.00	Por		5	B	TRF	- 2 - 2
	1929	AC7	75.00	CC		7	A	SG	- 2 - 2*
	1930	M5	55.00	Auto		5	S	SG	- 2 - 2
		D	50.00	Por		5	B	TRF	- 2 - 2
		A6	65.00	Por		5	B	SG	- 2 - 2
HYMAN & CO. INC., HENRY	1923		7.50				-	C	-
			25.00						
			29.00						
	1924	V60	150.00	T	2	5	E		- 1 - 3
	1925	V60 Imperial Bestone	150.00	T	2	5	E		- 1 - 3
		V60 Bestone	115.00		2	5	E		- 1 - 3
		"Aristocrat"	100.00	TS	2	5	E		- 1 - 3
		Bestone	165.00	T	3	5	S		- 2 - 2
		"	42.50	T	3	5	S		- 2 - 2
		"	59.50	T	3	5	S		- 2 - 2
		"	62.50	T	3	5	S		- 2 - 2
		"	72.50	T	3	5	S		- 2 - 2
		"	78.00	P	3	5	S		- 2 - 2
		"	85.00	T	3	5	S		- 2 - 2
		"	119.00		3	6	S		- 3 - 2
		"	88.00		3	6	S		- 3 - 2
		"	150.00						

MANUFACTURER	YEAR	MODEL NO. & NAME	PRICE	STYLE	D	T	P	CIR. & STAGES
ILLINOIS RADIO APPLIANCE CO.	1926	a-18 Emmons Premier	40.00	T	3	5	3	TRF - 2 - 2
		a-21 "	60.00	T	3	5	3	TRF - 2 - 2
		a-28 "	75.00	T	3	5	3	TRF - 2 - 2
		a-H18 "	150.00	C	2	5	2	TRF - 2 - 2
ILLINOIS RADIO ENGINEERS	1926	5	80.00	T	3	5		TRF - 2 - 2
IMPERIAL RADIO CORP.	1926	5	55.00	T	3	5	E	TRF - 2 - 2
	1927	a-5 Michigan	40.00	T	1	5	S	TRF - 2 - 2
		6	50.00	C	1	6	S	TRF - 2 - 3
		6	75.00	C	1	6	S	TRF - 2 - 3
		6	150.00	C	1	6	A	TRF - 2 - 3
IMPERIAL RADIO CO.	1927	T-6 Le Pilote	85.00	T		6	S	TRF - 3 - 2
		C-6 " "	140.00	C		6	S	TRF - 3 - 2
INCANDESCENT SUPPLY CO. "NEWLANDS"	1925	Cabinet	70.00	T	3	5	S	TRF - 2 - 2
		DeLuxe	125.00	T	3	5	S	TRF - 2 - 2
		"	170.00	C	3	5	S	TRF - 2 - 2
INDEPENDENT RADIO LABS.	1925	IRL	38.50	T	2		E	- 1 - 2
		IRL-Super 4	50.00	T	3		S	- 2 - 2
		IRL-5	65.00	T				
INDIANA MFG. & ELEC. CO.	1925	500 Hyperdyne	62.50	T	3	5	E	TRF - 2 - 2
		600 "	37.50	Panel	3	5	E	TRF - 2 - 2
		500 "	65.00	T	3	5	E	TRF - 2 - 2
		700 "	175.00	C	3	6	E	TRF - 2 - 3
		502 "	80.00	T	3	6	E	TRF - 2 - 3
		701 "	200.00	C	3	6	E	TRF - 2 - 3
		503 "	100.00	C	3	6	E	TRF - 2 - 3
		702 "	175.00	C	3	5	E	TRF - 2 - 3
	1926	503 (Case)	100.00	T	3	6		TRF - 2 - 3
		506 "	75.00	T	3	5		TRF - 2 - 2
		500 "	65.00	T	3	5	E	TRF - 2 - 2
		701 "	200.00	C	3	6		TRF - 2 - 2
		60A	75.00	T	2	6		TRF - 2 - 2
		60B	100.00	HBC	2	6		TRF - 2 - 2
		60C	125.00		2	6		TRF - 2 - 2
		60D	170.00	C	2	6		TRF - 2 - 3

MANUFACTURER	YEAR	MODEL NO. & NAME	PRICE	STYLE	D	T	P	CIR. & STAGES
INDIANA MFG. & ELEC. CO. (cont.)		503	85.00	T	2	6		TRF
		701	180.00	C	2	6		TRF
		702	160.00	C	2	5		TRF
		600	90.00					TRF
		606	100.00					TRF
		603	110.00					TRF
		703	170.00					TRF
	1927	60A	65.00	T		8	S/B	TRF - 3 - 2
		61A	85.00	T		6	S/B	TRF - 3 - 2
		61C	135.00	HB-C		6	S/B	TRF - 3 - 2
		62B	185.00	T		6	A	TRF - 3 - 2
		90A	225.00	T		9	S/B	TRF - 6 - 2
		62C	235.00	HB-C		6	A	TRF - 3 - 2
		92A	350.00	C		9	A	TRF - 6 - 2
		90C	350.00	C		9	S/B	TRF - 6 - 2
		92C	475.00	C		9	A	TRF - 6 - 2
INDUSTRIAL RADIO SERVICE	1924	Ultra-Marvel	70.00	T	2	3	S	Rfx - 2 - 1
		404	75.00	T	2	3	S	Rfx - 2 - 1
		404A	100.00	T	2	4	S	Rfx - 2 - 2
	1925	Ultra-Marvel "	120.00	T	3	4	S	TRF - 2 - 2
	1926	" "		T	2	5	S	TRF - 2 - 2
		Ultrola		C	2	6	S	TRF - 3 - 2
INMAN SPECIALTY STORE	1926		5.00	Kit				C - - - -
INTERCITY RADIO CO.								
INTERNATIONAL RADIO CO.	1925 1926		7.50	T	3	1	E	Reg. - - - -
INTERNATIONAL RADIO CORP.	1925	10 Rotofor	110.00	T	1			TRF
		20 "	145.00	T	1			TRF
		30 "	165.00	T	1			TRF
		40 "	260.00	T	1			TRF
		50 "	290.00	T	1			TRF
	1926	3	69.00	T	1	5	S	TRF - 2 - 2
		5	89.00	T	1	5	S	TRF - 2 - 2
		10	97.00	T	1	5	S	TRF - 2 - 2

MANUFACTURER	YEAR	MODEL NO. & NAME	PRICE	STYLE	D	T	P	CIR. & STAGES
INTERNATIONAL RADIO CORP. (cont.)		20	128.00	T	1	5	S	TRF - 2 - 2
		30	150.00	End-T	1	5	S	TRF - 2 - 2
		41	160.00		1	5	S	TRF - 2 - 2
		51	190.00	D	1	5	S	- 2 - 2
		40	235.00	HB	1	5	S	- 2 - 2
		50	250.00	C	1	5	S	- 2 - 2
INTERNATIONAL TEL. & TEL. CO.	SEE	Kolster Radio Inc.						
IRVING RADIO CORP.	1925	42 Irvington	55.00	T	3	5	S	TRF - 2 - 2
		44 Favorite	65.00	T	3	5	S	TRF - 2 - 2
		46 Aristocrat	85.00	T	3	5	S	TRF - 2 - 2
		Favorite	60.00	T	3	5	E	TRF - 2 - 2
			65.00	T	3	5	E	TRF - 2 - 2
	1926	42	125.00	C	3	5	E	TRF - 2 - 2
		44	49.50	T	3	5	S	TRF - 2 - 2
		46	65.00	T	3	5	S	TRF - 2 - 2
			80.00	T	3	5	S	TRF - 2 - 2
JACKSON BELL CO.	1928	5	69.50	T		5	A	
	1929	59	59.50	M		7	A	
		60	59.50	M		7	A	
		6	79.50	T		6	A	
		6	99.50	C		6	A	
		8	108.00	T		8	A	
		8	124.50	LB		8	A	
		8	134.50	H		8	A	
	1930	Imperial DeLuxe	144.50	C	1	6	A	SG - 3 - 1
		62 Modern	59.50	M	1	6	A	SG - 3 - 1
		62 Round Top	59.50	M			A	
JACKSON RESEARCH LABORATORY	1930	N-J-30	77.50	Ch	1	6	A	SG - 2 - 2
JAYNXON LABORATORIES	1923							C - - - -
	1924							C - - - -
	1925							
	1926							
JEWEL MANUFACTURING CO.	1930	M	59.50	M	1	5	A	SG - 2 - 1

Je

MANUFACTURER	YEAR	MODEL NO. & NAME	PRICE	STYLE	D	T	P	CIR. & STAGES
JEWETT RADIO & PHONOGRAPH CO.	1925	Jewett Receiver	140.00	T	2	5	E	TRF - 2 - 2
	1926	"	155.00	T	2	5	E	TRF - 2 - 2
JOLLEY RADIO CO.	1924							
JOLLEY RADIO COMPACT	1926							
JONES AGENCIES, EDWARD	1925	II Radiograph	150.00	T	3	5	S	TRF - 2 - 2
JONES RADIO CO.	1921	S/W Model H	29.00	T	3	1	S	Reg. 2
	1923	SMJ Symphony	150.00	T	3	4	S	Reg. 2
		502J	165.00	T	3	3	S	Reg. 3
		503J	175.00	T	3	4	S	Reg. 3
		Port	132.00	Por	3	4	S	Reg. 3
	1924	SMJ	150.00		3	4	S	Reg. 3
		502J	165.00		3	4	S	Reg. 3
		503J	175.00		3	3	S	Reg. 2
	1925	Symphony	165.00	T	3	4	E	Reg. 3
	1926							
	1927	29 Harmonic	100.00	T	3	4	S	Reg. 1 - 3
JONES RADIO MANUFACTURING CO. (Joseph W. New York)	1924	Semi-Portable	100.00	Por	2	4		RF
			50.00	Por	1	4		RF
			100.00	P	3	6		RF
			160.00	Por	3	4		RF
	1925	J-80	80.00	T	3	6	S	TRF - 1 - 2
		Port.	160.00	T	3	5	S	TRF - 3 - 2
		J-75S.P.	75.00	T	3	5	S	TRF - 2 - 2
		J-100B	100.00		3	6	S	TRF - 2 - 2
		J-175	175.00		3	5	S	TRF - 2 - 3
			125.00		3	6	S	TRF - 2 - 2
		J-100-C	150.00	Stand	3	6	S	TRF - 2 - 3
		J-175-C	250.00		3	5	S	TRF - 2 - 3
		J-175D	475.00		3	4	S	TRF - 2 - 3
		J-85	85.00	T	2	5	S	TRF - 2 - 3
		J-65	65.00	T	3	6	S	TRF - 2 - 2
		JW-90	90.00		3	5	S	TRF - 1 - 2
		J-195	195.00	T	3	6	S	TRF - 2 - 2
		J-75B	75.00		3	5	S	TRF - 2 - 2

MANUFACTURER	YEAR	MODEL NO. & NAME	PRICE	STYLE	D	T	P	CIR. & STAGES
JONES RADIO MANUFACTURING CO. (cont.) (Joseph W. New York)	1925	J-75-T	110.00	Stand	3	5	S	TRF - 2 - 2
	1926	J-621	65.00	T	3	6	E	TRF - 2 - 3
		J-700	125.00	T	3	6	E	TRF - 2 - 3
		J-675	85.00	T	3	6	E	TRF - 2 - 3
		J-655	75.00	T	3	6	E	TRF - 2 - 3
		J-175	175.00	T	3	6	E	TRF - 2 - 3
		J-195B	150.00	C	3	6	E	TRF - 2 - 3
	1927	J-621	45.00	T	3	6	S	TRF - 2 - 3
		J-625	45.00	T	3	6	S	TRF - 2 - 3
		J-600	60.00	T	3	6	S	TRF - 2 - 3
JONES RADIO MANUFACTURING CO.	1926	Jones DeLuxe	150.00	T	1	6		RF - 3 - 2
		Concerdyne	175.00	T	2	8		RF - 4 - 3
		Oriola	250.00	C	2	8		RF - 4 - 3
KAESS MANUFACTURING CORP.	1926	Clearview Six				6		
KARDON PRODUCTS CO..	SEE	Diva Radio Corp.						
KARDON RADIO CO.	SEE	Diva Radio Corp.						
KEHLER RADIO LABORATORIES	1924	Radola	150.00	T	3	5	B	TRF - 2 - 2
	1925	Tranadyne	110.00	T	3	5	S	TRF - 2 - 2
	1926	"						
KELLER-FULLER MFG. CO. LTD.	1930	F14	59.50	M	1	6	A	SG - 3 - 1
		Radiette		M	1	4	A	TRF - 1 - 1
KELLOGG SWITCHBOARD & SUPPLY CO. "WAVEMASTER"	1922	Kellogg	125.00	T	1	1	S	Reg. - - -
	1925	Wavemaster	145.00	T	3	5	S	TRF - 2 - 2
		"	225.00	T	3	5	S	TRF - 2 - 2
		"	235.00	CL	3	5	S	TRF - 2 - 2
		"	275.00	C	3	5	S	TRF - 2 - 2
		"	335.00	C	3	5	S	TRF - 2 - 2
		"	375.00	C	1	5	S	TRF - 2 - 2
		"	400.00	C	3	7	S	RFL - 4 - 2
	1926	504	75.00	T	3	5	S	TRF - 2 - 2
		505	125.00	C	3	5	S	TRF - 2 - 2
		506	135.00	CL	3	5	S	TRF - 2 - 2
		507	215.00	T	1	6	S	RFL - 3 - 2

MANUFACTURER	YEAR	MODEL NO. & NAME	PRICE	STYLE	D	T	P	CIR. & STAGES	
KELLOGG SWITCHBOARD & SUPPLY CO (cont.)		508	345.00	C	1	6	S	RFL	- 3 - 2
		601	200.00	T	1	5	S	RFL	- 2 - 2
		701	400.00	C	1	7	S	RFL	- 4 - 2
	1927	510	495.00	C	1	8	A	RFL	- 4 - 2
		511	365.00	CL	1	8	A	RFL	- 4 - 2
		512	495.00	C	1	8	A	RFL	- 4 - 2
	1928	514	495.00	C	1	8	A	RFL	- 4 - 2
		515	169.00	T	1	6	A	RFL	- 2 - 2
		516	375.00	C	1	8	A	RFL	- 4 - 2
		517	775.00	C	1	8	A	RFL	- 4 - 2
		518	225.00	CL	1	6	A	RFL	- 2 - 2
		519	275.00	T	1	6	A	RFL	- 2 - 2
		520	115.00	C	1	6	A	RFL	- 2 - 2
		521	199.50	C	1	6	A	RFL	- 2 - 2
		521B	199.50	C	1	9	A	SG	- 3 - 2*
	1929	523	250.00	C	1	10	A	SG	- 3 - 2*
		524	295.00	RP	1	10	A	SG	- 3 - 2*
		525	395.00	C	1	9	A	SG	- 3 - 2*
		526	185.00	C	1	10	A	SG	- 3 - 2*
		527	235.00	RP	1	10	A	SG	- 3 - 2*
	1930	528	405.00	C	1	8	A	SG	- 3 - 2*
		533		C	1	8	A	SG	- 3 - 2*
		534, 535, 536							
KEMPER RADIO CORP. LTD.	1930	SG-7	119.00	T	1	7	A	SG	- 2 - 2*
		SG-71	141.00	LB	1	7	A	SG	- 2 - 2*
		80 Kemper Kompak	69.50	M	1	6	A	SG	- 2 - 2
KEMPER RADIO LABORATORIES	1925	K51	135.00	Por	2	5	B	TRF	1 - - 2
	1926	K52	135.00	Por	2	5	B		
	1927	K53	135.00			5			
		Radiomobile	225.00						
	1928	K56	99.50			5			
	1929	K57 Kompak	74.50	Por		5	A		
		K53	65.00			5	B		
	1930	SG7	129.50	T		7	A	SG	- 2 - 2*
KEN-MAR RADIO CORP.	1925	10 }International 11 }Babydyne	10.00 13.50	B B	1 1	1	B B	Reg. Reg.	
		4 Ken Mar	85.00	T	2		B	TRF	

MANUFACTURER	YEAR	MODEL NO. & NAME	PRICE	STYLE	D	T	P	CIR. & STAGES	
KEN-MAR RADIO CORP. (cont.)		{10 International	10.00	B	1		B	Reg.	
		{11 Babydyne	13.50	B	1		B	Reg.	
		4 Ken Mar	85.00	T	2		B	TRF	
		Lincoln	30.00	T	3		B	TRF	
		" DeLuxe	35.00	T	3		B	TRF	
KENMAN ELECTRIC CO. INC.	1925	Kenman-5-1926	37.50	T	3	5	S	TRF	- 2 - 2
		" -5-1926	29.75	T	3	5	S	TRF	- 2 - 2
KENNEDY CO., COLIN B.	1919	Short Wave	210.00	T	4	1	-	PT	
	1921	220 Intermediate	200.00	T	4	1		Reg.	- - 2
	1922	281/54 Short Wave	285.00	2T	3	3		Reg.	- - 2
		220/525	250.00	2T	4	3		Reg.	- - 2
	1923	110 Intermediate Wave		2T	4	3		Reg.	- - 2
		Universal		Por	2	1	E	Reg.	- - ,
		311	75.00	T	2	1	E	Reg.	- - 2
		V	86.50	T	2	3	B	Reg.	- - 2
		X	285.00	C	2	3	B	Reg.	- - 2
		Jacobean	775.00	C	2	3	B	Reg.	- - 2
	1924	Spanish Desk	825.00	T	1	5	B	Reg.	- - 2
		22	185.00	T	2	4	E	Reg.	- - 3
		XI	142.50	T	2	5	E	TRF	- 2 - 2
		XV (430)	101.50	Por	2	3	E	Reg.	- - 3
	1925	III	105.00	T	2	4	E	Reg.	- - 2
		VI (420, 421)	235.00	C	2	5	E	TRF	- 2 - 2
		XVI Royal (430)	90.00	T	1	5	E	TRF	- 2 - 2
		20 (440)	145.00	T	2	5	E	TRF	- 2 - 2
		30 (XXX) (435)							
	1926	7 Coronet	125.00	T	1	7	D	TRF	1 3 - 2
	1927	"	125.00	T	1	7	A	TRF	- 3 - 2
		Imperial	225.00	C	1	7	D	TRF	
		"	225.00	C	1	7	A	TRF	- 3 - 2
		Spinet	195.00	Desk	1	7	D	TRF	
		"	195.00	Desk	1	7	A	TRF	- 3 - 2
	1928	60 Royal	95.00	T	1	7	A	TRF Reg.	- 3 - 2*
		70	250.00	C	1	8	A	TRF	- 4 - 2*
	1929	80 Royal	275.00	C	1	9	A	TRF	- 3 - 2*
		210	152.00	CL	1	8	A	TRF	- 3 - 2*
		Royal				8	A	TRF	

1929-1930: Last two digits are the chassis model, e. g. Model 10 chassis in 210 and 310, Model 26 chassis in 426, 526, 726.

MANUFACTURER	YEAR	MODEL NO. & NAME	PRICE	STYLE	D	T	P	CIR. & STAGES
KENNEDY CO., COLIN B. (cont.) 1930: Model 34 add-on superhet SW converter option available. Three S. G. tubes; RF, OSC, 1st Det. Converter was an integral part of Model 826B.	1930	220	159.00	CL	1	8	A	TRF - 3 - 2*
		310	182.00	C	1	8	A	SG - 3 - 2*
		320	189.00	C	1	8	A	SG - 3 - 2*
		222	159.00	LB	1	7	D	SG - 3 - 2*
		224	99.00	LB	1	7	S	SG - 3 - 2*
		426	159.00		1	8	A	SG - 3 - 2*
		526	169.00	HB	1	8	A	SG - 3 - 2*
		632	139.00	LB	1	8	A	SG - 3 - 2*
		726	229.00	HB	1	8	A	SG - 3 - 2*
		726A	285.00	HB	1	8	A	SG - 3 - 2*
		726B	390.00	RP	1	8	A	SG - 3 - 2*
		826	199.00	C	1	8	A	SG - 3 - 2*
		826A	242.00	RP	1	11	A	SG - 4 - 2*
		826B (SW/LW)	252.00	C	1	8	A	SG - 3 - 2*
		826C	304.00	RP	1	8	A	SG - 3 - 2*
		1030	114.50	LB	1	8	A	SG - 3 - 2*
KEYSTONE RADIO CO.	1925	Wondertone	90.00	T	3	5	B	TRF - 2 - 2
		" 5	65.00		3	5	E	TRF - 2 - 2
	1926	Classic 5	50.00	T	3	5	S	TRF - 2 - 2
		" 6	165.00	C	1/3	6	S	TRF - 2 - 3
KEYSTONE RADIO LABORATORIES	1926	1	35.00	T	3	5	S	TRF - 2 - 2
		2	50.00	T	3	5	S	TRF - 2 - 2
		5	55.00	T	3	6	S	TRF - 2 - 3
		3	60.00	T	2	5	S	TRF - 2 - 2
		4	60.00	T	2	6	S	TRF - 2 - 3
	1927	126	60.00	Ch		6	S	- 3 - 2
		226	60.00	T		5	S	- 3 - 2
		3-D-6	60.00	T		6	S	- 3 - 2
		126	70.00	T		6	S	- 3 - 2
		126-C	97.50	C		6	S	- 3 - 2
		126A	150.00	C		7	A	- 3 - 2
KEYSTONE RADIO SERVICE	1925	L-2-Ultradyne	99.00	Kit	2			Reg.SH
		Kit	30.00	Kit				Reg.SH
		L-2-Ultradyne	97.00	Kit	2			Reg.SH
KILBOURNE & CLARK MFG. CO.	1923	K & C	13.50					C - - - -
	1924	K & C						C - - - -

MANUFACTURER	YEAR	MODEL NO. & NAME	PRICE	STYLE	D	T	P	CIR.	& STAGES
KILBOURNE & CLARK MFG. CO. (cont.)	1925	Air Roamer	140.00		3	5	E	TRF	- 2 - 2
KILLARK ELECTRIC MFG. CO.	1923		4.50					C	: - :
	1924							C	: - :
KIMBERCH PHONO CO.	1924					8			
KING MANUFACTURING CORP.	1924			T					
King Quality Products 1925	1925			T					
King Hinners Radio Co. 1926-27				C					
King-Buffalo, Inc.		5		Kit					
King Mfg. Corp. 1927-1930	1926	10K1	101.00	T	3	5	S	Neut.	- 2 - 2
Absorbed by Colonial Radio Corp.		10SK			3	5	S	Neut.	- 2 - 2
		25	186.50	T	3	5	S	Neut.	- 2 - 2
		30	76.00	T	3	5	S	Neut.	- 2 - 2
		40			3	5	S	Neut.	- 2 - 3
		61	66.00	T	3	6	S	TRF	- 2 - 2
		62	101.00	T	1	6	S	TRF	- 2 - 3
		63	211.50	C	1	6	S	TRF	- 2 - 3
	1927	71 Commander	220.00	T	1	6	S	TRF	- 3 - 2
		80 Baronet	70.00	T	1	6	S	Neut.	- 3 - 2
		80H Viking	140.00	C	1	6	S	TRF	- 2 - 3
		81 Crusader	115.00	T	1	7	S	TRF	- 2 - 3
		81H Chevalier	210.00	C	1	6	A	TRF	- 2 - 2
		82			1	5	S	TRF	- 2 - 2
	1928	E	55.00	T	1	6	S	Neut.	- 3 - 2
		F	72.50	T	1	7	A	Neut.	- 3 - 2
		G	110.00	T	1	8	A	Neut.	- 3 - 2*
		H	130.00	C	1	8	A	Neut.	- 3 - 2*
		J			1	9	A	Neut.	- 3 - 2*
	1929	97 Royal	149.00	T	1	7	A	SG	1 3 - 2*
		98 Imperial	169.00	T	1	7	A	SG	- 3 - 1*
		101 Monark	159.00	C	1		A		
	1930	218	29.25	Ch					
KINGS RADIO SALES CO.	1925	RF5	45.00	T	3	5	E	TRF	- 2 - 2
	1926	RF5	45.00	T	3	5	S	TRF	- 2 - 2
		RF5	95.00	C	3	6	S	TRF	- 2 - 2

MANUFACTURER	YEAR	MODEL NO. & NAME	PRICE	STYLE	D	T	P	CIR. & STAGES
KINGS RADIO SALES CO. (cont.)	1927	RF5	40.00	T	3	5	S	TRF - 2 - 2
		RF-5-C	75.00	C	3	6	S	TRF - 2 - 3
KLAUS RADIO & ELECTRIC CO.	1923					2		
KLITZEN RADIO MANUFACTURING CO.	1923		80.00					Reg.
	1924	Klitzen Kent	42.50		2	3	E	DAA Reg. - - - 2
	1925	Wolverine	54.50		2	3	E	DAA Reg. - - - 2
		Badger			1		S	Reg.
KNICKERBOCKER TALKING MACH. CO.	1925		150.00	C	2	5	S	TRF - 2 - 2
KODEL MANUFACTURING CO.	1924	S-1	5.00	T	1	-	.	C - - - -
		C-11	10.00	T	1	1	E	D - - - 1
		C12	18.00	T	1	2	E	DA - - - 1
		C-13	28.00	T	2	3	E	Rfx - 1 - 2
		C-14	32.50	T	2	4	E	Rfx - 2 - 2
		P11 Camera	16.00	Por	1	1	B	D - - - 1
		P-12	22.50	Por	1	2	B	DA - - - -
	1925	C-1	5.00	T	1	-	.	C - - - -
		Gold Star (1-tube)	12.00	T	1	1	S	D - - - -
		" "	18.00	T	1	1	S	D - - - 1
		" (2-tube)	20.00	T	1	2	E	DA - - - 1
		Gold Star Reflex	25.00	Por	2	3	B	DA - 1 - 1
		P14	30.00	Por	2	4	B	Rfx - 1 - 1
		Logodyne	50.00	Kit	3	5	E	Rfx - 2 - 2
		"	50.00	Kit	3	5	E	TRF - 2 - 2
			65.00	Por	2	4	E	Rfx - 2 - 2
			75.00		3	5	E	TRF - 2 - 2
		Big 5 Logodyne	90.00	T	3	5	E	TRF - 2 - 2
		STD 5 "	165.00	C	3	5	E	TRF - 2 - 2
		Big 5 "	275.00	C	1	4	B	Rfx - 2 - 2
			37.50	Por	3	5	E	TRF - 2 - 2
		STD 5 Logodyne	70.00	T	3	5	E	TRF - 2 - 2
		Logodyne Unitrola	87.50	T	3	5	E	Rfx - 2 - 2
	1926	" 53	82.50	T	3	5	E	TRF - 2 - 2
			250.00	C	3	5	E	TRF - 2 - 2
KOLSTER RADIO INC.	1925	6A	175.00	T	2	6	E	TRF - 2 - 3

MANUFACTURER	YEAR	MODEL NO. & NAME	PRICE	STYLE	D	T	P	CIR. & STAGES	
KOLSTER RADIO INC. (cont.)									
Federal Tel. Co. 1925									
Federal Brandes, Inc. 1926-7									
Kolster Radio Corp. 1928-9									
Brandes Radio Corp. 1929									
	1926	6B	225.00	T	2	6	E	TRF	- 2 - 3
		8B	265.00	C	1	8	B	TRF	- 4 - 3
		8C	375.00	C	1	8	B	TRF	- 4 - 3
		6C	250.00	C	2	6	E	TRF	- 3 - 2
		6D	85.00	T	1	6	E	TRF	- 3 - 2
		6E	135.00	C	1	6	B	TRF	- 4 - 3
		8A	185.00	T	1	8	B	TRF	- 4 - 3
		6G	265.00	C	1	6	S	TRF	- 3 - 2
		6H	125.00	C	1	6	S	TRF	- 3 - 2
		7A	140.00	T	1	7	S	TRF	- 4 - 2
	1927	7B	160.00	T	1	7	A	TRF	- 3 - 2
		6F	250.00	C	1	7	A	TRF	- 3 - 2
		6K			1	7	A	TRF	- 3 - 2
		6J			1	7	A	TRF	- 3 - 2
		6L			1	7	A	TRF	- 3 - 2
	1928	6R	250.00	C	1	7	A	TRF	- 3 - 2
		K-20	135.00	T	1	8	A	TRF	- 3 - 2
		K-21	160.00	T	1	7	A	TRF	- 4 - 3
		K-22	200.00	T	1	8	A	TRF	- 3 - 2
		K-23	285.00	C	1	9	A	TRF	- 4 - 2
		K-24 (210), K-24 (250)	350.00	C	1	7	A	TRF	1 3 - 2
		K-25	135.00	T	1	6	D	TRF	- 3 - 2
		K-30	135.00	T	1	6	D	TRF	- 3 - 2
		K-32	200.00	C	1	4	A	TRF	- 3 - 0
		K-35	80.00	Ch	1	5	A	TRF	- 4 - 0
		K-36	95.00	Ch	1	11	A	TRF	- 3 - 2
		6M	325.00	C	1	7	A	TRF	- 4 - 2*
		K27, K37			1	8	A	TRF	- 3 - 2*
	1929	K28	235.00	C	1	8	A	SG	- 3 - 2*
		K42	325.00	C	1	9	A	SG	- 3 - 3**
		K43	500.00	C	1	11	A	SG	- 3 - 2
		K44	750.00	T	1	10	A	TRF	- 3 - 2*
		K45	85.00		1	7	A	SG	- 3 - 2*
		K38			1	8	A	TRF	- 3 - 2*
		B10			1	8	A	SG	- 3 - 2*
		B11			1	8	A		
		B12	125.50	C	1		A		
		B15	165.00	C	1		A		
		B16							

MANUFACTURER	YEAR	MODEL NO. & NAME	PRICE	STYLE	D	T	P	CIR. & STAGES
KO-RAD CO., THE	1924	Lafayette Neut. K40	140.00	T	3	5	E	Neut. TRF - 2 - 2
	1925	" K60	160.00	T	3	5	E	TRF - 2 - 2
KRANZ & SELL CO.	1927	4-1 Wayne	50.00			4	S	TRF - 2 - 1
		4-2	55.00			4	S	TRF - 2 - 1
		4 Daisy	65.00			4	S	TRF - 2 - 1
		3 Superior	95.00			4	S	TRF - 2 - 1
		5 DeLuxe	125.00			4	S	TRF - 2 - 1
KRASCO MANUFACTURING CO. INC.	1924	Monarch Loop Por.		Por				
LAKESIDE SUPPLY CO.	1923		80.00					
			150.00					
	1924 1925	550 EM Microdyne	400.00	D	2	7		SH - 2 - 2
LA MAR MANUFACTURING CO. INC. (Master Craft)	1925	12-4 Junior	60.00	T	2	4	S	TRF - 1 - 2
		18-4 DeLuxe	100.00	T	2	4	S	TRF - 1 - 2
		14-4 Grand	85.00	T	2	4	S	TRF - 1 - 2
		15-4 Aristocrat	65.00	T	2	4	S	TRF - 1 - 2
		Lasher Capacidyne	175.00	C	3	5	S	TRF - 2 - 2
LAMB, F. JOS.	1922	DA3	60.00	Box	0	3	B	DAA - - 2
LANGBEIN KAUFMANN CO.	1925	4-S Elkay Super Selector	70.00	T	2	4	E	TRF - 1 - 2
		5-S "	80.00	T	2	5	E	TRF - 1 - 3
		Kit	60.00	Kit	2	4	E	TRF - 1 - 3
		Kit	65.00	Kit	2	5	E	TRF - 1 - 3
	1926	5-S Elkay	80.00	T	2	5	S	RF - 2 - 3
		6-S "	125.00	T	1	6	S	TRF - 2 - 3
	1927	Jr. 6 "	80.00	T	1	6	S	TRF - 2 - 3
		Jr. 7 "	92.50	T	1	7	S	TRF - 3 - 3
		Sr. 6 "	125.00	T	1	6	S	TRF - 2 - 3
		Sr. 6E "		T		6	A	TRF - 2 - 3
LARKIN CO. INC.	1926	65	120.00	C	2	6	S	TRF - 2 - 3
LAUREL MOTORS CORP.	1926	Laurel & Sinclair	29.50 "up"	C	3	5	S	TRF - 2 - 2
				C	3	6	S	TRF - 3 - 2

MANUFACTURER	YEAR	MODEL NO. & NAME	PRICE	STYLE	D	T		CIR. & STAGE
LAUREL MOTORS CORP. (cont.)	1927	Laurel & Sinclair	29.50 "up"	C	3	5	S	TRF - 2 - 2
				C	3	6	S	TRF - 3 - 2
LEE ELECTRIC & MFG. CO. "LEMCO"	1923	Lemco	6.00					C - - - -
			9.00					C - - - -
			20.00					C - - - -
			30.00					
			50.00					Rfx - - - -
	1924	50 Lemco Neutroflex.	6.00					C - - - -
		340-A	6.00					C - - - -
		B	7.50					C - - - -
	1925	50 Lemco	40.00			2		Rfx - - - -
	1926	340A	6.00					C
			50.00			5		TRF - - - -
LEEDS RADIO LABORATORIES	1930	1930 Sp'l	44.00	T	2	3	E	DAAReg - - 2
LEICH ELECTRIC CO.	1925	1A	125.00		3		S	TRF
	1926	Special Neutralized	100.00		3		S	TRF
LE MOR RADIO INC.	1925	Uni Control	145.00		1		S	RF (pretuned) - 1 - 3
	1926	" "	145.00		1		S	TRF
LENFORD INC.	1926	Lenford Special		T	3	5		TRF - 1 - 3
LESTER RADIO SHOP	1926	AC	22.00	T	2	2		Rfx - 1 - 1
		5	50.00	T	3	5		TRF - 2 - 2
		Portable	54.00	Por	2	4		TRF - 1 - 2
		Grand	75.00	C	3	6		TRF - 3 - 2
		Transcontinental	200.00	T	2	9		- 5 - 3
LEUTZ, C. R. INC.	SEE	Experimenters Info. Service 1923-25 Golden-Leutz Corp. 1924-1927						
LEWIS & DeROY RADIO CORP.	1923	Conquerer						DAA
LIBERTY MAIL ORDER HOUSE	1924	14S93 Knock-Out	26.40	T	2	1	B	Reg. - - - 1
		14S95 " "	35.45	T	2	2	B	Reg. - - - 1
		14S96 " "	40.40	T	2	3	B	Reg. - - - 2
		Roberts Knock-Out	61.85	T	2	4	E	Reg. - - - 2*

MANUFACTURER	YEAR	MODEL NO. & NAME	PRICE	STYLE	D	T	P	CIR. & STAGES
LIBERTY MAIL ORDER HOUSE (cont.)	1925	Sherma Flex	53.78	T	2	2	B	Rfx - 1 - 1
		Kit	27.72	Kit	2	2	B	Rfx - 1 - 1
LIBERTY TRANSFORMER CO.	1925	Sealed Five	100.00	T	3	5	E	TRF - 2 - 2
LIGHTRITE CO. INC., THE	1923	Soundrite	20.00					DAA - - - -
	1924	"	25.00					C
	1924	"						
LILLIE CO., J. P.	1924	VT						
LINCOLN RADIO CORP.	1923		110.00					
			125.00					
	1924							
	1925							
	1926							
	1927							
	1928	8-80	92.65	Kit	2	8	S	SH - - 3 2
		Sargent-Rayment SM-710	120.00	Kit		7	S	TRF 12 - 2
		S-M 720 S-G Six	77.50	Kit	2	6	S	SH
		1929 Lab Super	95.70	Kit	2			
		Tyrman 72	98.50	Kit				
		" 72AC	153.40	Kit			A	
		" 80 Super	134.50	Kit				
	1929	8-80 One Spot Super		Ch	2	8	S	SH - - 3 2
	1930	8-40	190.00	Ch	1	9	A	SH - - 2 2*
		10,31		Ch	1	11	A	SH - - 4 2*
LISTENING POST, THE	1923		125.00					
			150.00					
LONE WOLF RADIO CORP.	1927		85.00	Por	1	9	B	Rfx - 3 - 2
LONG RADIO CO.	1930	C Comb.	99.50	M	1	6	A	TRF - 3 - 1
LOS ANGELES SALES CO.	1924	Lasco	96.50	TC	2	2	A	Rfx
	1925	" B	115.00	C	2	3	A	Rfx
		"					A	Rfx

MANUFACTURER	YEAR	MODEL NO. & NAME	PRICE	STYLE	D	T	P	CIR. & STAGES
LUXEM & DAZIS CO.	1925	DeLuxe	150.00	Por		4	B	
	1926	" VT						
LYRADION MANUFACTURING CO.	1923	Models from $135 to $180						
LYRIC	SEE	All-American Mohawk						
LYTTON INC., WALTER	1923	Models $45 to $545						
	1924	Models 15 to 545						
	1925	103A Compass	225.00	Por	1/2	7	S	RF TRF 2 1 - 3
		103	195.00	Por	1/2	6	S	RF TRF 2 1 - 2
			42.50	Por	1	2	B	
		100	75.00	T	3	5	B	TRF - 2 - 2
		101A Wav-O-dyne	165.00	T	2	5	B	TRF - 2 - 2
		99T Lytton Duplex	19.75	T	1	2	B	Rfx Cry - 2 - 2
		Port "	25.00	Por	1	2	B	Rfx Cry - 2 - 2
		103PL Masterpiece	160.00	Por	1/2	6	E	TRF - 3 - 3
		103-A-PL	190.00		1		S	TRF - 3 - 3
		105 Super Wav-o-dyne	195.00	T	2	6	E	TRF - 3 - 3
		201 Wav-o-dyne	195.00	T	2	5	E	TRF - 2 - 2
		100 Standard	195.00	C	3	5	E	TRF - 2 - 2
		401A Concert	350.00	C	2	5	E	TRF - 2 - 2
		305	500.00		2		E	TRF - 3 - 2
MC FADDEN & CO.	1924							
MC INTOSH STEREOPTICON CO.	1924	Excellophone						C - - - -
MC MILLAN RADIO CORP.	1926	DeLuxe Tel-o-air	175.00	HB	1	6	S	TRF - 3 - 2
		Standard "	100.00	T	1	6	S	TRF - 3 - 2
		Table Model "	160.00	T	1	6	S	TRF - 3 - 2
		Standard DeLuxe	65.00	T	3	5	S	TRF - 2 - 2
		1 McMillan	50.00	C	3	5	S	TRF - 2 - 2
		2 Superfine Five	71.00	HB	3	5	S	TRF - 2 - 2
		3 McMillan Five	99.50	T	3	5	S	TRF - 2 - 2
		1 McMillan	65.00	HB	1	6	A	TRF
	1927	Seville	From 170 to 325	HB	1	6	A	TRF
		Ivanhoe		HB	1	6	A	TRF
		Verdi		HB	1	6	A	TRF
		Orleans		LB	1	6	A	TRF

MANUFACTURER	YEAR	MODEL NO. & NAME	PRICE	STYLE	D	T	P	CIR. & STAGES	
MC MILLAN RADIO CORP. (cont.)	1928	Oxford Six	From 80 to 150	T	1	6	B	TRF	
		Northfield		C	1	6	B	TRF	
		Warwick 8	160.00	C	1	9	A	TRF	1 3 - 2*
		Westminster 8Y	210.00	C	1	9	A	TRF	1 3 - 2*
		York Comb. 185	285.00	T-C	1	9	A	TRF	1 3 - 2*
		Westchester 186	285.00	T	1	9	A	TRF	1 3 - 2*
	1929	959	159.50	C	1	9	A	TRF	1 3 - 2*
	1930	965	165.00	C	1	9	A	TRF	1 3 - 2*
		975	175.00	C	1	9	A	TRF	1 3 - 2*
		999	199.50	C	1	9	A	TRF	1 3 - 2*
		925A	225.00	C	1	9	A	TRF	1 3 - 2*
		925B	225.00	C	1	9	A	TRF	1 3 - 2*
		925D	225.00	C	1	9	A	TRF	1 3 - 2*
		935	235.00	C	1	9	A	TRF	1 3 - 2*
		937	237.50	C	1	9	A	TRF	1 3 - 2*
MACHEN ELECTRIC CO.	1924	RF Clearad							
MACHEN MFG. & DISTR. CO.	1926	W-5	180.00	T	3	5	S	TRF	- 2 - 2
MACHINE SPECIALTY CO.	SEE	Consolidated Radio Corp.							
MACK CO.	1925	Sincroflex	70.00		3	2	S	Rfx TRF	- 4 - 2
		"	50.00		2	2	E/B	Rfx TRF	- 4 - 3
		"	85.00		3	3	S	Rfx TRF	- 4 - 2
MAC LAREN MANUFACTURING CO.	1925	Dominaire	250.00	TC	3	5	B/D	TRF	- 2 - 2
	1926	"	250.00	T	3	5		TRF	- 2 - 2
		A & B	300.00	C	3	5	A/D	TRF	
MAGNAFORMER	SEE	Radiart Labs							
MAGNAVOX CO.	1924	TRF-50	150.00	CT		5	E	TRF	- 2 - 2
		TRF-5	125.00	T		5	E	TRF	- 2 - 2
		Jr.	85.00	Por	1	5	S	TRF	- 2 - 2
		10	110.00	T	1	5	S	TRF	- 2 - 2
	1925	TRF-5	125.00	T	1	5	E	TRF	- 2 - 2
		25	145.00	T	1	5	S	TRF	- 2 - 2
		TRF50	150.00	TC	1	5	E	TRF	- 2 - 2
		A, D, "One Dial"							

MANUFACTURER	YEAR	MODEL NO. & NAME	PRICE	STYLE	D	T	P	CIR. & STAGES
MAGNAVOX CO. (cont.)								
	1926	75 (7-5)	200.00	DC	1	5	S	TRF - 2 - 2
		Drawer	75.00	T	1	5	S	TRF - 2 - 2
		Drawer	75.00	T	1	5	S	TRF - 2 - 2
		Jr.	85.00	Por	1	5	S	TRF - 2 - 2
		25	145.00	T	1	5	S	TRF - 2 - 2
	1927	75	200.00	Desk C	1	5	S	TRF - 2 - 2
MAGNUS ELECTRIC CO.	1923	872	10.00	T	1			C - - -
		876	10.00	T	1			C - - -
		873	12.00	T	1			C - - -
		4	12.00	T	1			C - - -
		55	16.00	T	1	1		C - - -
		77	20.00	T	1	4	E	D - - -
	1924	868 Magnadyne 84	120.00	T	3	5	E	TRF - 2 - 2
	1925	940 Magnutrol	65.00	T	3	5	E	TRF - 2 - 2
		Magnutrol	60.00		3	5	E	TRF - 2 - 2
		" Sub-Panel	75.00		3	5	E	TRF - 2 - 2
		Magnutrol DeLuxe	75.00	T	3	5	E	TRF - 2 - 2
		" Sloping DeLuxe		T	3	5	E	TRF - 2 - 2
		Magnus	150.00	P	3	5	E	TRF - 2 - 2
		"	215.00	C	3	5	S	TRF - 2 - 2
		"	60.00	C	3	6	S	TRF - 2 - 2
	1926	" TRF	75.00		3	5	E	TRF - 2 - 2
		" Sub Panel	60.00		3	5		TRF - 2 - 2
		" DeLuxe	75.00	P	3	5		TRF - 2 - 2
		" Phono Panel	150.00	C	3	5	E	TRF - 2 - 2
MAJESTIC	SEE	Grigsby-Grunow Co.						
MALONE LEMON PRODUCTS, INC.	1923	See Carloyd Elec. Co.						
	1924	" " "						
	1925	SP 5	95.00	T	2	5	S	TRF - 1 - 3
	1926	Power Six	140.00	T	3	6	S	TRF - 2 - 3
		MR-6	195.00	T	2	6	S	TRF - 2 - 3
		8 Tube		T	2	8	S	TRF
		25		C	3	5	S	TRF - 2 - 2

MANUFACTURER	YEAR	MODEL NO. & NAME	PRICE	STYLE	D	T	P	CIR. & STAGES		
MALONE LEMON PRODUCTS, INC. (cont.)		31	78.50	T	2	5	S	TRF	- 1 -	3
		35		C	3	5	S	TRF	- 2 -	2
		52			2	5	S	TRF	- 2 -	2
		55			3	5	S	TRF	- 2 -	2
MANHATTAN RADIO CO.	1924									
MANEY RADIO CORP.	1923							Neut.		
MARATHON RADIO CO.	1924 1925	MRS 3	80.00	T	2	2	B	Rfx	- 1 -	1
		MR 3	65.00	T	2	3	B	TRF	- 1 -	1
		MX 5	100.00	T	2	3	B	TRF	- 1 -	1
		MR 5	140.00	T	2	3	B	TRF	- 1 -	1
		MP 5	170.00	T	2	3	B	TRF	- 1 -	1
		MX	100.00	T	3	5	S	TRF	- 2 -	2
		MP	200.00	T	3	5	S	TRF	- 2 -	2
MARINETTE ELECTRIC CORP.	1923 1924 1925 1926	Little Tatler	6.00				C	C	- :	-
		" "	6.00				C	C	- :	-
		Little Tatler	6.00					C	- :	-
MARLOW CO.	1926	Marlodyne VT								
MARSHALL GERKEN CO., THE	1924	Thorobred KD								
MARSHALL RADIO PRODUCTS INC.	1924 1926	4	120.00	CT	2	4	S	TRF	- 1 -	2
		5		T	3	5	S	TRF	- 2 -	2
MARTIAN MANUFACTURING CO. INC.	1923 1924	Big 4	7.50	T	1	-	·	C	- :	-
		" "	7.50	T	1	-	·	C	- :	-
		Special VT	4.00	T	1	1	E	D	- :	-
		DeLuxe	15.00	T	1	1	E	D	- :	-
MARTI ELECTRIC RADIO CO. INC.	1926 1927	B-Power	125.00	T	1	7	A	TRF	- 2 -	3
		Electric Power	175.00	T	1	7	A	TRF	- 2 -	3
		TA-2	235.00	D	1	7	A	TRF	- 2 -	3
		TA-10	250.00							
		DC-2	275.00							

MANUFACTURER	YEAR	MODEL NO. & NAME	PRICE	STYLE	D	T	P	CIR. & STAGES
MARTI ELECTRIC RADIO CO. INC.	1928	DC-10	290.00	D	1	7	A	TRF - 2 - 3
		CS-2	325.00	C	1	7	A	TRF - 2 - 3
		CS-10	350.00	C	1	7	A	TRF - 3 - 3
			225.00	T	1	8	A	TRF - 3 - 3
			395.00	C	1	8	A	TRF - 3 - 3
	1929 1930	E	199.00	C	1	7	A	SG - 2 - 2*
MARTIN COPELAND CO.	1925	Reactodyne Mar-Co	25.00	Kit	2	4	S	TRF - 1 - 2
MARTIN RADIO & ELECTRIC CO.	1925	Packard-5	45.00	T	3	5	E/S	TRF - 2 - 2
	1926	"	45.00	T	3	5	E/S	TRF - 2 - 2
MARWOL RADIO CORP.	1925	A-1	60.00	P	3	5	S	TRF - 2 - 2
		Phono Panel	70.00		3	5	S	TRF - 2 - 2
		Kit	15.00	Kit	3	5	S	TRF - 2 - 2
		Baby Grand	36.50	T	3	5	S	TRF - 2 - 2
		Jewel	39.50	T	3	5	S	TRF - 2 - 2
		A-1	55.00	T	3	5	S	TRF - 2 - 2
		Table Console	75.00	TC	3	5	S	TRF - 2 - 2
		Console Grand	130.00	CG	3	5	S	TRF - 2 - 2
		Six	100.00	T	3	6	S	TRF - 2 - 2
		Portable	115.00	Por	3		S	TRF
		Console Table	40.00	CT	3		S	TRF
		Phono Panel	45.00	P	3		S	TRF
		Home Builder	35.50	T	3	5	S	TRF - 2 - 3
MARWOOD RADIO CORP.	1927	6	43.85	T	1	6	B/A	
		6	36.85	T	3	6	A	
		8	69.00	T	1	8		
		8	98.00	C	1	8	B/A	
		6	47.00	T	1	6		
MASTER ELECTRIC CO.	1923		6.00					C - - - -
	1924							C - - - -
MASTER RADIO MANUFACTURING CO.	1930	70	59.50	M	1	6	A	TRF - 3 - 1
		50	66.50	T	1	6	A	TRF - 3 - 1
		Console	89.50	C	1	6	A	TRF - 3 - 1
MATTATUCK	1922	RP-1	35.00					

MANUFACTURER	YEAR	MODEL NO. & NAME	PRICE	STYLE	D	T	P	CIR. & STAGES
MAXWELL RADIO CORP.	1928	AS Louis XIV	375.00	C	1	6	A	TRF - 2 - 2
		Coliseum	375.00	C	1	6	A	TRF - 2 - 2
MAZDA RADIO MANUFACTURING CO.	1924	Consomello Grand	235.00	C	3	6	S	RF 2 - - 3
	1925	" "	235.00		3	6	S	RF
		Consonello	250.00	C	2		S	RF
		" "	150.00		2		S	RF
		Jr.	40.00	Por	2		S	Rfx
	1926		225.00		2		S	RF
		Consomello Concert	85.00	T	1	5	S	RF
		Premier	175.00	T	2	8	S	RF
		DeLuxe	235.00	C	2	8	S	RF
		Royal	285.00	C	2	8	S	RF
		Consomello Grand	500.00	C	2	10	S	RF
		Jr.	175.00	T	2	8	S	Rfx
		Port.	75.00	T	2	5	B	RF
		Special	225.00	Por	2		S	RF
			275.00		2	10	S	RF
MEEPON	1923	The Meepon		Box	1		-	C - - - -
MELCO	SEE	Amsco						
MELLODYNE	1924	1-Tube	19.95	T		1	B	
		2-Tube	32.95	T		2	B	
		3-Tube	49.95	T	2	3	B	
		4-Tube	57.95	T		4	B	(S optional)
MELLODYNE RADIO CO., THE (Cincinnati, Ohio)	1926		96.95			5	S	
			49.95			3	B	
			29.95			2	B	
			18.95			1	B	
MELODEE RADIO MANUFACTURING CO.	1926	Mel-o-dee 5	35.00	T	2	5	E	TRF - 2 - 2
		" 5	90.00	C	2	5	E	TRF - 2 - 1
		" 6	125.00	C	2	6	E	TRF - 2 - 3
MELODIAN LABORATORIES	1923		4.00					C - - - -
			25.00					D - - -
			45.00					DAA - - - 2

MANUFACTURER	YEAR	MODEL NO. & NAME	PRICE	STYLE	D	T	P	CIR. & STAGES
MELODIAN LABORATORIES (cont.)	1924							C — - - - 2
								— - - - 2
	1925	Melody King	50.00					TRF
	1926	Melodian	125.00					TRF
MELODYNE RADIO CO. (New York City)	1926	10 (Electric)	200.00	T	3	5	A/D	RF - 2 - 2
		11 "	300.00	C	1	6		RF - 2 - 3
		11A "	300.00	C	1	6		RF - 3 - 2
		12 "	350.00	C	2	7		RF - 3 - 3
MENZEL CO., THE	1924	Etherson VT						
MERCURY ELECTRIC CO. "HETRO MAGNETIC"	1926	Super 5 Hetro Magnetic	45.00	T	3	5	E	TRF - 2 - 2
		" " "	39.50		3	5	E	TRF - 2 - 2
		" " "	83.50		3	5	E	TRF - 2 - 2
		" " "	73.50		3	5	B	TRF - 2 - 2
MERCURY RADIO PRODUCTS CO.	1923	Grimes						Rfx
		2-5-4				4		Rfx
	1924	Four-Tube Rfx	150.00	T	3	4		Rfx
		1-A-3				3		Rfx
	1925	165	165.00	T	3		B	Rfx - 2 - 3
MERRELL CO., THE	1926							
METEOR PHONO CO.	1925	4	50.00	T	2	4	B	TRF - 1 - 2
		30	80.00	T	1	5	S	TRF - 1 - 3
		6	100.00	C	1	5	S	TRF - 1 - 3
		7	125.00	C	1	5	S	TRF - 1 - 3
		9	140.00	C	1	5	S	TRF - 1 - 3
		20	175.00	C	1	5	S	TRF - 1 - 3
METRO ELECTRICAL CO.	1923	Little Gem	6.50					C
		Little Giant	8.00					C
		Metro Jr.	2.50					C
	1924	Little Gem						
		Little Giant						
		Metro Jr.						

MANUFACTURER	YEAR	MODEL NO. & NAME	PRICE	STYLE	D	T	P	CIR. & STAGES
METRO ELECTRIC CO. "METRODYNE"	1925	Metrodyne	38.50	T	3	5	S	TRF - 2 - 2
	1926	" Super 5	88.00	T	1	5	S	TRF - 2 - 3
		" 7	75.00	T	1	7	S	TRF - 3 - 3
	1927	" 6	48.50	T	3	6	S	TRF - 3 - 3
		" 7	75.00	T	1	7	S	TRF - 3 - 3
		" 6	48.50	T	1	6	A	TRF - 3 - 3
	1928	" All Electric		C	1	7	A	TRF - 3 - 3
		" "		C	1	7	B/A	TRF - 3 - 3*
		" Super 8		C	1	8	A	TRF - 3 - 3*
	1929	" "		Ch	1	8		TRF - 3 - 3*
METROPOLITAN ENG. SERVICE CO.	1925	B	175.00	T	3	5	B	Neut. - 2 - 2
	1926	B2	175.00	T	3	5	B	Neut. - 2 - 2
		B2		T	3	5		Neut. - 2 - 2
METROPOLITAN ELECTRIC CO.	1925	Meco 2	60.00	T	2		S	TRF - 2 - 2
		" 10	100.00	T	2		S	TRF - 2 - 2
		" 6	125.00	SC	2	6	S	TRF - 2 - 2
		" 5	200.00	C			S	TRF - 2 - 2
			250.00	C				TRF - 2 - 2
METROPOLITAN RADIO CORP.	1922	Little Giant	15.00	Box	0			C - - - -
MICHIGAN RADIO CORP.	1922	Senior	125.00	T	2	3		Reg. - - - 2
	1923		27.00					
			48.00					
		MRC-3	57.50	T	2	3	B	Reg. - - 2
		MRC-7	125.00	T				Reg.
		Midget	27.00	T	2	2	B	Reg. - - 1
		Junior	57.50	T	2	1	E	Reg.
	1924	MRC-4 Bon Voyage	150.00	T	2	4	E	Reg. - - 3
		M-10 Midget	27.00		0	2		DA - - 1
		MRC-11 Amp	30.00		2	2		AA
		MRC-2	32.50	T	2	2	E	Reg. - - 1
		MRC-3	87.50	T	2	3	E	Reg. - - 2
		MRC-12	57.00	T	2	3	E	Reg. - - 2
	1925	MRC-14 DeLuxe	87.00	DLS	2	4	E	RF 1 - - 2
MIDLAND ELECTRIC CO.	1924							

116

MANUFACTURER	YEAR	MODEL NO. & NAME	PRICE	STYLE	D	T	P	CIR. & STAGES	
MIDLAND ELECTRIC CO. (cont.)									
	1925	Midland R. F. Rec.	35.00		2	4	E	TRF	- 1 - 2
		Night Owl	15 to 35		1/3				
MIDWEST RADIO CO. "MIRACO"	1922	Miraco	20.00	Box	1	1	E	D	- 1 -
	1923	K	29.50	T	2	2	E	RF	1 - -
		MW	54.50	T	2	4	E	RF	1 - 2
			32.50	T	1	1	B		- - -
			18.50	T	1	1	B		- - -
	1924	K	29.50	T	2	2	E	RF	1 - -
		MW	54.50	T	3	4	E	RF	1 - 2
		Ultra 5	75.00	T	1	5	S	TRF	- 2 - 2
	1925	R	14.35	T	1	1	E	D	- - -
		R3	29.50	T	2	3	E	DAA	- 1 - 2
		MW	54.50	T	3	4	E	RF	1 - 2
		Ultra 5	59.50	T	1	5	E	TRF	- 2 - 2
	1926	R	13.75	T	1	1	E	D	- - -
		R3	27.35	T	3	3	E	DAA	- 2 - 2
		Unitune	89.50	T	1	5	S	TRF	- 2 - 2
	1927	Ultra 5	49.75	T	1	5	E	TRF	- 2 - 2
		Unitune	69.75	Ch	1	8	A/S	TRF	- 4 - 2
		8 Tube	49.75	T	1	7	A/S	TRF	- 3 - 2
		7 "	36.75	T	3	6	A/S	TRF	- 3 - 2
	1928	8 "	69.75	Ch	1	8	A/S	TRF	- 4 - 2
		7 "	49.75	T	1	7	A/S	TRF	- 3 - 2
		6 "	36.75	T	3	6	A/S	TRF	- 3 - 2
		DeLuxe	83.75	Ch	1	9	S	TRF	
		AC9	71.50	Ch	1	8	A	TRF	
		AC8	49.88	Ch	1	7	A	TRF	
	1929	AC8	49.88	Ch	1	6	B	TRF	
			91.50	Ch	1	8	A	TRF	
			98.50	C	1	8	A	TRF	
			108.85	SC	1	8	A	TRF	
			114.52	AC	1	8	A	TRF	
			32.29		1	8	B	TRF	
			49.88	Ch	1	9	A	SG	
	1930	AC7	39.85		1	7	A	SG	
			29.50		1		S	SG	
		A	118.00	HB	1	8	A	SG	- 3 - 2

MANUFACTURER	YEAR	MODEL NO. & NAME	PRICE	STYLE	D	T	P	CIR. & STAGES	
MIDWEST RADIO CO. (cont.)		B	98.75	CL	1	8	A	SG	- 3 - 2
		H	154.00		1	8	A	SG	- 3 - 2
		J	99.00	HB	1	8	A	SG	- 3 - 2
		K	110.00	LB	1	8	A	SG	- 3 - 2
		L	102.00	HB	1	8	A	SG	- 3 - 2
		M	118.00	HB	1	8	A	SG	- 3 - 2
MIESSNER RADIO CO.	1925	Electrik	175.00		3		A	TRF	
		Diamond T	185.00		4		S	TRF	
		"	49.50		3		S	TRF	
		"	80.00		3		S	TRF	
		"	160.00		3				
MIGNON	1914	RLC2		T	1	-	-	C	: - : - :
MILLER, BERTRAND F. CO.	1924 1925	KD Hercules	85.00		3	5	S	TRF	
MILLS RADIO & ELECTRIC CO.	1924								
MINERVA RADIO CO.	1925	Distantia DeLuxe 5	60.00	T	3	5	S	TRF	- 2 - 2
		5M	90.00	T	3	5	S	TRF	- 2 - 2
		Elite	125.00	T	3	5	S	TRF	- 2 - 2
		Serenade	200.00	C	3	5	S	TRF	- 2 - 2
		Grand	255.00	C	3	5	S	TRF	- 2 - 2
	1926	Studio Console	130.00	C	1	6		TRF	
		DeLuxe	200.00	T	1	6		TRF	
		1A	75.00		1	6		TRF	
		Library Console	140.00	C	1	6		TRF	
		Parlor Console	165.00	C	1	6		TRF	
		Consolette	110.00	CL	1	6		TRF	
	1927	F-26	250.00	C	1	8	A	TRF	- 3 - 3
	1928	F-27	250.00	C	1	8	A	TRF	- 3 - 3
		F-28	250.00	C	1	8	A	TRF	- 3 - 3
		F-29	250.00	C	1	8	A	TRF	- 3 - 2
	1929	1	125.00	C	1	8	A	TRF	
		2	175.00	C	1	8	A	TRF	
	1930	3	250.00	C	1	8	A	TRF	
		4	350.00	C	1	8	A	TRF	
		13	149.00	C	1	9	A	SG	

MANUFACTURER	YEAR	MODEL NO. & NAME	PRICE	STYLE	D	T	F	CIR. & STAGES
MINERVA RADIO CO. (cont.)		14	169.00	C	1	9	A	SG
		M-28	100.00	C	1	7	A	SG
		M-29	129.00	C	1	8	A	
		M-30	169.00	C	1	9	A	SG
MIRACLE	SEE	Uncle Al's Radio Shop						
MISSION BELL RADIO MFG. & DIST. CO.	1928	AC	69.50	Por	1	6	A	
	1929		89.50	C	1	6	A	
			59.50	M	1	4	A	TRF - 2 - 2
		D	79.50	T	1	6	A	TRF - 2 - 2
		E	99.50	C	1	6	A	SG - 2 - 2
	1930	Mantle	69.50	M	1			
MISSISSIPPI VALLEY RADIO CO.	1924	M-V	4.00	T	3		S	C - . -
	1925	5 Lafayette	65.00	T	3	5	S	TRF - 2 - 2
	1926	Lafayette	65.00					TRF - 2 - 2
MITCHELL BLAIR CO.	1923	Blairco-Trainon 11			1		E	
M & M ELECTRIC MFG. CO.	1924	Custom made						
MODERNOLA CO. INC.	1926	Caddy	50.00	T	2	5	E	TRF - 1 - 2
		Sheraton	75.00	T	2	5	E	TRF - 1 - 2
		Delano	135.00	C	2	5	E	TRF - 1 - 2
MOE MANUFACTURING CO.	1925	Aladdin	65.00	T	3	5	E	TRF - 2 - 2
		" Deluxe	115.00	T	3	5	E	TRF - 2 - 2
		5 Tube Wonder Set	32.50	T	3	5	E	TRF
			45.00	Por	2	3		
		Kit	17.00	C				
MOHAWK CORPORATION OF ILLINOIS See also All American Mohawk Corp.	1925	A5	150.00	T	1	5	E	TRF - 2 - 2
		110	175.00					
		115	225.00	C				
	1926	X	250.00	C	1	5	E	TRF - 2 - 2
		XLI	300.00	C	1	5	E	TRF - 2 - 2
		CX	133.50	C		5		
		A	205.00	C		5		

MANUFACTURER	YEAR	MODEL NO. & NAME	PRICE	STYLE	D	T	P	CIR. & STAGES
MOHAWK CORPORATION OF ILLINOIS (cont.)	1927	B	250.00	C	2	5	B	TRF - 3 - 2
		Portable	135.00	Por		6		
		Seneca	62.50	Ch		6		
		Geneva	200.00	C		6		
		Pontiac	155.00	C		6		
		Winona	85.00	T		6		
	1928	Cherokee	70.00	T		6		
		Chippewa	125.00	C		6		
		Navajo	117.00	T		6		
		Pawnee	167.00	C		6		
		Iroquois	189.50	C		6		
		Hiawatha	224.50	C		6		
		Cortez	254.50	C		6		
		Seminole	290.00	C		6		
MOHAWK ELECTRIC CO.	SEE	All American Mohawk Corp.						
MOHAWK RADIO CORP.	SEE	" " " "						
MONARCH	1929	1D	100.00	LB		7		SG
		D1	100.00	LB		7		
		E	115.00	C		7		
		E3	115.00	C		7		
		G	125.00	HB		7		SG
		G3	125.00	C		7		
		H	195.00	RP		7		
MONROE RADIO MANUFACTURING CO.	1925	V Monrona	75.00		3		S	- 2 - 2
		VI "	100.00		2		S	- 2 - 2
	1926	Monrona	8.00					C - - -
		" 300	150.00	Por	2	5	E	TRF Rfx - 3 - 2
MONTGOMERY WARD CO.	1925	Airline			1	1		
	1926	Airline			1	5		
	1930	Alexander			1	8	A	TRF - 3 - 2*
MONTROSE-HAST RADIO LABS.	1926	Naturelle						
MOON RADIO CORP.	1923	Satellite Antennaless			2		B	

MANUFACTURER	YEAR	MODEL NO. & NAME	PRICE	STYLE	D	T	P	CIR. & STAGES
MOON RADIO CORP. (cont.)	1924	C-1	127.00					
		C-2	157.00					
		C-2-A	135.00					
	1925	Terafone TA	100.00		1	5	E	RF 2 - - 2
MOONEY RADIO CO., THE	1924	Harkness						Rfx C - - - -
MORELEY RADIO CO.	1926							
MORRIS, WALTER C.	1924	Gold Medal	35.00 50.00					"Reflectodyne"
MORRIS REGISTER CO.	1926	Monarch	60.00	T	3	5		TRF - 2 - 2
MORRISON RADIOPHONE CO.	1924	Morradyne III		T	3	5	E	TRF - 2 - 2
MORTON, GEORGE	1926	A-102	85.00	T	1	5		TRF - 2 - 2
MULTIPHONE CO.	1924	Multiphone		Box	1	-	-	C - - - -
MUNN-LANDON	1925			T	2			
MU-RAD LABORATORIES INC.	1922	MA-12	128.00	T	2	4	E	TRF - 3 - -
		MA-13	160.00	T	2	6	E	TRF - 3 - 2
	1923	MA-17		T	3	6	E	TRF - 3 - 2
	1924	MA-15		T	2	6	E	TRF - 3 - 2
		MA-18	110.00	T	1	5	E	TRF - 2 - 2
		MA-20	185.00	T	3	5	A	TRF - 2 - 2
		Triplex	75.00	C	2	4	B	TRF - 1 - 2
	1925	MA-20	345.00	T	3	5	A	TRF - 2 - 2
		Transcontinental A	180.00	T	1	5	S	TRF - 2 - 2
		B	125.00	T	1	5	S	TRF - 2 - 3
	1926	Super Six	195.00	T	1	6	S	TRF - 2 - 3
	1927	Super Six T	98.00	C	1	6	S	TRF - 2 - 3
		SC	172.00	C	1	6	A/S	TRF - 2 - 3
		SE	265.00					
MURDOCK CO., WM. J.	1923 1924	5 Tube Neutrodyne		T	3	5	S	Neut. - 2 - 2

MANUFACTURER	YEAR	MODEL NO. & NAME	PRICE	STYLE	D	T	P	CIR. & STAGES
MURDOCK CO., WM. J. (cont.)	1925	5 Tube Neutrodyne 100	100.00	T	3	5	E	Neut. - 2 - 2
		204	350.00	C	2	6		Neut. - 3 -
		200		T	3	5		Neut.
		203		T	3	6		Neut.
		CS-32	130.00	T	3		S	Neut. - 2 - 2
		CS-33	140.00	T	3		S	Neut. - 2 - 2
		101	92.50	T	3	5		Neut. - 2 - 2
		110	110.00	T	3	5		Neut. - 2 - 2
	1926	M-26	65.00	T	3	5	S	Neut. - 2 - 2
	1927	350	52.50	T	1	7	B	Neut. - 2 - 2
		65	65.00	T	1	7	B	Neut. - 3 - 3
		75	75.00	T	1	7	B	Neut. - 3 - 3
MUSIC MASTER CORP. (See Ware)	1924	360	360.00	T	1	6	S	TRF - 3 - 2
	1925	175	175.00	Desk	2	6	S	TRF - 2 - 2
		400	400.00	T	2	5	A	TRF - 2 - 2
		60	60.00	T	3	5	S	TRF - 2 - 2
		100	100.00	Desk	2	5	S	TRF - 3 - 2
		215	215.00	Desk	2	6	S	TRF - 2 - 2
		300	300.00		2	5	S	TRF - 1 - 1
		50 Ware	50.00		2	3	B	Neut. - 2 - 2
		140	140.00	T	1		S	TRF - 4 - 4
		250 Ware	250.00		1	7	Neut.	Neut. - 4 - 2
		460 "	460.00	Desk	2	7	S	TRF - 4 - 2
	1926	301	300.00				S	TRF
MUSICAL PRODUCTS DISTR. CO.	1925	210 Radio Art	95.00	C-LS	3	5	S	TRF - 2 - 2
		Federal Danersk	325.00		2	5	E	TRF - 2 - 2
MUSIC RADIO CO.	1923	Musio	12.50					
			45.00					
			115.00					
			160.00					
			400.00					
		AC-5	175.00					RF
		AC-4	140.00					RF
MUTUAL RADIO CO.	1925	5 Super Six	115.00		2		B	TRF - 3 - 2
		L "	140.00		2		B	TRF - 3 - 2
		P " "	175.00		2		B	TRF - 3 - 2

MANUFACTURER	YEAR	MODEL NO. & NAME	PRICE	STYLE	D	T	P	CIR. & STAGES
MUTUAL RADIO CO. (cont.)	1926	S Super Six	95.00	T	2	6		TRF - 3 - 2
		4 "	110.00	T	2	6		TRF - 3 - 2
		TC "	140.00	C	2	6		TRF - 3 - 2
		FC "	175.00	FC	2	6		TRF - 3 - 2
MYRADIO CO.	1925	3	25.00	T	2	4	S	Rfx - 1 - 2
NASSAU RADIO CO.	1923	LR-70	175.00	T	2	7	S	TRF - 3 - 3
	1924	LR-70	175.00	T	2	7	S	TRF - 3 - 3
	1925	LR-170 Unitune	195.00	T	2	7	S	TRF - 3 - 3
		VR215 Magadyne	115.00	T	3	6	E	TRF - 2 - 3
		MR60 "	130.00	T	3	6	E	TRF - 2 - 2
		VR400 "	130.00	T	3	5	E	TRF - 2 - 3
	1926	MR60 "	130.00	T	3	6	E	TRF - 2 - 2
		VR400 "	130.00	T	3	5	E	TRF - 2 - 3
		VR215	115.00	T	3	6	E	TRF - 2 - 2
		C	175.00					
		DLP	300.00					
NATIONAL AIRPHONE CORP.	1923	G	12.50	T	1	1		C -
		GT-1 Monodyne	10.00	T	1	1	B	D -
	1924	GT-1 "	10.00	T	1	1	B	D -
	1925	4A Stratford	65.00	T	2	4	E	TRF - 1 - 2
		5A Somerset Mars	75.00	T	3	5	E	TRF - 2 - 2
		4B Shelbourne	85.00	T	1	4	E	TRF - 1 - 2
		4C Smrst. Standish	150.00	T	1	4	E	TRF - 2 - 2
		Monodyne		BB	1		B	TRF - 2 - 2
		Somerset 5	60.00	T	3	5		TRF - 1 -
NATIONAL CARBON CO. "EVEREADY"	1927	1	110.00	T	1	8	A	TRF - 3 - 2*
	1928	2	90.00	T	1	8	A	TRF - 3 - 2*
		3	110.00	T	1	8	A	TRF - 3 - 2*
	1929	11	145.00	C	1	8	A	TRF - 3 - 2*
		20	40.00	T	1	6	B	TRF - 3 - 2
		21	40.00	T	1	6	B	TRF - 3 - 2
		31	115.00	T	1	8	A	TRF - 3 - 2*
		32	175.00	C	1	8	A	TRF - 3 - 2*
		33	210.00	C	1	8	A	TRF - 3 - 2*
		34	225.00	C	1	8	A	TRF - 3 - 2*
		42	180.00	C	1	8	A	TRF - 3 - 2*

Na

MANUFACTURER	YEAR	MODEL NO. & NAME	PRICE	STYLE	D	T	P	CIR. & STAGES
NATIONAL CARBON CO. (cont.)		43	215.00	C	1	8	A	TRF - 3 - 2*
		44	230.00	C	1	8	A	TRF - 3 - 2*
		52	185.00	C	1	8	A	SG - 3 - 2*
		53	220.00	C	1	8	A	SG - 3 - 2*
		54	235.00	C	1	8	A	SG - 3 - 2*
NATIONAL CHELSEA RADIO CORP.	SEE	Chelsea Radio Corp.						
NATIONAL CO. INC. S/A fil's operable from AC or Storage battery. SW-5 used 5880 power box, but also available in lo-drain battery model.	1924	Browning-Drake	22.00	Kit	2	2	E	Reg - - 1
	1929	SG-4 Thrill Box		MT	1	4/5	S/A	SG Reg. - 1 - 2
		SG-5 Thrill Box	54.75	MT	1	5/6	S/A	SG Reg. - 1 - 3
		SW-4 Thrill Box		Ch	1	4/5	S/A	SG Reg. - 1 - 2*
		MB29	114.00	MT	1	9	A	SG 1 3 - 2*
	1931	SW-5 A-C Thrill Box		MT	1	6	A	SG Reg. - 1 - 2*
		SW-3 Thrill Box		MT	1	3/4	S/A	SG Reg. - 1 - 1
NATIONAL INDUSTRIES INC.	1923	Black Diamond	2.50 / 40.00 / 100.00					C - - - -
NATIONAL RADIO & TELEVISION CO.	1929	30 Minuet	115.00	LB	1	8	A	
		31 "	118.00	LB	1	8	A	
		32 "	125.00	LB	1	8	A	
		33 "	132.00	LB	1	8	A	
		34 "	145.00	HB	1	8	A	
		35 "	145.00	HB	1	8	A	
		38	249.00	HB	1	8	A	
NATIONAL RADIO CORP.	1925				3	5	S	TRF - 2 - 2
NATIONAL RADIO ENGINEERING CO.	1923	Nareco	15.00 / 25.00 / 30.00 / 50.00 / 75.00 / 100.00 / 150.00					
NATIONAL RADIO MANUFACTURING CO.	1923	70	72.00					
		71	96.00					

MANUFACTURER	YEAR	MODEL NO. & NAME	PRICE	STYLE	D	T	P	CIR. & STAGES
NATIONAL RADIO MANUFACTURING CO. (cont.)		72	123.00					
		73	165.00					
		77	198.00					
		82	180.00					
		83	240.00					
		88	270.00					
		93	291.00					
		99	399.00					
		473	475.00					
		Ford Jr.	67.50					
		Ford Sr.	125.00					
	1924	072	160.00					
		372	160.00					
	1925	Country Gentleman	80.00	Por	2	4	B	TRF - 1 - 2
		"	110.00		2	4	B	TRF - 1 - 2
NATIONAL RADIO PRODUCTS CORP.	1923	Radiolean Jr.	12.50		1	-	-	C - - - -
NATIONAL TRANSFORMER MFG. CO.	SEE	Balkeit Radio Co.						
	SEE	National Transformer Co.						
NAYLOR RADIO CORP.	1926	Sterling	39.50	T	2	5	S	TRF - 1 - 3
		" 5	64.50	TC	2	5	S	TRF - 1 - 3
		"	69.50	C	2	5	S	TRF - 1 - 3
	1927	"		T	2	5	S	TRF - 1 - 3
NEON LAMP WORKS	1923	Neon Simplex						
	1924	"						
NEUTROWOUND RADIO MFG. CO. (Advance Automobile Accessories Co.)	1925	1926	85.00	T	3	6	S	TRF - 2 - 3
	1926	1927	85.00	T	3	6	S	TRF - 2 - 3
		1927 Super Power	95.00	T	3	6	S	TRF - 2 - 3
	1927	1928		T	2	6	S	TRF - 2 - 3
NEWPORT RADIO CO.	1924	Series V	115.00	T	3	5	S	TRF - 2 - 2
		Newport	118.00	T	3	5	S	TRF
			170.00	CT	3	5	S	TRF
			250.00	C	3	5	S	TRF
NEW YORK ALBUM & CARD CO.	1925	R-2 Nyaccoflex	32.50	T	2	2	B	Cry.Rfx - 2 - 2
		RP-1	55.00	Por	3	2	B	Cry.Rfx - 2 - 2

MANUFACTURER	YEAR	MODEL NO. & NAME	PRICE	STYLE	D	T	P	CIR. & STAGES
NEW YORK ALBUM & CARD CO. (cont.)	1926	R-5 Nyacco	40.00	T	3	5		TRF - 2 - 2
		Nyacco Portable	65.00	Por	3	6		TRF - 2 - 3
NEW YORK COIL CO.	1922	Entertain-a-phone 2	50.00	T	2	3	E	NonReg. - - - 2
NIEHOFF, PAUL G. CO.	1921	Rezodon		T	6	5		Reg.
NO-BATTERY RADIO CO.	1926	Electrola	125.00				A	
		Electroformer	135.00				A	
		Electrola	195.00				A	
NORBERT RADIO SERVICE	1926	Melodee	75.00	C	3		E	TRF
			75.00	C	3		E	TRF
		S-6 Melodee	53.50	T	3		E	TRF
		N-5 "	53.50	T	3		E	TRF
		Famous 5	28.50	T	3		E	TRF
NORDEN-HAUCK CO. C-7 and C-10 were the famous Leutz Superhet design. See Experimenters Information Service.	1925	C-7	250.00	T	2	7	S	SH - - 2 2
		C-10 Navy Model	60.00	T	2	10	S	SH - 3 2 2
	1926	6 Pliodyne		T	2	6	E/A	TRF - 2 - 3
		Universal Plio 6		T	2	6	E/A	TRF - 5 - 4
		Admiralty Super 10	307.00	T	2	10	E/A	TRF - 5 - 4
		Super 10		T	2	10	E/A	TRF - 5 - 4
		" " Specialty		T	2	10	E	TRF - 5 - 4
		Admiralty Super 10		T	2	10	E	TRF - 5 - 4
		Improved Super 10		T	2	10	E	TRF - 5 - 4
	1928	Improved Super 10		T	2	10	E	TRF - 5 - 4
		Shielded Super 10	125.00	T	1	8	A/E	TRF - 3 - 3
		Electrophonic Super		T/C	2	10	A	TRF - 3 - 3
	1929	Shielded Super 10		T	2	10	A/E	TRF - 5 - 4
		Admiralty Super 10 Grid		MT	2	10	A/E	SG - 5 - 4
	1930	Super DX-5		MT	2	6	A/E	TRFReg. - 1 - 2*
NORTHERN ELECTRIC SALES CO.	1923	Roycroft	2.50			-	-	C - - - -
			5.00			-	-	C - - - -
			27.50					D
			40.00					D
NORTHLAND RADIO CO.	1926	$97.00 to $250.00						

126

MANUFACTURER	YEAR	MODEL NO. & NAME	PRICE	STYLE	D	T	P	CIR. & STAGES
NORTHWESTERN RADIO MFG. CO.	1922	22-2	150.00	Box 2	3	3		DAA	- - - 2
	1923	SR-25	95.00						
	1924	Nor-wes-co	150.00						
	1925	SR-25	65.00	T	3		S	TRF	
		Norco	100.00	T	3		S	TRF	
		" Type D	150.00	T	3		S	TRF	
	1926	" DeLuxe	75.00	T	3	5		RF	2 - - 2
		" 55	165.00	C	3	5		RF	2 - - 2
NOVELTY RADIO MANUFACTURING CO.	1924	Nickelette						C	- - - -
NUNN LANDON CO.	1925	E. D. Nunn	90.00	T	3	5	S	TRF	- 2 - 2
		" " "	110.00	T	3	5	S	TRF	- 2 - 2
		" " "	130.00	T	3	5	S	TRF	- 2 - 2
	1926	Cascade	135.00	T	2	5	S	TRF	- 2 - 2
			260.00	C	2	5	S	TRF	- 2 - 2
NUTONE RADIO CO.	1925	N-R-8A	175.00	T	3	5	B	TRF	- - - 2
		N-R-6A	145.00	T	3		B	TRF	
		N-R-5A	110.00	T	3		B	TRF	
		N.R. DeLuxe 25	310.00		3		B	TRF	
		N.R. 7A	180.00	T	3		B	TRF	
OARD RADIO LABORATORIES (Sold by Atlantic-Pacific Radio Supply)	1922	AR-2	135.00	T	5	3	E	Reg.	- - - 2
		DR-5	85.00	T	3	1	E	Reg.	- - - -
		AP-4	45.00	T				C	- - - ,
		AP-5 Amp.	50.00	Por		2	E	AA	- - - 2
		Oard Phantom Receptor	75.00	T	1	3	B	DAA	- - - 2
	1923	AR-10			2	3	S	DAA	- - - 2
OHIO STAMPING & ENGINEERING CO.	1925	5 and 5D "No-Dial"	98.00	T	1	5	E	TRF	- 1 - 3
OKAY RADIO CORP.	1922	VT	26.50	Box	2	1	B	Reg.	- - - -
	1926	RF-2	50.00	T	3	5		TRF	- 2 - 2
		2 DeLuxe	65.00	T	3	5		TRF	- 2 - 3
		RF-4	70.00	T	2	5		TRF	- 2 - 2
		RF-3	85.00	T	2	6		TRF	- 2 - 3
OLDROYD, WALTER J.	1924	Custom Made							

MANUFACTURER	YEAR	MODEL NO. & NAME	PRICE	STYLE	D	T	P	CIR. & STAGES
OLDROYD, WALTER J. (cont.)	1925	Custom Made						
	1926	" "						
O'NEILL, WM.	1926	VT						
OPERADIO CORP.	1923							
	1924	2	195.00	Por	2	6	B	TRF - 2 - 2
	1925	"1925"	190.00	Por	2	6	B	TRF - 3 - 3
		"1926"	189.00	Por		7	B	
		Windsor	195.00	Por			B	
		Empire	389.00	C				
		C	273.50	T				
	1926	C	160.00	Por	1	6	B	TRF - 3 - 2
			180.00		1			TRF 1 2 - 3
	1927	7	146.00	Por	1	7	B	TRF 1 2 - 3
		With power unit	190.00	Por				TRF 1 2 - 3
	1928	7	112.00	Por			B	
ORATOR RADIO CORP.	1925	III Popular	45.00		2		B	- 1 - -
		IV	58.50		3		B	- 1 - 2
		III Aristocrat	90.00				B	C
	1926	Midget	15.00					
		3 Popular	45.00	T	2	4	S	TRF - 1 - 2
		4	58.50	T	3	5	S	TRF - 2 - 2
		Light 6	98.50	Por	1	6	S	TRF - 3 - 2
		Console4	150.00	C	2	5	S	TRF - 2 - 2
		Master 8	550.00	T	2	5	S	TRF - 2 - 2
ORIOLE RADIO	SEE	Continental Radio						
ORTHOCRAFT	1928	Sextet	78.75	C		6		
		Septet	107.50	C		7		
ORTHODYNE RADIO MANUFACTURING CO.	1926	Air-Master	60.00	Ch	3	5	S	TRF - 2 - 2
		" " Concert	75.00	T	3	5	S	TRF - 2 - 2
		" " High Boy	130.00	C	3	5	S	TRF - 2 - 2
OTT RADIO, INC.	1923	WC-5-SW	85.00		3	4	E	TRF - 1 - 2
OWENS RADIO CO. INC.	1923							

MANUFACTURER	YEAR	MODEL NO. & NAME	PRICE	STYLE	D	T	P	CIR. & STAGES
OZARKA, INC.	1924	RC200	65.00	Por	2	3	B	DAA	- - - 2
	1925	299 Junior	39.50	T	4	4	B	TRF
			100.00	T	3	4	B	
			75.00	Por	3	4		
		Senior Console	125.00	T	3	5	S	TRF	- 2 - 2
			197.00	C	3	4		TRF
		Viking (5A)	58.00			5		TRF	- 2 - 2
	1926		64.00	C	2	4		
			160.00	Por	2	4		
			55.00	Por	3	4		
			75.00	Por	3	5		
		Senior (5A)	125.00	T	3	5	S	TRF	- 2 - 2
		Junior (5A)	100.00	T	3	5	S	TRF	- 2 - 2
		5A	210.00	C	3	5	S	TRF	- 2 - 2
		Senior (85)	132.00	T	3	5	S	TRF	- 2 - 2
		S7	215.00	C	3	7	S	TRF	- 2 - 3*
		Senior (5A)		T		7	S	TRF	- 2 - 3*
		S7		C		5	S	TRF	- 2 - 2
	1927	Senior (S5)	132.00	T	3	7	S	TRF	- 2 - 3*
		S7		T		5	S	TRF	- 2 - 2
		Junior (5A)		T	3	7	S	TRF	- 2 - 3*
		S8	215.00	C	3	5	S	TRF	- 2 - 2
	1928	S7		C		7	S	TRF	- 2 - 3
		78			3	6	S	TRF	1 - 3 - 2*
		89			1	9	A	TRF	1 - 3 - 1
		90			1	9	A	TRF	- 3 - 1
	1929	Viking			1	6	S	SG	- 3 - 2*
		91 Battery			1	7	A	SG	- 4 - 1
		92			1	7	S	SG	- - - -
	1930	93			1	6	A	SG SH	- - - -
		93A			1	7	S	SH	- - - -
		93B			1	7	A	SH	- - - -
		94AVC				8	A	SH	- - - -
PACIFIC CLARATONE	1925	Claratone	75.00	T	3	5	S	TRF	- 2 - 2
PACIFIC SCREW CO.	1923	Pasco	3.00					C	- - - -
	1924		5.00					C	- - - -
			3.00					C	- - - -

MANUFACTURER	YEAR	MODEL NO. & NAME	PRICE	STYLE	D	T	P	CIR. & STAGES
PACIFIC SCREW CO. (cont.)	1924	Pasco	6.00					C - - - -
	1925	Acme	3.50					C - - - -
	1926	Pasco	5.00					C - - - -
PACKARD RADIO PRODUCTS CO.	1925	"Five"	45.00	T	3	5	S	TRF - 2 - 2
	1928	Super 8	99.00	C	1	8/9	A	
			53.00					
PAIGE RADIO CO.	1924		5.00			1		C - - - -
			17.50				E	D
PALMER ELEC. & MFG. CO.	1924	Du-Wa		T	2	-	-	C - - - -
PAL RADIO CO. INC.	1926	Pal				1		C - - - -
P AND M RADIO CO.	1920	Penn C	48.00	T	2	1	-	Reg. - - - -
PANDORA	1922	Pandora	2.50	B	0	0	-	C - - - -
PARAGON	SEE	Adams-Morgan						
PARKER METAL GOODS CO.	1923							C - - - -
	1924							C
PARKIN MANUFACTURING CO.	1924	Peak of Perfection	124.00		3	1	E	D - - - -
	1925	" " "	17.00	Por	1	4	B	Rfx - - - -
	1926	" " "				1	B	D
PARMAK	1924	Parmak	85.00	T	3	5		TRF - 2 - 2
PATHE PHONO & RADIO CO.	1924	Minute Man	125.00	T	3	5	E	TRF - 2 - 2
	1925	"	90.00	T	3	5		TRF - 2 - 3
		B-5 Minute Man	60.00	T	3	5	E	TRF - 2 - 2
PATTERSON RADIO CORP.	1926	Supreme C	65.00	T	3	5	S	TRF - 2 - 2
		" T	75.00	T	2	4	E	TRF - 1 - 2
		"	90.00	T	3	5	S	TRF - 2 - 2
		" K	100.00	C	3	5	S	TRF - 2 - 2

MANUFACTURER	YEAR	MODEL NO. & NAME	PRICE	STYLE	D	T	P	CIR.	& STAGES
PATTERSON RADIO CORP. (cont.)	1927	Supreme B	125.00	C	3	5	S	TRF	- 2 - 2
		Supreme	69.75	C	1	6			
		K	99.50	C	1	7			
	1928	D	107.50	C	1	7			
		SD	129.50	C	1	7			
		SD	149.50	C	1	7			
			79.50	T	1	6			
	1929	Aristocrat	79.50	C	1	6	A		
		DeLuxe	97.50	C	1	7	A		
		89	89.50	T	1	7	A		
		99	99.50	LB	1	7	A		
		119	119.50	HB	1	7	A		
		169	169.50	RP	1	6	A	SG	
	1930	5-69	59.50	M	1	7	A	SG	- 2 - 2
		7-69	69.50	M	1	6	A	SG	- 3 - 2
		6-59	59.50	T	1	6	A	SG	- 2 - 2
		6-69	69.50	LB	1	6	A	SG	- 2 - 2
		7-69	69.50	T	1	7	A	SG	- 4 - 2
		7-69	79.50	LB	1	7	A	SG	- 4 - 2
PEARSON DIV. ELEC. RESEARCH LABS.	SEE	Elec. Research Labs.							
PEERLESS RADIO CO.	1922	International	175.00	T	2	5	S	TRF	- 2 - 2
	1924	Electradyne	125.00		2	2	A	Rfx	
	1925	"	110.00		3	4	B/A	Rfx / TRF	- 1 - 2
PENNSYLVANIA RADIO LABS.	1924	Parla	125.00		3	3			
	1925								
	1926		125.00		3	3			
PENN. RADIO MANUFACTURING CO.	1926	5 DeLuxe	85.00	T	3	5	E	TRF	- 2 - 2
		6	90.00	T	1	6	E	TRF	- 2 - 3
		5	150.00	C	3	5	E	TRF	- 2 - 2
PENNSYLVANIA WIRELESS MFG. CO.	SEE	Penn. Radio Mfg. Co.							
PENN WIRE MANUFACTURING CO.	SEE	Penn. Radio Mfg. Co.							
PENTZ RADIO FACTORY	1926	Pentzlyne	7.50		-	-	-	C	- - - -
		Pocket Radio	2.00		-	-	-	C	- - - -

MANUFACTURER	YEAR	MODEL NO. & NAME	PRICE	STYLE	D	T	P	CIR. & STAGES	
PENTZ RADIO FACTORY (cont.)		"Power" Crystal Sets ($25. to $50.)						C	- - - -
PERKINS PHONOGRAPH CO.	1926	Perkins Super Value		RP					
PERLESZ RADIO CORP.	1926	$275. to $1000.		T		7	S	TRF	
				S-C		8	S	TRF	
				C		9	S	TRF	
PERRY RADIO SUPPLY CO. "PERASCO"	1923	Perasco Kewpie	25.00						
		PRD-11	55.00						
		Petite Grand	250.00						
	1924	Perasco	25.00						
		PRD-11	50.00						
		Petite Grand	175.00						
	1925	Perasco Kewpie	25.00	T			E	D (non-reg.)	
		PA-111 Perasco Amp.	35.00	T			E	Reg.	- - 2
		Perasco Petit Grand	175.00	T	2		E	Grimes	- 3 - 3
		PRD-11 Perasco	50.00	T	2		E	Harkness	- 1 - 1
		PA IV Perasco Amp.	40.00	T			E	Reg.	- - 2
PFANSTIEHL RADIO CO. (Became Balkeit in 1928. Pfanstiehl name later changed to Fansteel.)	1924	7 Overtone	150.00	T	3	5	S	TRF	- 2 - 2
	1925	8	85.00	T	2	5	S	TRF	- 2 - 2
		8C	135.00	C	2	5	S	TRF	- 2 - 2
		8E	135.00	C	1	5	S	TRF	- 2 - 2
		10 Overtone	155.00	T	1	6	S	TRF	- 2 - 3
		10C	450.00	C	1	6	S	TRF	- 2 - 3
		10S	200.00	C	1	6	S	TRF	- 2 - 3
	1926	20	125.00	T	1	6	S	TRF	- 2 - 3
		201	170.00	C	1	6	S	TRF	- 2 - 3
		202	210.00	C	1	6	S	TRF	- 2 - 3
			235.00	HB	1	6	S	TRF	- 2 - 3
		18	95.00	T	2	5	S	TRF	- 2 - 2
		181	135.00	C	2	5	S	TRF	- 2 - 2
		182	170.00	C	2	5	S	TRF	- 2 - 2
	1927	28 Junior	65.00	T	1	6	S	TRF	- 3 - 2
		30	105.00	T	1	6	S	TRF	- 3 - 2
		32	150.00	T	1	7	S	TRF	- 3 - 3
		302	185.00	C	1	6	S	TRF	- 3 - 2
		322	250.00	C	1	7	S	TRF	- 3 - 3

MANUFACTURER	YEAR	MODEL NO. & NAME	PRICE	STYLE	D	T	P	CIR. & STAGES	
PFANSTIEHL RADIO CO. (cont.)									
		34	175.00	T	1	7	A	TRF	- 3 - 2
		50	135.00	T	1	7	A	TRF	- 3 - 2
PHENIX RADIO CORP. Specialized in R. E. LaCault version of superheterodyne.	1924	Ultradyne	24.50	T	2	8		SH	- - 2 2
		" Kit		Kit	2			SH	- - 2 2
	1925	" L-2		T				SH	
		" Kit	30.00	Kit				SH	
	1926	L-3	135.00	Kit					
		L-3 Ultradyne	135.00	CT	2	6	S		
		L-1			2	6		SH	
		L-2	175.00	C				SH	
		L-3							
PHILCO (Philadelphia Storage Battery Co.) Acquired Automobile Radio Corp. in 1931, along with the Transitone name.	1928	551	275.00	HB	1	7	A	Neut.	- 3 - 2*
		561	285.00	HB	1	7	A	Neut.	- 3 - 2
		531	200.00	LB	1	7	A	Neut.	- 3 - 2
		541	210.00	LB	1	7	A	Neut.	- 3 - 2
		511	115.00	T	1	7	A	Neut.	- 3 - 2
		521	125.00	T	1	7	A	Neut.	- 3 - 2
		512	125.00	T	1	7	A	Neut.	- 3 - 2
		513	125.00	T	1	7	A	Neut.	- 3 - 2
		514	125.00	T	1	7	A	Neut.	- 3 - 2
		515	125.00	T	1	7	A	Neut.	- 3 - 2
		522	135.00	T	1	7	A	Neut.	- 3 - 2
		523	135.00	T	1	7	A	Neut.	- 3 - 2
		524	135.00	T	1	7	A	Neut.	- 3 - 2
		525	135.00	T	1	7	A	Neut.	- 3 - 2
		86	275.00	HB	1	8	A	Neut.	- 3 - 2*
	1929	82	285.00	HB	1	8	A	Neut.	- 3 - 2*
		86 Neutrodyne Plus	215.00	LB	1	8	A	Neut.	- 3 - 2*
		86 "	157.00	C	1	8	A	Neut.	- 3 - 2*
		82	225.00	LB	1	8	A	Neut.	- 3 - 2*
		82	167.00	C	1	8	A	Neut.	- 3 - 2*
		65 DeLuxe	195.00	HB	1	6	A	SG	- 2 - 1*
		65	139.50	HB	1	6	A	SG	- 2 - 1*
		65	119.50	LB	1	6	A	SG	- 2 - 1*
		62 DeLuxe	67.00	T	1	6	A	SG	- 2 - 1*
		62	195.00	HB	1	6	A	SG	- 2 - 1*
		62	139.50	HB	1	6	A	SG	- 2 - 1*
		62	119.50	LB	1	6	A	SG	- 2 - 1*
		87 DeLuxe	67.00	T	1	6	A	SG	- 2 - 1*
			205.00	HB	1	8	A	Neut.	- 3 - 2*

MANUFACTURER	YEAR	MODEL NO. & NAME	PRICE	STYLE	D	T	P	CIR. & STAGES
PHILCO (cont.)	1930	87	149.50	HB	1	8	A	Neut.	- 3 - 2*
		87	129.50	LB	1	8	A	Neut.	- 3 - 2*
		83 DeLuxe	205.00	HB	1	8	A	Neut.	- 3 - 2*
		83	149.50	HB	1	8	A	Neut.	- 3 - 2*
		83	129.50	LB	1	8	A	Neut.	- 3 - 2*
		65	99.50	T	1	7	A	SG	- 2 - 2*
		76	115.00	T	1	7	A	SG	- 2 - 1*
		65	145.00	Tudor	1	6	A	SG	- 2 - 1*
		62	145.00	Tudor	1	6	A	SG	- 2 - 1*
		87	155.00	Tudor	1	8	A	Neut.	- 3 - 2*
		83	155.00	Tudor	1	8	A	Neut.	- 3 - 2*
		95 DeLuxe	225.00	HB	1	9	A	SG	- 3 - 3*
		95	169.50	HB	1	9	A	SG	- 3 - 3*
		95	149.50	LB	1	9	A	SG	- 3 - 3*
		95	97.00	T	1	9	A	SG	- 3 - 3*
		92 DeLuxe	235.00	HB	1	9	A	SG	- 3 - 3*
		92	179.50	HB	1	9	A	SG	- 3 - 3*
		92	159.50	LB	1	9	A	SG	- 3 - 3*
		92	107.00	T	1	9	A	SG	- 3 - 3*
		76 DeLuxe	195.00	HB	1	7	A	SG	- 2 - 2*
		76	139.50	HB	1	7	A	SG	- 2 - 2*
		76	119.50	LB	1	7	A	SG	- 2 - 2*
		76	112.00	C	1	7	A	SG	- 2 - 2*
		30	67.00	T	1	7	A	SG	- 2 - 2*
		30	129.00	HB	1	8	B	SG	- 3 - 3*
		Baby Grand	99.50	LB	1	8	B	SG	- 2 - 2*
		Concert Grand	350.00	M	1	7	A	SG	- 2 - 2*
		20	49.50	LB	1	8	A	SG	- 2 - 2*
		20A	56.50	M	1	7	A	SG	- 2 - 2*
		96	85.00	M	1	9	A	SG	- 3 - 3*
		77	85.00	T	1	7	A	SG	- 2 - 2*
		296A Comb.	365.00	RP	1	9	A	SG	- 3 - 3*
		296A Comb.	210.00	RP	1	9	A	SG	- 3 - 3*
		96A	155.00	HB	1	9	A	SG	- 3 - 3*
		77A	120.00	LB	1	7	A	SG	- 2 - 2*
		77A	105.00	C	1	9	A	SG	- 2 - 2*
		96A	95.00	T	1	7	A	SG	- 3 - 3*
		77A	65.00	T	1	9	A	SG	- 3 - 3*
		41, 42	149.00	HB	1	6	D	SG	- 2 - 2*
		41, 42	119.00	LB	1	6	D	SG	- 2 - 2*

MANUFACTURER	YEAR	MODEL NO. & NAME	PRICE	STYLE	D	T	P	CIR. & STAGES
PHILCO (cont.)								
		41, 42	99.50	C	1	6	D	SG - 2 - 2*
		29 Comb.	350.00	RP	1	9	A	SG - 3 - 3*
		296 Comb.	198.00	RP	1	9	A	SG - 3 - 3*
		96	145.00	HB	1	9	A	SG - 3 - 3*
		77	110.00	LB	1	7	A	SG - 2 - 2*
		77	95.00	C	1	7	A	SG - 2 - 2*
		76	112.00	C	1	7	A	SG - 2 - 2*
		87	149.50	HB	1	8	A	Neut. - 3 - 2*
		87 DeLuxe	205.00	HB	1	8	A	Neut. - 3 - 2*
		87	129.50	LB	1	8	A	Neut. - 2 - 2*
		77		Ch	1	7	A	SG - 2 - 2*
		96		Ch	1	9	A	SG - 3 - 3*
		77	55.00	T	1	7	A	SG - 2 - 2*
PICARD RADIO CORP.	1923	Ames $35. & $40.			2		S	DAA - - 2
PIERCE AIRO INC.	1930	524		M	1	5	A	SG - 2 - 1
		AC-724		Ch	1	7	A	SG - 2 - 2*
		AC-725			1	7	A	SG - 2 - 2*
		DC-727		Ch	1	7	D	SG - 2 - 2*
		B-22		Ch	1	6	B	SG - 3 - 2
PIERCE RADIO LABORATORIES	1926							
PIERCE RADIO SALES CORP.	1924	Piercetone						
PIERSON CO., THE	1929	#71			1	8	A	TRF - 3 - 2*
PILOT ELECTRICAL MFG. CO.	SEE	Pilot Radio & Tube. Corp.						
PILOT RADIO & TUBE CORP.	1926	Universal	17.90	Kit	2	3/5/7		(Several)
	1927							
	1928	Super Wasp K110	29.50	Kit	2	4	S	Reg. TRF - 1 - 2
	1929	A.C. Super Wasp K115/111	34.50	Kit	2	5	A	Reg. TRF - 1 - 2
		Pilotone			1	7	A	TRF - 2 - 2*
		Air Scout			1	6	A	TRF - 2 - 2
		Air Hound			1	5	A	Reg. TRF - 1 - 2*
		SG105			1	6	A	SG - 1 - 2*
		K106			1	7	A	SG 13 - 1
		K108			1	7	A	TRF - 2 - 2*
		K117 Twin S. G. 8			1	8	A	SG - 3 - 2*
	1930	Auto Pilot	49.50	Kit A	1	6	S	SG - 3 - 2

PILOT RADIO & TUBE CORP.
Tube count includes separate AC power supply unit. Super Wasp was a very popular set, designed by Krause and Sleeper.

MANUFACTURER	YEAR	MODEL NO. & NAME	PRICE	STYLE	D	T	P	CIR. & STAGES
PINE-TREE RADIO CORP.	1926	Pine Tree						
PIONEER RADIO CORP.	1929	66	99.50	C	1	8	A	TRF	- 3 - 2*
		68	125.00	C	1	8	A	TRF	- 3 - 2*
		70	135.00	C	1	8	A	TRF	- 3 - 2*
		72	150.00	C	1	8	A	TRF	- 3 - 2*
		74	135.00	C	1	8	A	TRF	- 3 - 2*
		76	145.00	C	1	8	A	TRF	- 3 - 2*
		60A	70.00	C	1	8	A	TRF	- 3 - 2*
	1930	100	136.00	HB	1	7	D	SG	- 3 - 2*
PITTSBURGH RADIO SUP. HOUSE INC.	1923	SP-2	100.00			4		
	1924	SP-2						
	1925							
	1926							
PLAZA MUSIC CO.	1926	R-1 Fine Arts	37.50	T	3	5/6	E	TRF	- 2 - 2
		R-2 "	52.50	T	3	5/6	E	TRF	- 2 - 2
		R-6 "	52.50	T	3	5/6	E	TRF	- 2 - 2
		R-3 "	87.50	C	3	5/6	E	TRF	- 2 - 2
		R-99 "	92.50	HB	3	5/6	E	TRF	- 2 - 2
		R-4 "	125.00		3		E	TRF	
		R-5 "	150.00		3		E	TRF	
PLYMOUTH RADIO CORP.	1930	3	64.50	M	1	5	A	SG	- 2 - 1
PONTREE RADIO LABORATORY	1925	Engler-SDV	65.00	T	2	5	E	TRF	- 2 - 2
		"	70.00		2	5	E	TRF	- 2 - 2
PORTER, FRANK	1926	Coriola 7	350.00	T		6	B	RF	- 3 - 3
	1927	Superior 25	75.00			7	B	TRF	- 3 - 3
			150.00	T		7	B	TRF	
PORTOLA RADIO CO.	1925	101	160.00	Por	2	6	B	RF	3 - - 2
PORTS MANUFACTURING CO.	1924	PRMCO KD	60.00	T	3	5	E	C	- - - -
	1925	102 Premco	65.00		3	5	E	TRF	- 2 - 2
		Pormco	40.00		3	5	E	TRF	- 2 - 2
		Perkwell Super 5							

MANUFACTURER	YEAR	MODEL NO. & NAME	PRICE	STYLE	D	T	P	CIR. & STAGES	
PORTS MANUFACTURING CO (cont.)	1926	105A PRMCO	42.00	T	3	5	S	TRF - 2 - 2	
		105 "	70.00	T	3	5	S	TRF - 2 - 2	
		110 "	75.00	T	3	6	S	TRF - 2 - 2	
POWELL MANUFACTURING CO.	1930	Cathedral	59.50	M	1	6	A	SG - 3 - 1	
POWER RADIO CO.	1924	A	165.00			6		RF	
		B	110.00			4		Rfx	
		C	220.00	Por				Rfx	
	1925	Power		T	2			Rfx	
POWEROLA RADIO CO.	1925	C-3	115.00		3	5	D	TRF - 2 - 2	
	1926	"	165.00		3	6	A	TRF - 2 - 2	
		"	115.00		3		D	TRF	
		"Electric Panel"	165.00		3		A	TRF	
		"	100.00		3		D	TRF	
		" DeLuxe 114	150.00		3	5	A	TRF	
		"	280.00	HB	3	6	D	TRF	
		" Highboy 113	320.00	HB	3	5	A	TRF	
		" " 111	230.00	HB	3	6	D	TRF	
		" "	280.00	HB	3	6	A	TRF	
		" " 110	245.00	HB	3	6	D	TRF	
		" "	295.00		3	5	A	TRF	
		" "	245.00		3	6	D	TRF	
		" "	295.00		3		A	TRF	
POWERPHONIC CO.	1928		60.00		3	6	A	TRF	
PRECEL RADIO MANUFACTURING CO.	1924	Super Five	130.00	T	3	5	E	TRF - 2 - 2	
	1925	Super Five	130.00	T	3	5	E	TRF - 2 - 2	
PRECISE RADIO MANUFACTURING CO.	1926		34.50					TRF	
PRECISION EQUIPMENT CO.	SEE	Crosley Radio Corp.							
PRECISION PRODUCTS CO.	SEE	Consolidated Radio Corp.							
PREMIER ELECTRIC CO.	1926	Ensemble	35-175	Kit	3	5	B	TRF - 2 - 2	
			24.50	T		5	B	TRF - 2 - 2	
				C			B	TRF	

MANUFACTURER	YEAR	MODEL NO. & NAME	PRICE	STYLE	D	T	P	CIR. & STAGES
PREMIER ELECTRIC CO. (cont.)	1927	6 in line	24.50	T	3	5	B	TRF - 2 - 2
	1928	PT28-29RAC	45.20	C	3	5	B	TRF - 2 - 2
		PT28-29DC	50.00	Ch	1	6	B	TRF - 2 - 2
		PC28-29RAC	90.00	T	1	6	A	TRF - 3 - 2
		PC28-29DC	60.00	C	1	6	D	TRF - 3 - 2
		PC28RAC	140.00	C	1	7	A	TRF - 3 - 2
		PC28DC	110.00	C	1	6	D	TRF - 3 - 2
		PC80RAC	153.00	C	1	7	A	TRF - 3 - 2
		PC80DC	123.00	C	1	6	D	TRF - 3 - 2
		PC47RAC	157.00	C	1	6	A	TRF - 3 - 2
		PC47DC	127.00	C	1	7	D	TRF - 3 - 2
	1929	601	167.00	Ch	1	6	A	TRF - 3 - 2
		771M	137.00	Ch	1	6	B	TRF - 3 - 2
		745C	45.00	Ch	1	8	A	TRF - 3 - 2
		845-V	66.00	Ch	1	8	A	TRF - 4 - 2
		724D	70.00	MT	1	9	A	SG - 3 - 2
		PT-771-M	74.00		1	8	A	TRF - 3 - 2
		2930 7-M	78.00		1	8	A	TRF - 3 - 2*
		2930 7-D	74.00		1	8	A	TRF - 3 - 2*
		R-53			1	8	A	TRF - 3 - 2*
		R-57			1	8	A	TRF - 3 - 2*
		R-55			1	8	A	TRF - 3 - 2*
		R-54			1	8	A	TRF - 3 - 2*
		R-47			1	8	A	TRF - 3 - 2*
	1930	2375	265.00	RP	1	8	A	SG - 4 - 1*
		824	78.00	Ch	1	8	A	SG - 4 - 1*
		Home-Pal	62.50	M	1	6	A	SG - 3 - 1
PREMIER RADIO CO.	1925	7-A	290.00	C	2	5	E	Rfx - 4 - 3
		7-B	160.00	T	2	5	E	Rfx - 4 - 3
	1926	6B	100.00		3			TRF
		8A	350.00	C	2		S	Rfx
		Allen's Rectaflex 20	37.50	T	2	5	S	RfxTRF - 1 - 4
	1927	30	75.00	T	3	7	S	TRF - 2 - 4
		40	75.00	T	1	7	S	TRF - 2 - 4
		50B	350.00	C	1	7	S	TRF - 2 - 4
		50	375.00	C	1	7	S	TRF - 2 - 4

MANUFACTURER	YEAR	MODEL NO. & NAME	PRICE	STYLE	D	T	P	CIR. & STAGES	
PRIESS RADIO CORP.	1925	PR-3	145.00	T	2	5	S	Rfx	3 - 3
		PR-5	225.00	C	2	5	S	Rfx	3 - 3
		PR-4 Straight 8	165.00	T	2	8	E	Rfx	3 - 2
		PR-6 " "	275.00	C	2	8	E	Rfx	3 - 2
		PR-4 " "	175.00	Por	2	8	E	Rfx	3 - 2
	1926	PR-6 " "	285.00	T	2	8	S	Rfx	3 - 5
		PR-4 " "	175.00	C	1	8	S	Rfx	5 - 2
		PR-6 " "	285.00	T	1	8	S	Rfx	5 - 2
		Straight 9 "	195.00	C	1	9	S	Rfx	6 - 2
		"	335.00		1	9	S	Rfx	6 - 2
PRIMA PRODUCTS CORP.	1926	V.T.							
PRITCHARD ROEVER RADIO	SEE	Autophone Co.							
PROGRESSIVE SPECIALTY CO.	1924							C	- - -
Q-T LIGHT CO.	1923	Q.T.	8.50						
		79	17.00						
		718	45.00			3			
Q. T. RADIO PRODUCTS CO., THE	1924							D	
	1925	PT Little Giant	60.00		3	1	E	DAA	2 - 2
		QT "	39.50		3	3	E	TRF	2 - 2
		QT Evening Hour	100.00		3	5	E	TRF	2 - 2
	1926	QT-3	45.00	T	3	5	E	TRF	2 - 2
		QT-A	60.00	T	3	5	S	TRF	2 - 3
		QT-C	95.00	C	1	6	S	TRF	2 - 3
	1927	EH-7 Evening Hour	225.00	C	1	6	S	TRF	3 - 3
						8	A	TRF	
QUEEN QUALITY RADIO CORP.	1926	V.T.							
QUEENS RADIO CO. INC.	1922	Five Unit System	70.00	5 Box	1	2		DA	- - 1
	1923		70.00					Reg.	
RACON ELECTRICAL CO.	1923		2.00					C	- - -
RADIART LABS	1926	Magnaformer 9-8	200.00	T	2	9	S	SH	- - 4 2

Ra

139

MANUFACTURER	YEAR	MODEL NO. & NAME	PRICE	STYLE	D	T	P	CIR. & STAGES		
RADIETTE	1929		59.50 79.50	M C		6 6				
RADIO APPARATUS CO.	1919 1923 1924	5A & 5C Traco RX1 Etherphone RX1 "	45.00	B		-	-	PT		
RADIO AUTO DISTRIBUTORS	1925 1926	3D Airtone Airtone	60.00 85.00 125.00 200.00	Auto	2	3	E	Special		
RADIO BUYERS SYNDICATE	1925	LeCalle	98.50 98.50		3 3	6 6	S S	TRF - 3 - 2 TRF - 3 - 2		
RADIO CENTER	1925	H5 Reinen Reflex	135.00		3		S	Rfx - 2 - 2		
RADIO CONSTRUCTION CO. INC.	1924									
RADIO CORPORATION OF AMERICA	SEE	R. C. A. Victor Co. R. C. Victor Corp. of America								
RADIO COURSES INC.	1923 1924	"Assembly Detector" "	35.00							
RADIO CRAFT CO.	SEE	DeForest Radio Co.								
RADIO DEVICES CO.	1923 1924	Cymo (RF and D) Audio Unit Cymo (RF and D) Audio Unit	32.50 45.00 32.50	T T		1 2 1 2	E E E E	D - - - AA - - 2 D - - - AA - - 2		
RADIODYNE	SEE	Western Coil & Electrical Co.								
RADIO ELECTRIC CO.	1923	Reco	125.00			4	E	RF - 1 - 2		
RADIO & ELECTRICAL CO.	1926									
RADIO ENGINEERING CO.	1923	Reco " "	25.00 35.00 75.00							

MANUFACTURER	YEAR	MODEL NO. & NAME	PRICE	STYLE	D	T	P	CIR. & STAGES
RADIO ENGINEERING CO. (cont.)	1924	Reco	125.00					
		"	25.00					
		"	35.00					
		"	75.00					
		"	125.00					
RADIO EQUIPMENT CO.	1923							
	1924		20.00		2	-	-	C - - - - -
	1925							
	1926							
	1927							
	1928	6 Superphonic	16.95	Ch	1	6		TRF - 4 - 2
		7	16.95	Kit	1	7		TRF - 4 - 2
	1929	7 "	16.95	Kit	1	7		TRF
RADIO EXCHANGE & SUPPLY CO. INC.	1923	Airscout	40.00					C - - - - -
		Jr.	60.00					
	1924	IV	40.00					
		Jr.	60.00					
		IV						
RADIO-FONE-O-GRAF CO.	1924	Combinations						
RADIOGEM CORP., THE	1923	Radiogem	1.00					C -
	1924	" KD	2.50					C -
	1925	" KD	2.50					C -
	1926		1.00					C -
RADIO GUILD INC., THE	1922	Harkness Super-Reg.	75.00	Kit	2	3		S. Reg.
	1923	Armstrong Super-Reg.	95.00	T	2	3		S. Reg.
		Guild Seal	38.50					
			42.50					
		"Broadcast Receiver"	400.00					
		RG510	95.00	T	1	1		RF
	1924	Harkness Reflex	195.00	T	2	2		RF
						3		Rfx - - - - -
	1925	Counterflex Reflex						Rfx
	1926							

MANUFACTURER	YEAR	MODEL NO. & NAME	PRICE	STYLE	D	T	P	CIR. & STAGES	
RADIO INDUSTRIES CORP.	1925	Ricotrode DeL. Std. A	60.00	T	3	5	E	TRF	- 2 - 2
		Ricodyne DeL. B	75.00	TS	3	5	E	TRF	- 2 - 2
		Ricodyne AristocrT	100.00	C	3	5	E	TRF	- 2 - 2
		Kit	38.75	Kit	3	5	E	TRF	- 2 - 2
RADIO INSTRUMENTS CO.	1921	JM	95.00	T	0	5			2 - - 2
RADIO MAIL ORDER CO.	1924		.60					C	- - - -
RADIO MASTER CORP. OF AMERICA	1925	100 Simpliform	135.00	T	2	4	E	TRF	- 1 - 2
		275 "	225.00	C	2	4	E	TRF	- 1 - 2
		375 "	315.00	C	2	5	E	TRF	- 2 - 2
		5-T-50	85.00		3	5	E	TRF	- 2 - 2
		5-T-14	125.00	C	3	5	E	TRF	- 2 - 2
		5-T-15	150.00		3	5	E	TRF	- 2 - 2
		10 Simpliform	200.00	RP	2		E	TRF	
		11 "	200.00	RP	2		E	TRF	
		12 "	230.00	RP	2		E	TRF	
		5-T-1	85.00	T	2		E	TRF	
		110 "	80.00	T	3		E	TRF	
		5-T-215 "	250.00		3		E	TRF	
	1926	19-AS	85.00						
		15	125.00						
		10 Simpliform	150.00	RP	2		E	RF	
		11 "	200.00	RP	2		E	RF	
		12 "	200.00	RP	2		E	RF	
		5-T-1 "	230.00	T	3		E	TRF	
		5-T-14 "	85.00	C	3		E	TRF	
			125.00						
RADIO PANEL SHOP	1923	The Radio Flivver	45.00	Por					
	1924	"		Por					
RADIO PARTS CO. LABORATORIES	1925	Pliodyne 6	60.00	T					- 2 - 3
	1926	"	60.00	T					- 2 - 3
		Universal	46.50			4			
RADIO PRODUCTS CORP. OF AMERICA	1923		3.00					C	- - - -
RADIO PRODUCTS MANUFACTURING CO.	1923	RPM	6.00					C	- - - -

MANUFACTURER	YEAR	MODEL NO. & NAME	PRICE	STYLE	D	T	P	CIR. & STAGES
RADIO PRODUCTS MANUFACTURING CO. (cont)	1924	RPMODYNE	100.00	B-B	3	6	E	TRF - 2 - 3
	1925	RPM-50	110.00	B-B	3	6	E	TRF - 2 - 3
		RPM-51	135.00	T	3	6	E	TRF - 2 - 3
		RPM-52	230.00	C	1	6	E	TRF - 2 - 3
		RPM-53	80.00	Por	1	4	B	TRF - 1 - 2
	1926	RPMODYNE A	90.00	C	1	4	B	TRF - 1 - 2
		" B	139.00	C	1	4	B	TRF - 1 - 2
		" C						
	1927	Same Models as 1926						
	1928	C	184.00	C	1	5	A	TRF - 1 - 2
		D	125.00	T	1	5	A	TRF - 1 - 2
	1929	4AC			1	7	A	TRF - 3 - 2
		3AC			1	7	A	TRF - 3 - 2
		"RPL"		RP	1	7		TRF - 3 - 2
RADIO RECEPTOR CO. INC.	1923	Home-O-Fone	24.00			2		C - - -
	1924	Receptrad Multiflex	50.00	Kit		4		Rfx - 1 - 2
		"	65.00	Box		2		Rfx - - -
	1925	SW-5	135.00		2	7	D	Rfx - 3 - 3
		Receptrad Multiflex	180.00		2	8	A	TRF - 3 - 3
		Batteryless	125.00		2	4		Rfx - 2 - 3
	1926	RM-2-DC	142.00	T	2	5		RF 2 - - 3
		M-DC	150.00	T	2	6		TRF - 2 - 3
		RF-6	180.00	T	2	4		Rfx - 2 - 3
		RM-2-AC	182.00	T	2	5		RF 2 - - 3
		M-AC	250.00	C	2	6		TRF - 2 - 3
		P-F-6						
RADIO RITE SERVICE LABS.	1925	451 Selectodyne	17.50		3	1	E	D - - -
		453 "	42.50		3	3	E	DAA - - 2
RADIO SERVICE LABS.	1923	R212	120.00	T	3	5	S	Neut. - 2 - 2
RADIO SERVICE & MFG. CO.	1923		15.00					C - - - - -
RADIO SHACK, THE	SEE	Schwab, H.M. Inc.						
RADIO SHOP, THE	1920	S.W. Regen	50.00		3	1		Reg. - - - - -
	1923	Leroy	15.00 to 150.00					

MANUFACTURER	YEAR	MODEL NO. & NAME	PRICE	STYLE	D	T	P	CIR. & STAGES
RADIO SHOP, THE (cont.) Three associated companies located in Chicago, Ill., Long Beach, Calif. and Sunnyvale, Calif. Echophone Corp. was sales agent for most of their output; See Echophone Corp.								
	1924	Leroy	15.00			1		C — — — —
		"	25.00			5		
		"	85.00			8		Neut. — — — —
		"	175.00			3		SH — — — —
	1925	V-3 Standard	50.00	T	2	3		Reg. — 2 — 2
		F-Grand Consolette	165.00		2	5	B	TRF — 2 — 2
		V-3-Consolette	87.50	T	2	3		Reg. — 2 — 2
		F-Standard	110.00		2	5	B	TRF — 2 — 2
		3	50.00	T	2	3		Reg. — 1 — 2
		4	75.00	Por	2	3		TRF — 1 — 2
		Echophone 3	75.00	Por	2	4		Reg. — 1 — 2
		" 4	98.00			4	B	TRF — 1 — 2
RADIO SPECIALTIES CO.	1922	Cry. Det.	15.00			1		C — — — —
		Audion Det.	50.00			3	B	D — — — —
		Det 25T6 Amp.	105.00		3			DAA — — — 2
	1925	M-2 Master	15.00					C — — — —
RADIO SPECIALTY CO.	1925	Tropadyne Superadio	60.50	Kit	2	6		
		No-Sod-Er Kits		Kit				
RADIO SUPPLY HOUSE	1924	Paramount	20.00	T	2	1	B	D — — —
	1925	" X3	18.00		1	1	B	D — — —
		" 1	78.00		3	1	B	D — — —
	1926	" #5	20.00			5	S	TRF — 2 — 2
			75.00					
RADIOTEL MANUFACTURING CO.	1925	SA2	70.00		3		S	— 2 — 2
		SA3	85.00		3		S	— 2 — 3
RADIOTROPE	1929	27R, 74R	115.00		1	5	A	SG — 2 — 1
		R1	140.00	C		7	A	
		R2		C		7	A	
RADISTO SALES CO.	1925		85.00		1	4		
RAMSTONE CORP.	1925	Ramstone Special	15.50	T	2	1	E	NonReg. — — — 2
		" Tritube	34.50	T	2	3	E	NonReg. — 2 — 2
		V			3	5	S	TRF — 2 — 2
RANDLE RADIO CO.	1925	RF4	100.00		3		E	— 1 — 2
	1926	VT						

MANUFACTURER	YEAR	MODEL NO. & NAME	PRICE	STYLE	D	T	P	CIR. & STAGES
RANDOLPH RADIO CORP.	1924	Acme 1 Tube	17.45	Kit		1	B	Rfx - - - -
		" 4 "	39.85	Kit		4		Rfx - - -
		Harkness	17.95	Kit	2	2	B	Rfx - 1 - 2
		Neutrodyne	33.75	Kit	3	5	E	TRF - 2 - 2
		Cockaday	19.59	Kit	2	3	B	Reg.
	1925	Superheterodyne	59.75	Kit	2	8	S	SH
			39.50	T		5		TRF
			81.30	T	3	5		TRF
		Acme	15.85	Kit	3	1		Rfx
		Reinartz	10.45	Kit		1		Reg.
		"	17.55	Kit		3		RFX
		Neut.	33.45	Kit		5		Neut.
		Superhet.	52.75	Kit		8		SH
		Cockaday	39.65	Kit		5		TRF
		"	18.55	Kit		3		Rfx
		"	10.10	Kit		1		Reg.
			65.80			8		SH Rfx
	1926	Acme	17.45			1		Rfx
		Cockaday	55.80			8		Rfx
		Symphonic Five	24.90	T	3	5	S	TRF
		Columbia Sr. Six	36.50	T	3	6	S	TRF
		Columbia Grand	42.65	C	3	6	S	TRF
		Ampliphonic Six	79.50	C	2	6	S	TRF
	1927	Senior Six	55.00	T	1	6	E	TRF
		Senior Seven	77.00	T	1	7	A/E	TRF
		Randolph	99.00	C	1	7	A/E	TRF
RANGER COIL CO.	1927	R-6-28 Ranger	70.00			6	B	TRF - 3 - 2
		R-7-28 "	80.00			7	B	TRF - 3 - 3
		R-8-28 "	125.00			8	B	TRF - 4 - 3
RASLA	1925					3	S	Rfx
RAULAND MANUFACTURING CO.	1925	"All-American" Jr.	22.00	OP	1	1	D	Rfx - - -
		Sr.	42.00	OP	2	3	S	Rfx
RAUSCHENBERG RADIO SHOPS	1926	Midget Magnatone	25.00	T	3	5		TRF - 2 - 2
		W-3-D "	45.00	T	3	5		TRF - 2 - 2
		W-1-D "	55.00	T	1	5		TRF - 2 - 2
		C-3-D "	125.00	C	3	5		TRF - 2 - 2

MANUFACTURER	YEAR	MODEL NO. & NAME	PRICE	STYLE	D	T	P	CIR. & STAGES
RAVEN RADIO INC.	1924	Superhet	70.00		3		E	TRF
	1925	Five	170.00	C	3	5	E	TRF - 2 - 2
			90.00		3		E	TRF
			125.00		2		E	
RAY-DEE ARTCRAFT PRODUCTS	1925	S-3-RRV	135.00	T	3	3	S	TRF - 1 - 1
RAY ISLER RADIO CO.	1925		70.00	T		3		Reg. 2
	1926	3-A	65.00	T	2	3		Reg. 2
		3	70.00	T	3	3		TRF - - 2
		55	90.00	T		5		TRF - 2 - 2
	1927	55	275.00	T	1	5	A	TRF - 2 - 2
			375.00	C		5	A	TRF - 2 - 2
R. B. RADIO CO.	1924	Standard	165.00	T	3/4	5	S	RF - 2 - 2
	1925		250.00	C	3/4	5	S	TRF - 2 - 2
		Knickerbocker	350.00	HB	3/4	5	S	TRF - 2 - 2
		"Page 5"	57.50	T	3	5	S	TRF - 2 - 2
		"Page 6"	37.50	T	3	6	S	TRF - 2 - 3
		Belle Claire	135.00	C	1	6	S	TRF - 2 - 3
R. C. A. VICTOR CO., VICTOR DIV. (Radio Corporation of America)	1926	Hyperion	900.00	a	2	10	A	SH
		Borgia I	675.00	b	2	8	B	SH
		Borgia II	1000.00	b	2	10	A	SH
	1927	Florenza	550.00	b	2	8	B	SH - 2 - 2
a "Electrola"		Alhambra I	350.00	b	3	5	B	Reg.
b "Orthophonic"		Alhambra II	425.00	b	2	6	B	SH
		7-30	325.00	b		5	B	Reg.
c "Electrola Radiola"		R-20	135.00	c		8	B	Reg. - 2 - 2
		9-15	600.00	b		10	B	SH
d "Victrola Radiola"		9-25	1150.00	c	2	10	A	SH
		9-40	1000.00	b		10	A	SH - 2 - 2
e "Automatic Electrola Radiola"		9-55	1550.00	c	2	10	A	SH
	1928	7-10	275.00	c	1	6	B	TRF
f "Auto Electric"		7-11	250.00	d	1	7	A	TRF - 3 - 2
		7-25	385.00	b	1	7	A	TRF - 3 - 2
g "Radio Electrola"		7-26	425.00	c	1	7	A	TRF - 3 - 2
		9-16	750.00	c	2	8	A	SH

MANUFACTURER	YEAR	MODEL NO. & NAME	PRICE	STYLE	D	T	P	CIR. & STAGES
R. C. A. VICTOR CO., VICTOR DIV. (cont.)	1929	9-54	1350.00	e	2	11	A	SH
		9-18	925.00	a	2	11	A	SH
		9-56	1750.00	f	2	11	A	SH
		R-32	155.00	C	1	10	A	TRF 14 - 2*
		RE-45	275.00	g	1	10	A	TRF 14 - 2*
	1930	R-52 Radiola	215.00	RP	1	10	A	TRF 14 - 2*
		RE-75 Electrola	350.00	RP	1	10	A	TRF 14 - 2*
		RE-154 "	495.00	RP	1	10	A	TRF 14 - 2*
		RE-156 "	595.00	LB	1	8	A	SG - 3 - 2*
		R-35		C	1	8	A	SG - 3 - 2*
		R-39		RP	1	8	A	SG - 3 - 2*
		RE-57						
R C A VICTOR CORP. OF AMERICA (Radio Corporation of America)	1922	Concert	40.00	Box	1			C - - -
		Aeriola Jr.	25.00	Box				C - - -
		Aeriola Amp	68.00	Box		2	B	AA - - -
		Aeriola Sr.	65.00	Box	1	1	B	Reg.
	1923	AR 1300	50.00	T	2	4		C - 2*
		Aeriola Grand	350.00	CT	1		B	Reg.
		Radiola Concert	40.00	MT	1			C
		RE Ant. Tuner	(225.00 Comb.)	M				PT
		AR R.F. Amp		T		3	B	RF
		RA Reg. Tuner		T	1			PT
		DA Det-Amp	30.00	MT				DAA
		Radiola Special	142.50	T	1	3	B	Reg. - 2
		RC (RA, DA Comb.)	65.00	Box	1	1	B	Reg.DAA - - 2
		Radiola Sr.	80.00	2 Box		3	S	Reg.
		" AC AA-1520	350.00	CT	1	5	B	RFDAA 2 - - 2*
		" Grand	87.50	T		4	B	Reg.DAA - 1 - 2*
		RS	25.00	Box		2		DA Reg. - - 1
		Radiola I	275.00	Por	1		B	C
		" II	97.50	CT		2	B	Reg.DA - - 1
		" IV	142.50	2 MT	3	3	B	DAA - - 2
		" V	162.50	2 MT	2	3	S	Reg.DAA - - 2
		" VI	245.00	CT		6	B	RD 3 - - 2
		" VIIB, IX	35.00	Box	2	5	B	Reg.TRF - 2 - 2
	1924	III	30.00	Box	1	2	B	Reg.DA - - 1
		III Amp	65.00	Box		4	B	A - - - 1*
		IIIA	425.00	C	2	6	B	Reg.DAA - - - 2*
		VIII Super	245.00	CT	2	4	B	SH - 1 2 2
		X						TRFReg. - 1 - 2*

RCA was first set up to prevent British controlled Marconi from taking over the U.S. market. In its earlier years RCA sold sets made by General Electric, Westinghouse and Wireless Specialty Apparatus Co.

CAUTION: The Victor Division and RCA Victor Corp. of America used similar type numbers for different sets. For instance, Victor R-32 is not the same set as Radiola 32.

Models VIII, Superheterodyne, 24, 25, 26, 28, 30, and 32 use the impregnable "Catacomb" structure and a complex circuit. Get help before attempting repairs.

147

MANUFACTURER	YEAR	MODEL NO. & NAME	PRICE	STYLE	D	T	P	CIR. & STAGES
R C A VICTOR CORP. OF AMERICA (cont.)								
	1925	Superheterodyne	220.00	T	2	6	B	SH - - 2 2
		Regenoflex	150.00	T	2	4	B	TRF Reg. - 1 - 2*
		20	102.50	T	1	5	B	TRF Reg. - 2 - 2
		24	195.00	Por	2	6	B	SH - 1 2 2
		25	165.00	T	1	6	A	SH - 1 2 2
		26	225.00	Por	2	6	B	SH - 1 2 2
		28	260.00	Stand	1	8	A/E	SH - 1 2 2
	1926	30	575.00	C	1	10	A	SH - 1 2 2
	1927	28 and 104	570.00	2 pcs	1	12	D/A	SH - 1 2 2
		16	69.50	T	1	6	B	TRF 1 2 - 2
		17	130.00	T	1	7	A	TRF 1 2 - 2
		18	115.00	T	1	6/7	D/A	TRF 1 2 - 2
		30A	495.00	C	1	10	D/A	SH - 1 2 2
		32	895.00	C	1	10	D/A	SH - 1 2 2
		51	195.00	C	1	6/7	D/A	TRF 1 2 - 2
	1928	41 AC	215.00	T	1	7	D/A	TRF 1 2 - 2
		60	175.00	C	1	9	A	SH - 2 2 1
		62	375.00	C	1	9		SH - 2 2 1
		64 DeLuxe	550.00	T	1	11		SH - 2 2 1
	1929	21	69.50	C	1	5	B	SG Reg. - 2 - 2
		22	135.00	T	1	5	B	SG Reg. - 2 - 2
		33	69.50	C	1	7	A	TRF 1 2 - 2
		33	77.50	C	1	7	A	TRF 1 2 - 2
		33	87.50	C	1	7	D	TRF 1 2 - 2*
		44	75.00	T	1	5	A	SG - 2 - 1
		46	139.00	C	1	5	A	SG - 2 - 1
		46 DC	189.00	C	1	6	D	SG - 2 - 2*
		47	195.00	RP	1	5	A	SG - 2 - 1
		66	179.00	C	1	8	A	SH - 1 2 1
	1930	67	690.00	RP	1	10	A	SH - 1 2 1
		48	112.50	C	1	7	A	SG 3 - 1*
		80		C	1	9	A	SH - 1 2 1*
		82		C	1	9	A	SH - 1 2 1*
		Comb. 86		RP	1	9	A	SH - 1 2 1*
RECEPTOR RADIO CORP.	1925	Five	60.00	T	3	5	S	TRF - 2 - 2
REEPS RADIO CORP.	1925	26	115.00	T	3	5	S	TRF - 2 - 2
		22	200.00		3	5	S	TRF - 2 - 2
		77	225.00		3	5	S	TRF - 2 - 2

MANUFACTURER	YEAR	MODEL NO. & NAME	PRICE	STYLE	D	T	P	CIR. & STAGES
REEPS RADIO CORP. (cont.)		55			3	5	S	TRF - 2 - 2
REICHMANN CO. (Thorola)	1924	51 Thorola	85.00	T	2	5	S	TRF - 2 - 2
	1925	50 Thorola Islodyne	85.00	T	3		S	TRF - 2 - 2
		55 "	115.00	T	3		S	TRF - 2 - 2
		Thorola Islodyne	100.00	T	3	5		TRF
		New 51	85.00	T	3			TRF
	1926	Thorola Islodyne Console	225.00	C	3	5	S	TRF - 2 - 2
		60	60.00	T	2	5		TRF
		57	60.00	T	2	5		TRF - 2 - 2
		58 Thorola	125.00	C	2			TRF
		59 "	185.00	T	3			TRF - 2 - 2
		55	100.00	C	3			TRF
		50	85.00	C	3			TRF
		51	85.00		3			TRF
		52	225.00		3			TRF
REINARTZ, J.L. CO.	1921	Reinartz		T	2	1		Reg. - - -
REMLER RADIO MANUFACTURING CO.	1921	Remler	5.00	B	0	0		C - - -
		400/300	22.00	2B	0	1	B	D - - -
	1922	505/502/330/331/333	45.00	5 Ch	2	3	B	DAA - - -
	1925	9 Tube Super	90.00	Kit	2	9	S	SH Various
REPUBLIC RADIO CO.	1930	31C	39.00	Ch	1	5	A	SG - 2 - 1
		31M	59.50	M	1	5	A	SG - 2 - 1
		31J Junior	64.50	M	1	5	A	SG - 2 - 1
		31L	90.00	LB	1	5	A	SG - 2 - 1
		31H	100.00	HB	1	5	A	SG - 2 - 1
		1PC Comb.	175.00	RP	1	5	A	SG - 2 - 1
RESAS, INC. (Tone-A-Dyne)	1924	5-T	78.00	T	3	5	S	TRF
	1925	Compact	78.00		3	5	E	TRF - 2 - 2
		DeLuxe	60.00		3	5	S	TRF - 2 - 2
			85.00					TRF - 2 - 2
REYNOLDS RADIO SPECIALTY CO.	1920	Multi-Wave	55.00	T	2	1	B	Reg. - - -
REZODON	SEE	Niehoff, Paul C.						

MANUFACTURER	YEAR	MODEL NO. & NAME	PRICE	STYLE	D	T	P	CIR. & STAGES		
RHAMSTINE, J. THOS.	1922	Det. & Amp. Cabinet	50.00	Box	0	3		DAA	- - 2	
RHASON MANUFACTURING CO.	1926	B Air Tune	45.00	T	3	5	E	TRF	- 2 - 2	
		A "	65.00		2	6	E	TRF	- 2 - 3	
		H "	135.00	C		5		TRF	- 2 - 2	
RICH, GEORGE H.	1925	2-T-12	29.50		2	2	E	Rfx	- 2 - 2	
		3-T-22	50.00		3	3	E	Rfx	- 2 - 3	
		2-T-22	35.00		2			Rfx	- 1 - 2	
		5	60.00		3		E	TRF		
		Special	55.00		2		E	"Special"		
		3	60.00		3		E	Rfx		
		5 Custom Built	25.00		2		E	TRF		
		Custom Built Dragon	225.00		2		E	"Special"		
	1926	3	35.00	T	3	3		Reg.	- -	
			50.00	T	3	3		Rfx	- 2 - 2	
		4	55.00	T	3	4		Reg.TRF	- 1 - 2	
		5 Special	75.00	C	3	5		TRF	- 3 - 2	
		6	200.00	T	2	6		TRF	- 2 - 3	
	1927	6-S Custom Built	110.00	T		6	B	TRF	- 3 - 2	
		6	110.00	T		6		TRF	- 3 - 3	
		7	125.00	C		7	B	TRF	- 2 - 3	
		EP-6-S	300.00	C		6	B	TRF	- 2 - 3	
		EP-6	300.00	C		6		TRF	- 3 - 2	
		EP-7	325.00	C		7		TRF	- 3 - 3	
RICHARDS, C. W.	1925	CWR-6	150.00	T	3	5	S	TRF	- 2 - 2	
		CWR-7	195.00	T	2	6	E	TRF	- 3 - 2	
RICHARDS & CO. INC., GEORGE	1924	Hemco		Por						
RICHARDSON RADIO INC.	1925	5	65.00	T	3	5	S	TRF	- 2 - 2	
		5	49.00	Kit	3	5	S	TRF	- 2 - 2	
			75.00	C	3	5	S	TRF	- 2 - 2	
			95.00	C	2	5	S	TRF	- 2 - 2	
		Imperial	150.00	C	2	7	S	TRF	- 3 - 3	
		"	75.00	C	2	5	S	TRF	- 2 - 2	
			125.00	T	2	7	S	TRF	- 3 - 3	
	1926	Sophomore	38.50	T	3	5	S	TRF	- 2 - 2	

Manufacturer	Year	Model No. & Name	Price	Style	D	T	P	Cir. & Stages
RIPPNER BROS. MANUFACTURING CO.	1926	Monarch						C - - -
RITTENHOUSE CO., THE A. E.	1923		5.00					C - - -
	1924							C - - -
RITTER RADIO CORP.	1923							
	1924	Grand	3.50					C - - -
	1925		3.50					
	1926	Grand	2.50					C - - -
RIVERO & CO.	1924	Brownie Airphone	7.50					C - - -
ROBBINS & FUERST	1924	Ambassador			3			"Special"
ROBBINS RADIO CO.	1926							
ROBERTS RADIO CO., HENRY C.	1924	Air Key	15.00	KD		1		
			30.00	KD		3		
	1925	Oriole	100.00		3	5	E	TRF - 2 - 2
		" 5	47.50			5		
ROBINSON SPECIALTY CO.	1923	Q-R	25.00	C	1			
	1924	Q-R $25. to $300.	300.00					
RODGERS RADIO CO.	1926		395.00	C	1	7	E	TRF - 4 - 3
ROEMER FURNITURE CO., RUDOLPH	1929			C	1			
ROLA	1929	80	99.00	LB		6	A	
		90	129.00	LB		6	A	
ROLLO-O-RADIO CORP., THE	1924	5 in 1 Super Set	6.00					C - - -
ROSE RADIO CO.	1926	2-A Aurora	35.00	T	3	5	S	TRF - 2 - 2
		2-B "	80.00	C	3	5	S	TRF - 2 - 2
ROSELLE MANUFACTURING CO.	1924	Custom Built						
ROSENDALL & CO.	1924							

MANUFACTURER	YEAR	MODEL NO. & NAME	PRICE	STYLE	D	T	P	CIR.	& STAGES
ROSSITER MANNING	1925	B-T3 Nameless	198.00	T	3	5			- 2 - 2
		B-T3	325.00	C	3	5			- 2 - 2
ROTH-DOWNS MANUFACTURING CO.	1925	Orphens F	65.00	T	3	5	S	TRF	- 2 - 2
	1926	" A	130.00	C	2	5	S	TRF	- 2 - 2
		" C	100.00	C	2	5	S	TRF	- 2 - 2
	1927	" H	75.00	T	2	5	S	TRF	- 2 - 2
		" H	60.00	T		4	B	TRF	- 1 - 3
		25	75.00	CL		4	B	TRF	- 1 - 3
		C	95.00	C		4	B	TRF	- 1 - 3
		A	120.00	C		4	B	TRF	- 1 - 3
	1928	30	140.00			4	B	TRF	- 1 - 3
	1929	40	240.00			4	B	TRF	- 1 - 3
	1930	82	220.00	RP	1	8	A	SG	- 3 - 2*
		62	130.00	HB	1	7	A	SG	- 3 - 2
		52	112.00	LB	1	6	A	SG	- 2 - 2
		Caradio	96.00	Auto	1	4	S/B	SG	- 2 - 1
ROTH RADIO CO.	1925	Melodee	45.00		3		S		- 2 - 2
ROYAL MANUFACTURING CO.	1923 1924	Neon Simplex	9.75	Por		1		D	
ROYALE	1928	80	93.50	T		7			
		81	136.50	T		7			
		82	151.50	T		7			
ROYCRAFT CO., THE	1924		15.00			1			
RUCHELHAUS, JOHN	1925	Rutic Super V	65.00	T	3				
SAMPSON ELECTRIC CO.	1925	TC		Kit	2	4	S	TRF	- 1 - 2
SANGAMO ELECTRIC CO.	1925			T	1	7	S	SH	
SAN PEDRO RADIO LABORATORIES	1925	AC	100.00	T	2		A		
SARGENT		SLF6		T	3	6	S	TRF	- 3 - 2

MANUFACTURER	YEAR	MODEL NO. & NAME	PRICE	STYLE	D	T	P	CIR.	& STAGES
SCHENECTADY RADIO CORP.	1923		5.00 30.00					C	- - - -
SCHWAB INC., HAROLD M.	1925	Type 5726WK 718RF	64.50 60.00	T T	3 3	5 5	S 8	Neut. TRF	- 2 - 2 - 2 - 2
SCIENTIFIC ENGINEERING ASS'N	1922	Radiovox	150.00	C	1	6	S	RF	3 - - 2
SCOTT TRANSFORMER CO. Scott sold chasses and cabinets separately for custom sets.	1928 1929 1930	Super 9 " " AC Nine Symphony Automobile World's Record A-C 10 1931 All Wave Super		Kit Kit Kit Kit Kit A Ch Ch	2 2 1 1 1 1 2	9 9 9 11 4/5 7 11/12 12/13	S S A A A S A A	SH SH SH SH TRF SH SH SH	- 1 3 2 - 1 3 2 - 1 3 2 - 1 3 2 - 1 - 2 - 2 2 - 1 3 2**
SEARS MANUFACTURING CO.	1925	A Acme Reflex B " Standard " Torodyne	150.00 150.00 160.00 200.00 70.00	Por Por	1 2 1 2 3	4 5	S S E	Rfx Rfx Rfx Rfx Rfx (Acme)	
SEARS ROEBUCK & CO.	1923 1929	Armstrong Reg. 36AC Silvertone 115 1150 1170 1152 1174 1250 1252 1260 1260 1290 1292 1300 1302 1310 1312	23.25			6 6 6 6 5 5 5 6 6 6 6 6 7 7	A A A A A A A A S S S S A A	SG SG SG SG SG SG SG SG SG SG SG SG SG SG	- 2 - 1* - 2 - 1* - 2 - 2 - 2 - 2 - 2 - 1 - 2 - 1* - 2 - 2 - 2 - 2* - 2 - 2* - 2 - 2* - 2 - 2* - 2 - 2 - 3 - 2 - 3 - 2

MANUFACTURER	YEAR	MODEL NO. & NAME	PRICE	STYLE	D	T	P		CIR. & STAGES
SEARS ROEBUCK & CO. (cont.)	1930	1330			2	7	A	SG	- 3 - 2
		1370				4	A	SG	- 1 - 1
		1320				8	A	SG	- 3 - 1*
		1322				8	A	SG	
		1324				8	A	SG	- 3 - 1*
		1390				6	A	SH	
		1400				6	A	SH	
		1402				6	A	SH	
		1404				6	A	SH	
		1406				6	A	SH	
		1430				9	A	SH	
SEC-TRON RADIO CO.	1923	A Sectron DeLuxe		T	2	6			- 3 - 2
		B "		Por					
		C "Business Man's"							
SEELEY ELECTRIC CO.	1930	5	79.50	M	1	5	A	SG	- 2 - 1
		6	89.50	M	1	6	A	SG	- 3 - 1
SEERY BARTELL CO.	1925	Seeryola	125.00	Por	3	5	S	RF	2 - - 2
	1926		150.00	T	3	5	S		
SELECTOR RADIO CO.	1926							TRF	
SELECTROL RADIO CORP.	1925	Super Five	60.00	T	3	5	S	TRF	- 2 - 2
SENTINEL	SEE	United Air Cleaner Corp.							
SERVICE RADIO CO.	1923	212	150.00	T	3	5	S	TRF	- 2 - 2
	1924	212	150.00	T	3	5	S	TRF	- 2 - 2
SHAMROCK MANUFACTURING CO.	1925	Shamrock Harkness	35.00	Kit	2	2		Rfx	- 2 - 3
		"	39.50			3		Rfx	- 2 - 3
		Grand Console	160.00	C	1/2	6		TRF	
		Spec. Consolette	130.00	T	1/2	6		TRF	- 2 - 3
		DeLuxe	95.00	T	1/2	6	E	TRF	- 2 - 3
			260.00						
	1926	A DeLuxe Grand	95.00	T	1	6	B	TRF	- 2 - 3
		B	130.00	CL	1	6	B	TRF	- 2 - 3

MANUFACTURER	YEAR	MODEL NO. & NAME	PRICE	STYLE	D	T	P	CIR. & STAGES	
SHAMROCK MANUFACTURING CO. (cont.)	1927	D or C	275.00	HB	1	6	B	TRF	- 2 - 3
		A	75.00	T	1	6	B	TRF	- 2 - 3
		B	98.50	C	1	6	B	TRF	- 2 - 3
		C	150.00	C	1	6	A	TRF	- 2 - 3
		BL	185.00	C	1	7	A	TRF	- 2 - 3
		CL	250.00	C	1	7	A	TRF	
	1928	Standard	95.00	C	1	7	A	TRF	
	1929	Console Electric	167.50		1	7	A	TRF	
			139.50	HB/C		7	A	TRF	
SHELBY MANUFACTURING CO.	1929	52				8		TRF	- 3 - 2*
		H-42				8		TRF	- 3 - 2*
		H-32				8		TRF	- 3 - 2*
SHELDON RADIO CO.	1926								
SHEPARD POTTER CO. INC.	1924	Thermiodyne	21.00	T	2	6			- 3 - 2
		"Shepco"			1	1			
	1925	TFS Thermiodyne	140.00	T		6	B	TRF	- 3 - 2
SHERMAN RADIO MANUFACTURING CO.	1925	D Clearfield DeLuxe	115.00		3	6	S	TRF	- 2 - 2
SHORTWAVE & TELEVISION LAB.	1929		60.00	Por	1	4	B	SG	- 1 - 1
			87.50	Por	1	4	D	SG	- 1 - 1
			97.50	Por	1	5	A	SG	- 1 - 2
SHOWERS BROS. CO.	1926	556 Console		C	1	6			
SIDBENEL RADIO EQUIP. MFG. CO.	1924		47.50		3	5		Neut.	- 2 - 2
	1925	5-H Hetro Magnetic	75.00		3	5	B	TRF	- 2 - 2
			55.00			5			
			150.00						
SIGNAL ELECTRIC MFG. CO.	1926								
SIGNAL RADIO & ELECTRIC CORP.	1923	No-1-A Triumph	30.00	Box	2	1	S	D	- - - -
SILVER-MARSHALL INC. Also sold by Lincoln Radio Corp. and Western Radio Mfg. Co.	1924	Silver Six		Ch	3	6	S	TRF	
	1925	S-M		Ch	2	7	S	SH	
	1927	A.C. Improved Shielded Six		Ch	1	6	A		- - 2 2

MANUFACTURER	YEAR	MODEL NO. & NAME	PRICE	STYLE	D	T	P	CIR. & STAGES
SILVER-MARSHALL INC. (cont.)	1928	SCII Silver				5	S	TRF - 2 - 2
		620 Cockaday				4	E	TRF Reg. - 1 - 2
		630				6	S	TRF - 3 - 2
		642		Kit		2	A	Reg. TRF - 1 - .
		644SG	72.50	Tuner		4	S	Reg. TRF - 1 - 2
		720 S. G. Six	102.00	Tuner		6	S	TRF 1 2 - 2
		730 Round-World 4	51.00	Kit	2	4	E	SG Reg. - 1 - 2
			66.00	T				
		740 Coast-Coast 4	51.00	Kit	2	4	E	SG Reg. - 1 - 1
			75.00	T				
	1929	712 Boss of the Air	64.90		1	8	A	SG - 3 - 2*
		714	87.50		1	9	A	SG - 1 2 2*
		716	130.00	Kit	1	10	A	SH 1 2 - 2*
		710	175.00		1	8	A	SG - 4 - 2
		720AC	78.00	Kit	2	8	A	SG - 3 - 2
		720AC	117.00	Wired	2	7	A	SG - 3 - 2
		720	44.79	Kit	2	7	S	SG - 3 - 2
		720	66.30		2	6	A	SG - 2 - 2*
		722 Band Selector 7	52.90		1	6	A	SG - 2 - 2*
		722DC			1	7	D	SH - 1 2 1*
		724	99.50		1	6	A	SH - 1 2 1*
		724DC	82.50		1	9	D	SH - 1 2 1*
		726			1	8	A	SH-SH - 1 2 1*
		726SW			1	9	A	SH - 1 2 1*
		727SW			1	11	A	SH - 1 2 1*
		730	31.71	Kit	1	9	E	SG Reg. - 1 - 2
		730	42.90	Wired	1	4	E	SG Reg. - 1 - 2
		731	22.86		1	4	E	SG Reg. - 1 - 2
		731	30.00		1	4	E	SG Reg. - 1 - 2
		735AC Round the World	64.90		1	6	A	SG Reg. - 1 - 2*
		737			1	5	A	SG Reg. - 1 - 2
		740	48.60	Wired	1	4	D	SG Reg. - 1 - 2
		740AC	32.97	Kit	1	5	A	SG Reg. - 1 - 2
		740AC	50.70	Wired	1			
		770 Auto	112.00	A	1	5	s	SG - 2 - 2
	1930	782 Midget		M	1	8	A	SH - . 2 1*
		30A Princess	170.50		1	8	A	SG 1 2 - 2*
		30B "	155.50		1	7	A	SG - 1 2 2*
		30			1	8	A	SG - 1 2 - 2
		Bearcat Midget			1	5	A	SH - . 2 1*
		" S-W						TRF Reg. - 1 - 2

MANUFACTURER	YEAR	MODEL NO. & NAME	PRICE	STYLE	D	T	P	CIR. & STAGES
SILVER-MARSHALL INC. (cont.)								
		30C			1	8	A	SG 1 2 - 2*
		30D			1	8	A	SG 1 2 - 2*
		30E			1	8	A	SG 1 2 - 2*
		34	135.00	LB	1	7	A	SG - 2 - 2*
		34A	185.00	LB	1	7	A	SG - 2 - 2*
		35	225.00	LB	1	9	A	SG - 3 - 2*
		35A		HB	1	9	A	SG - 1 2 1*
		36			1	9	A	SH - 1 2 1*
		36A		M	1	8	A	SH - 2 1*
		37 Midget		M	1	8	A	SH - 2 1*
		38		M	1	8	A	SH - 2 1*
		39	155.00	LB	1	8	A	SG - 3 - 2
		39 "	160.00	LB	1	8	A	SG - 2 - 2*
		55	145.00	LB	1	7	A	SG (PT) - 3 - 2
		60	173.00		1	8	A	SG - 2 - 2*
		60B	173.00		1	8	A	SG - 2 - 2*
		70	158.00		1	7	A	SG (PT) - 2 - 2*
		75			1	7	A	SG (PT) - 2 - 2*
		75 Concert Grand			1	7	A	SG (PT) - 2 - 2*
		90B			1	8	A	SG - 3 - 2
		95B	195.00	HB				
		95						
SILVERSET RADIO CO.	1925		125.00	T	3	5	S	TRF - 2 - 2
SILVEY ELECTRIC CO.	1926							
SIMPLEX RADIO CO. (Philadelphia)	1921	Panels	38.00	4 Ch	3	1	B	PTD - - - -
		Panels	58.00	5 Ch	3	2	B	PTDA - - - 1
	1923	RJ	70.00					RF
		RFB	80.00			4	S	TRF
		RF	120.00			4	S	RF
	1924	RF	120.00			4	B	TRF
		RJ	70.00			3		TRF
		RFB	80.00			4		TRF
	1925	RFB	80.00	Por	2		B	TRF
		Travel	80.00	Por	2		B	RF
		RX	80.00	T	2		B	RF 1 - - 2
		RF	120.00	T	3		B	RF 2 - - 2
		SR-8	65.00	T	3	5	S	TRF 2 - - 2
		SR-5	57.00	T	3	5	S	TRF - 2 - 2

MANUFACTURER	YEAR	MODEL NO. & NAME	PRICE	STYLE	D	T	P	CIR. & STAGES
SIMPLEX RADIO CO. (cont.)	1926	SR-5 DeLuxe	65.00	T	3	5	S	TRF
		SR-8	65.00	T	3	5	S	
		Compact	45.00	T	3	5	S	TRF
		SR-9	65.00	CL	3	5	S	TRF
		SR-9 Grand	95.00	C	3	5	S	TRF
			185.00	C	3	5	S	TRF
		SR-9	125.00	T	3	5	S	TRF
	1927	SR-9	64.00	T	1	5	B	TRF - 2 - 2
		SR-10	70.00	T	1	6	B	TRF - 2 - 2
		SR-11	70.00	CL	1	6	B	TRF - 3 - 2
		SR-11	95.00	CL	1	5	B	TRF - 3 - 2
		SR-10	95.00	CL	1	5	B	TRF - 2 - 2
		SR-9	95.00	C	1	6	B	TRF - 2 - 2
		SR-11	145.00	C	1	5	B	TRF - 3 - 2
		SR-10	145.00	C	1	5	B	TRF - 2 - 2
		SR-9	145.00	C	1	5	B	TRF - 2 - 2
SIMPLEX RADIO CO. (Sandusky, Ohio)	1925	6-A	120.00	T	1	5	E	TRF - 1 - 3
	1926	6-A	135.00	CL	1	6	S	TRF - 2 - 3
		6-A	175.00	C	1	6	S	TRF - 2 - 3
	1927	B Electric	195.00	C	1	6	S	TRF - 2 - 3
	1928	D	250.00	MT	1	7	A	TRF - 2 - 3
	1929	S Louis XV	145.00		1	8	A	TRF - 3 - 2*
	1930	G	98.00	LB	1	7	A	SG - 2 - 2*
		G	108.00	LB	1	7	A	SG - 2 - 2*
		G	115.00	HB	1	7	A	SG - 2 - 2*
		G	125.00	HB	1	7	A	SG - 2 - 2*
		G	129.00	HB	1	7	A	SG - 2 - 2*
		G	139.00	M	1	6	A	SG - 2 - 2*
		F	59.50	M	1	5	A	SG - 2 - 1
		H	69.50	M	1	6	D	SG - 3 - 1
		I	59.50	M	1	6	B	SG - 3 - 1
		J	59.50	M	1	6	B	SG - 3 - 1
SIMPLI-DYNE ELECTRIC CO.	1926	Jr.	60.00	T	3	5	S	RF 2 - - 2
		DeLuxe	145.00	C	2	5	S	RF 2 - - 2
SINGER CO., E.	1924	Compendyne	95.00	T	3	5	E	TRF - 2 - 2
	1925	Singer Compendyne	65.00	T	3	5	E	TRF - 2 - 2

MANUFACTURER	YEAR	MODEL NO. & NAME	PRICE	STYLE	D	T	P	CIR.	& STAGES
SINGER CO., E. (cont.)	1926	26	70.00	T	3	5	E	TRF	- 2 - 2
		27-P	80.00	T	2	7	E	TRF	- 3 - 3
		27-6	135.00	D	2	7	E	TRF	- 3 - 3
SLAGLE RADIO CO.	1925	Five	150.00	T	3	5	E	TRF	- 2 - 2
		IV	110.00	T	3	5	E	TRF	- 2 - 2
		V	165.00	T	3	5	E	TRF	- 2 - 2
	1926	10	70.00	T	3	5		RF	2 - - 2
		12	100.00	T	3	5		RF	2 - - 2
		4	100.00	T	3	5		RF	2 - - 2
		5	150.00	T	2	5		RF	0 - - 2
		9	175.00	C	3	5		RF	2 - - 2
		Console 4	300.00	C	3	5		RF	2 - - 2
		Console 5	350.00	C	3	5		RF	2 - - 2
		VII	70.00	T	3	5		RF	2 - - 2
	1927	XX	150.00	C	1	6	A	TRF	- 3 - 2
	1928	A "Ten 29"	360.00	C	1	6	B	TRF	- 2 - 2
		B "	500.00	C	1	6	B	TRF	- 2 - 2
		C "	600.00	C	1	9	A	RF	6 - - 1
		D "	750.00	RP	1	10	A	RF	6 - - 2
			850.00	RP	1	10	A	RF	6 - - 2
SLEEPER RADIO CORP. (M. B. Sleeper)	1920	3300	35.00	T	2	1	B	Reg. Rfx	- - - -
	1923	Monotrol			1		S/E	Grimes Inv. Dupx	3 - 3
	1924	" 54						"	
	1925	Scout 57	130.00	T	2	4	S	TRF	- 2 - 2
		Serenader 58	75.00	T	2	5	S	TRF	- 2 - 2
		Super Symphon 59	100.00	T	2	5	S	TRF	- 2 - 2
		Scout 57	150.00	C	2	5	S	TRF	- 2 - 2
		Serenader 58	110.00	C	2	5	S	TRF	- 2 - 2
	1926	Scout 57	135.00	T	2	5	s	TRF	- 2 - 2
		Serenader	90.00	T	2	5		TRF	- 2 - 2
		Super Symphonetic 56	115.00	T	2	5	s	TRF	- 2 - 2
	1927	Scout 64	65.00	T	2	5	s	TRF	- 2 - 2
			160.00	T		5		TRF	- 2 - 2

MANUFACTURER	YEAR	MODEL NO. & NAME	PRICE	STYLE	D	T	P	CIR. & STAGES
SLEEPER RADIO CORP. (cont.)		Serenader 65	175.00	T		5		TRF - 2 - 2
		Scout 66	175.00	T CL		5		TRF - 2 - 2
		" 67	235.00	C		5		TRF - 2 - 2
		Imperial 68	265.00	C		5		TRF - 2 - 2
		Monotrol 69	350.00	C		5		TRF - 2 - 2
		Electric Chassis	148.00	ch		5		TRF - 2 - 2
		"	240.00	ch		6		TRF - 3 - 2
SOMERSET RADIO CORP.	1926	4C Standish	110.00	T	1	4	E	
SOMERSET	SEE	National Air Phone Co.						
SONGBIRD, THE	1925		28.90	T	3	5		
SONORA PHONOGRAPH CO.	1924	241 Ware Neut.	235.00	RP	3	5	B	RfxNeut. - 1 - 2
		242 " " Type T	475.00	RP	2	3	B	RfxNeut. - 2 - 2
	1925	800C	90.00	T	3	5	E	TRF
		Plymouth	275.00	RP HB	3	5	S	TRF
		Hampden	325.00	RP HB	3	5	S	TRF
		C	200.00	HB	3	5	S	TRF
		Chatham	225.00	RP	2	5	S	TRF
	1926	D800	125.00	T	2	6	S	TRF - 2 - 2
		D820 Standard	185.00	C	2	6	S	TRF - 2 - 2
		D830 DeLuxe	225.00	C	2	6	S	TRF - 2 - 2
	1927	E300	495.00	C	1	6	S	TRF 1 2 - 2
		E850	99.50	T	1	6	S	TRF 1 2 - 2
		E860	165.00	Jr. HB	1	6	S	TRF 1 2 - 2
		E865 Standard	200.00	HB	1	6	S	TRF 1 2 - 2
		E870 DeLuxe	250.00	HB	1	7	S	TRF - 4 - 2
		F875	375.00	LB	1	6	S	TRF 1 2 - 2
		G880 Light	69.50	T	1	7	S	TRF 1 2 - 2
		G885 "	135.00	HB		7	S	SG
	1928	A20	455.00	Ch		7	A	SG - 3 - 2*
		A30	190.00	Ch		8	A	TRF - 4 - 2*
		A31	149.50	C		9	A	SG - 3 - 2*
		A32	250.00	RP		8	A	TRF - 4 - 2*
		A33	179.50	C		9	A	SG - 4 - 2*
		A35	235.00	C		9	A	SG - 4 - 2*
		A36	470.00	C		10	A	TRF - 4 - 2*
		A40	375.00	RP		8	A	TRF - 3 - 2*

MANUFACTURER	YEAR	MODEL NO. & NAME	PRICE	STYLE	D	T	P	CIR. & STAGES
SONORA PHONOGRAPH CO. (cont.)	1929	A44	695.00	RP		10	A	TRF - 4 - 2*
		A46	930.00	RP		10	A	TRF - 4 - 2*
		A50				6	A	TRF - 4 - 2*
SOVEREIGN ELECTRIC MFG. CO.	1926							
SPARKS-WITHINGTON CO. "SPARTON" "The Pathfinder of the Air"	1925	5-15	63.00	T	3	5	S	TRF - 2 - 2
		5-26	83.00	T	3	5	S	TRF - 2 - 2
	1926	AC5	260.00	T		6	A	TRF - 2 - 2
		6-15	375.00	C	1	6	A	TRF - 2 - 2
	1927	6-26	68.00	T	1	6	S	TRF - 3 - 2
		AC7, 62, 63	8.00	T	1	6	S	TRF - 3 - 2
		AC62	375.00	C	1	8	A	TRF - 3 - 2
		AC63	188.00	T	1	8	A	TRF - 3 - 2
	1928	39	215.00	T	1	8	A	TRF - 3 - 2
		69 Sparton	149.00	T	1	9	S	RF 5 1 - 2
		79	199.00	C	1	8	A	RF 4 1 - 1
		79A		C	1	8	A	RF 4 1 - 1
		89	375.00	C	1	8	A	RF 4 1 - 1
		89A	375.00		1	9	A	RF 4 1 - 1
		99		C	1	11	A	RF 4 1 - 2*
		109	495.00	C	1	10	A	RF 4 1 - 1*
	1929	101			1	13	A	RF 4 1 - 3*
		110	395.00	C	1	12	A	RF 4 1 - 2**
		111		T	1	12	A	RF 4 1 - 2**
		49	76.00	C	1	8	S	RF 5 1 - 2
		301	274.00	C	1	10	A	RF 4 1 - 1*
		301DC		C	1	8	D	RF 4 1 - 1*
		930	169.00	C	1	9	A	RF 4 1 - 1*
		931	179.00	C	1	9	A	RF 4 1 - 1*
		931DC		C	1	8	D	RF 4 1 - 1*
	1930	31, 32		RP	1	6	S	SG - 3 - 1*
		103 Emsemble		T	1	13	A	RF 5 1 - 2*
		111A	280.00	T	1	13	A	RF 5 1 - 2*
		235	56.00	C	1	10	A	RF 4 1 - 1*
		410			1	6	A	SG - 2 - 1*
		410DC			1	5	D	SG - 2 - 1*
		420	96.50	C	1	6	A	SG - 2 - 1*

MANUFACTURER	YEAR	MODEL NO. & NAME	PRICE	STYLE	D	T	P	CIR.	& STAGES
SPARKS-WITHINGTON CO. (cont.)		420DC		C	1	5	D	SG	- 2 - 1*
		564		HB	1	11	A	RF	
		570		LB	1	11	A	RF	
		574		LB	1	13	A	RF	
		589	136.00	LB	1	10	A	RF	4 2 - 1*
		591	115.00	HB	1	10	A	RF	4 2 - 1*
		593	115.00	HB	1	10	A	RF	4 2 - 1*
		600	136.00	HB	1	9	D	RF	4 2 - 1*
		600DC		HB	1	9	A	RF	4 2 - 1*
		610	136.00	HB	1	10	D	RF	4 2 - 1*
		610DC		HB	1	9	A	RF	4 2 - 1*
		620	151.00	HB	1	9	D	RF	4 2 - 1*
		620DC		AB	1	11	A	RF	
		740	182.00	HB	1	11	A	RF	
		740DC		HB	1	9	D	RF	
		750	222.00	HB	1	9	A	RF	
		750DC		HB	1	13	A	RF	
		870	323.00		1		A	RF	
		AR19		Auto	1	5	S	SG	- 3 - 1
		AR50 (Police)		Auto	1	5	S	SG	- 3 - 1
		AC55 (Headquarters)			1	6	A	SG	- 3 - 1
SPIELMAN ELECTRIC CO. INC.	1923	Seco	15.00					C	- - -
	1924	Seco	14.50					C	- - -
	1925	Air Pilot	55.00	T	3			TRF	- 2 - 2
	1926	" "	55.00			5	S	TRF	
		" "	60.00		3			TRF	
SPLITDORF ELECTRICAL MFG. CO. (Chasses also used by Thomas A. Edison Inc.)	1924	R100	150.00	T	3	5	S	TRF	- 2 - 2
	1925	R102	235.00	Desk	3	5	S	TRF	- 2 - 2
		R200	150.00	T	3	5	S	TRF	- 2 - 2
		R400 Sonata	60.00	T	2	4	S	TRF	- 1 - 2
		R500 Polonaise	75.00	T	3	5	S	TRF	- ? - 2
		R150D Nocturne	150.00	T	3	5	S	TRF	- 2 - 2
		R410C Rhapsody	410.00	T	3	5	S	TRF	- 2 - 2
		R110D Geisha	110.00	T	3	5	S	TRF	- 2 - 2
		R425C Mikado	425.00	C	3	5	S	TRF	- 2 - 2
	1926	C200	200.00	C	3	5	S	TRF	- 2 - 2
		C215	215.00	C	2	6	S	TRF	- 3 - 2

MANUFACTURER	YEAR	MODEL NO. & NAME	PRICE	STYLE	D	T	P	CIR. & STAGES
SPLITDORF ELECTRICAL MFG. CO. (cont.)								
	1927	R560	60.00	T	3	5	S	TRF - 2 - 2
		RV580	80.00	T	3	5	S	TRF - 2 - 2
		RV695	95.00	T	2	6	S	TRF - 3 - 2
		Abbey	100.00	T	1	6	S	TRF - 2 - 2
		Concerto	112.00	C	1	5	S	TRF - 2 - 2
		Virtuoso	127.50	C	1	5	S	TRF - 2 - 2
		Maestro	170.00	C	1	6	S	TRF - 3 - 2
		Intermezzo	135.50	C	1	6	S	TRF - 3 - 2
		Warwick	275.00	C	1	6	S	TRF - 3 - 2
		Lorenzo	350.00	C	1	6	S	TRF - 3 - 2
		Winthrop	600.00	C	1	6	S	TRF - 3 - 2
	1928	Buckingham	800.00	T	1	7	A	TRF - 3 - 2
		Abbey Jr.	135.00	T	1	7	A	TRF - 3 - 2
		Abbey Sr.	175.00	C	1	7	A	TRF - 3 - 2
		Warwick	325.00	C	1	7	A	TRF - 3 - 2
		Avon	290.00	C	1	8	A	TRF - 3 - 2
		Lorenzo	390.00	C	1	8	A	TRF - 3 - 2*
		Salem	575.00	RP	1	8	A	TRF - 3 - 2*
		Como	450.00	C	1		A	TRF - 3 - 2*
		Winthrop	750.00	C	1		A	TRF - 3 - 2*
		Devon	850.00	C	1		A	TRF - 3 - 2*
SQUARE DEAL RADIO & ELECTRIC CO.	1925	III Autophone	29.50		2	3	S	Rfx - 2 - 2
		V-3 Celestaphone	39.50		4		E	NonReg. - 2
		I Harmodyne	49.50		4	4	S	TRF - 2 - 2
		I Goldtone	55.00		3	5	E	TRF - 1 - 1
		Tonaphone	18.00		2	2	E	DA - 1
		Alestaphone	25.00		2	3	E	TRF - 1 - 1
	1926	Harmodyne	35.00		3		E	TRF
		Goldtone	45.00		3	5	E	TRF - 2 - 2
		Alestaphone	25.00					Reg.
		Harmodyne	40.00					TRF
		Goldtone	50.00					TRF
		Super Six	150.00					TRF
		" " 2						TRF
STAFFORD RADIO CO.	1925		2.00					C - - - -
	1926		2.00					C - - - -
			5.00					C - - - -
			6.50					C - - - -

MANUFACTURER	YEAR	MODEL NO. & NAME	PRICE	STYLE	D	T	P	CIR. & STAGES
STANDARD RADIO & ELECTRIC CO.	1922	Giblin Radioear	50.00	3 Box	1	3	E	DAA - - 2
	1923	"	50.00	T				DAA - - 2
	1924	"	125.00	T		6		RF - -
	1925	Brown Teletone	100.00		2		E	RF 1 - - 2
		RL Giblin	125.00	T	2	6	S	RF 2 - - 3
		TM "	425.00	RP	2			RF 2 - - 2
		C "	185.00	T	2	6	S	RF 2 - - 3
		2RA3 "	110.00	T	2	6		RF 2 - - 3
STANDARD RADIO CORP.	1925	I or B Standardyne	60.00	T	2/3	5	E	TRF - 2 - 2
		BH "	135.00	C	3	5	S	TRF - 2 - 2
		Standard Portable	75.00	Por	2	4	B	TRF - 1 - 2
		Standardyne		T	2	3	E	(Special)
	1926	"		T	3	6		TRF - 2 - 2
	1927	"				8	A	TRF 1 3 - 2
	1929	" AC29			1	8	A	TRF 1 3 - 2
STANLEY RADIO CO.	1924	Ultra Synchrodyne	120.00					
		Super Ultra	175.00					
STANLEY RADIO PRODUCTS CO.	1925	Concert Master Jr.	60.00	Por	3	6	B	
STANWOOD ELECTRIC CO.	1923	Pink-a-Tone $8. to						
	1924	" " " $650.						
STARR EQUIPMENT CORP.	1925	LD Star Harmonic	150.00	T	3	5	S	TRF - 2 - 2
STEIN, FRED W.	1930	130A	50.00	Auto		6	B	SG - 3 - 2
		130B	50.00	T		6	B	SG - 3 - 2
		130C	59.50	T		5	A	SG - 2 - 1
STEINITE LAB. (Steinite Radio Co.)	1925		6.00		1	-	-	C - - - -
		26-1	6.00	T	2	1	S	Reg. D - - - -
		25-1	12.00	T	2	1	S	Reg. D - - - -
		26-2	12.50	T	1	1	S	Reg. D - - - -
		25-2	17.00	T	2	2	S	Reg. DA - - 1
		5	60.00	T	3	5	S	TRF - 2 - 2

MANUFACTURER	YEAR	MODEL NO. & NAME	PRICE	STYLE	D	T	P	CIR.	& STAGES
STEINITE LAB. (cont.)									
	1926	27	40.00	T	3	5	S	TRF	- 2 - 2
	1927	27C	70.00	C	3	5	S	TRF	- 2 - 2
		85	125.00	T	2	6	A	TRF	- 2 - 2
		100	100.00	T	2	7	A	TRF	- 2 - 2
		125	125.00	T	2	7	A	TRF	- 2 - 2
		150	150.00	C	2	7/8	A	TRF	- 2 - 2
		990	85.00	T	2	7/8	A	TRF	- 3 - 2
		991	125.00	C	2	7/8	A	TRF	- 3 - 2
		992	150.00	C	2	7/8	A	TRF	- 3 - 2
		993	175.00	C	2	7	A	TRF	- 3 - 2
990-993 had several different power supply configurations.	1928	261	75.00	T	1	7	A	TRF	- 3 - 2
		262	75.00	T	1	7	A	TRF	- 3 - 2
		263	115.00	C	1	7	A	TRF	- 3 - 2
		264	115.00	C	1	7	A	TRF	- 3 - 2
		265	130.00	C	1	7	A	TRF	- 3 - 2
		266	150.00	C	1	7	A	TRF	- 3 - 2*
	1929	40	135.00	HB	1	8	A	TRF	- 3 - 2*
		45	165.00	HB	1	8	A	TRF	- 3 - 2*
		50	185.00	HB	1	9	A	TRF	- 3 - 2
		60	167.00	HB	1	8	A	SG	- 3 - 1*
		70	118.00	C	1	7	A	SG	- 3 - 1*
		80	179.50	HB	1	7	A	SG	- 3 - 1*
		95	112.00	C	1	7	A	SG	- 3 - 1*
		100	129.00	HB	1	7	A	TRF	- 3 - 2*
		102	250.00	RP	1	9	A	SG	- 2 - 2
		105	205.00	RP	1	7	A	SG	- 3 - 1*
	1930	410	64.00	M	1	6	A	SG	- 2 - 2
		420		LB	1	6	A	SG	- 3 - 1*
		412			1	6	A	SG	- 2 - 2
		450			1	6	A	SG	- 3 - 1*
		210			1	6	A	SG	- 3 - 1*
		230		M	1	6	A	SG	- 3 - 1*
		421		M	1	6	A	SG	- 3 - 1*
		425		M	1	6	A	SG	- 3 - 1*
STEINMETZ WIRELESS MFG. CO.	1923	Superior	4.75				-	C	- - - -
			8.50				-	C	- - - -
	1924		4.75	Por			-	C	- - - -
STENODE	1926	Radiostat				10	A	TRF	- 5 - 3*

165

MANUFACTURER	YEAR	MODEL NO. & NAME	PRICE	STYLE	D	T	P	CIR. & STAGES
STERLING MANUFACTURING CO.	1929	A-2-60 Troubadour	129.50	C	1	8	A	SG	- 3 - 2*
		A-3-60 Serenader	149.50	LB	1	8	A	SG	- 3 - 2*
		B-2-60 Imperial	187.50	C	1	8	A	SG	- 3 - 2
	1930	722	123.50	Ch	1	7	A	SG	- 3 - 2
		C Minstrel	107.50	HB	1	8	A	SG	- 3 - 2*
		E Chorister	69.50	M	1	5	A	SG	- 2 - 1
		F Little Symphony	82.50	M	1	5	A	SG	- 2 - 1
STEWART-WARNER SPEEDOMETER CORP. (Stewart-Warner Corp.)	1925	300	65.00	T	3	5	S	TRF	- 2 - 2
		300 A	65.00		3	5	B	TRF	- 2 - 2
		305 Aeromaster	115.00	T	3	5	S	TRF	- 2 - 2
		310	175.00	C	3	5	S	TRF	- 2 - 2
		315	285.00	C	3	5	S	TRF	- 2 - 2
		320	450.00	T	3	5	S	TRF	- 2 - 2
		325	80.00	TC	3	5	S	TRF	- 2 - 2
	1926	330	65.00	TC	3	5	B	TRF	- 2 - 2
		335	175.00		3	5	B	TRF	- 2 - 2
		340	80.00	TC	3	5	B	TRF	- 2 - 2
		345	80.00	TC	1	6	B	TRF	1 2 - 2
		350	110.00	TC	1	6	S	TRF	1 2 - 2
		355	150.00	CL	1	6	S	TRF	1 2 - 2
		360	400.00	HB	1	6	S	TRF	1 2 - 2
		365	65.00	T	2	5	S	TRF	1 2 - 2
		375	175.00	C	2	6	S	TRF	1 2 - 2
		385	75.00	T	1	6	S	TRF	1 2 - 2
	1927	390		C	1	6	S	TRF	- 3 - 2
		500	55.00	Ch	1	6	S	TRF	- 3 - 2
		520 Compact	125.00	C	1	6	S	TRF	- 3 - 2
		525	80.00	T	1	7	S	TRF	- 3 - 2
		530	170.00	C	1	7	A	TRF	- 3 - 2
		535	120.00	T	1	7	A	TRF	- 3 - 2
		700	90.00	Ch	1	6	S	TRF	- 3 - 2
		705 DeLuxe	125.00	T	1	6	S	TRF	- 3 - 2
		710 "	255.00	C	1	7	S	TRF	- 3 - 2
		715	170.00	T	1	7	A	TRF	- 3 - 2*
		720	325.00	C	1	8	A	TRF	- 3 - 2
		750			1	7	A	TRF	- 3 - 2
	1928	801 Series A	94.50	MT	1	7	A	TRF	- 3 - 2
		802 Series A	110.00	MT	1	7	A	TRF	- 3 - 2

MANUFACTURER	YEAR	MODEL NO. & NAME	PRICE	STYLE	D	T	P	CIR. & STAGES
STEWART-WARNER SPEEDOMETER CORP. (cont.)		806 Series A	67.50	MT	1	6	S	TRF - 3 - 2
		811 Series A	94.50	MT	1	7	A	TRF - 3 - 2
		812 Series A	110.50	MT	1	7	A	TRF - 3 - 2
		801, 801A Series B	96.00	MT	1	8	A	TRF - 3 - 2*
		802 Series B	112.00	MT	1	8	A	TRF - 3 - 2*
		806 Series B	69.00	MT	1	7	A	TRF - 3 - 2*
		811, 811A Series B	96.00	MT	1	8	A	TRF - 3 - 2*
		812 Series B	112.00	M	1	8	S	TRF - 3 - 2*
	1929	900	72.50	MT	1	7	A	TRF - 3 - 2*
		900AC	89.75	MT	1	8	A	TRF - 3 - 2*
		900AC	97.75	MT	1	8	A	TRF - 3 - 2*
		901-2-3	89.75	T	1	8	A	TRF - 3 - 2*
		911-12-13	95.25	T	1	8	D	TRF - 3 - 2*
		921DC	97.25	MT	1	7	D	TRF - 3 - 2*
		921-22-23-50 DC	97.25	T	1	7	S	TRF - 3 - 2*
		931-32-33-50 Batt.	72.50	T	1	7	A	SG - 3 - 2*
		950-51-52	95.00	T	1	8	A	SG - 3 - 2*
	1930	953	91.50	Ch	1	8	A	SG - 3 - 2*
		1 Avon	99.75	LB	1	8	D	SG - 3 - 2*
		" "	81.25	LB	1	7	S	SG - 3 - 2*
		2 Graham	137.00	LB	1	8	A	SG - 3 - 2*
		"	162.00	LB	1	8	D	SG - 3 - 2*
		3 Raphael	197.00	HB	1	8	D	SG - 3 - 2*
		4 St. James	197.00	HB	1	8	A	SG - 3 - 2*
		" "	215.00	HB	1	7	A	SG - 3 - 2*
		5 Comb.	215.00	HB	1	7	D	SG - 3 - 2*
STORY & CLARK RADIO CORP.	1930	36	208.00	C	1	7	A	TRF - 3 - 1*
		43	248.00	C	1	8	A	TRF - 3 - 1*
		51	317.00	C	1	8	A	TRF - 3 - 1*
STILES MANUFACTURING CO.	1925		97.50	T	2	5	S	TRF - 2 - 2
STROMBERG CARLSON MFG. CO.	1923	1A	180.00	T	3	5	S	Neut. - 2 - 2
	1924	2	310.00	T	3	5	S	Neut. - 2 - 2
	1925	1B	180.00	Desk	3	5	S	Neut. - 2 - 2
		3A	95.00	P	2	4	S	Neut. - 1 - 2

MANUFACTURER

STROMBERG CARLSON MFG. CO. (cont.)

YEAR	MODEL NO. & NAME	PRICE	STYLE	D	T	P	CIR. & STAGES
	3B	95.00	P	2	4	S	Neut. - 1 - 2
	601	210.00	T	2	6	S	Neut. - 3 - 2
	602	340.00	C	2	6	S	Neut. - 3 - 2
1926	501	180.00	T	2	5	S	Neut. - 2 - 2
	501A			2	5	S	Neut. - 2 - 2
	501B			2	5	S	Neut. - 2 - 2
	502	290.00	C	2	5	S	Neut. - 2 - 2
	502A	325.00	C	2	5	S	Neut. - 2 - 2
	502B			2	5	S	Neut. - 2 - 2
	601B	225.00	T	2	6	S	Neut. - 3 - 2
	602B			2	6	S	Neut. - 3 - 2
1927	601A	225.00	T	2	6	S	Neut. - 3 - 2
	602A	365.00	C	2	6	S	Neut. - 3 - 2
	523	295.00	T	2	8	S	Neut. - 2 - 2
	523 DC			2	8	A	Neut. - 2 - 2#
	524	425.00	C	2	8	A	Neut. - 2 - 2
	524 DC		D	2	8	D	Neut. - 2 - 2#
	633	355.00	T	2	6	A	Neut. - 3 - 2
	634	505.00	T	2	8	A	Neut. - 2 - 2
	734	755.00	C	1	9	A	Neut. - 4 - 2
1928	744	1245.00	RP	1	11	A	Neut. - 4 - 2
	633W	365.00	T	1	11	A	Neut. - 3 - 2
	635 Treasure Chest	185.00	T	2	9	A	Neut. - 3 - 2
	636 "			1	7	A	Neut. - 3 - 2
	744B	245.00	C	1	7	A	Neut. 1 - 3 - 2#
	635 DC	1205.00	T	1	11	D	Neut. - 3 - 2*
1929	638	185.00	C	1	9	A	Neut. - 3 - 2#
	638 DC	380.00	C	1	8	D	Neut. - 3 - 2
	641	370.00	T	1	9	A	Neut. - 3 - 1
	641A	155.00	T	1	6	A	SG - 3 - 1
	641B	155.00	C	1	6	A	SG - 3 - 1
	642	247.00	C	1	6	A	SG - 3 - 1
	642A	259.00	C	1	6	A	SG - 3 - 1
	642B	259.00	C	1	6	A	SG - 3 - 1
	846	347.00	C	1	10	A	SG - 3 - 2*
	846A	347.00	C	1	10	A	SG - 3 - 2*
	846B			1	10	A	SG - 3 - 2*
	848			1	8	A	SG - 3 - 2*
1930	645	272.00	C	1		D	SG - 3 - 2*

MANUFACTURER	YEAR	MODEL NO. & NAME	PRICE	STYLE	D	T	P	CIR. & STAGES
STROMBERG CARLSON MFG. CO. (cont.)								
		652	239.00	C	1	6	A	SG - 3 - 1
		652A	239.00	C	1	6	A	SG - 3 - 1
		652B	239.00	C	1	6	A	SG - 3 - 1
		654	369.00	RP	1	6	A	SG - 3 - 1
		654A	369.00	RP	1	6	A	SG - 3 - 1
		654B	369.00	RP	1	6	A	SG - 3 - 1
		10	259.00	C	1	7	A	SG 1 2 - 1 *
		10A	259.00	C	1	7	A	SG 1 2 - 1 *
		10B	259.00	C	1	7	A	SG 1 2 - 1 *
		11	285.00	C	1	7	A	SG 1 2 - 1 *
		11A	285.00	C	1	7	A	SG 1 2 - 1 *
		11B	285.00	C	1	7	A	SG 1 2 - 1 *
		12	355.00	C	1	10	A	SG 1 2 - 2 *
		12A	355.00	C	1	10	A	SG 1 2 - 2 *
		12B	355.00	C	1	10	A	SG 1 2 - 2 *
		14	645.00	RP	1	10	A	SG 1 2 - 2 *
		14A	645.00	RP	1	10	A	SG 1 2 - 2 *
		14B	645.00	RP	1	10	A	SG 1 2 - 2 *
SUN MANUFACTURING CO.	1925	50 Sun Reflex	75.00		3	6	S/E	RfxTRF - 3 - 2
		60 " "	140.00		3	6	E	RfxTRF - 3 - 2
		70 " RP	237.00		3	6	E	RfxTRF - 3 - 2
		Sun Radio DeLuxe	100.00		3	6	E	RfxTRF - 3 - 2
		Super Sun	125.00		2	6	B	RF Spl 3 - - 2
	1926	Sun " Radio DeLuxe						
	1927	27-A	75.00	T		5	B	TRF - 2 - 2
		27-B	80.00			5	B	TRF - 2 - 2
SUN RADIO CO.	1925	Sun Set	150.00	Por	3		S	RF 1 - - 2
SUN RADIO MANUFACTURING CO.	1924	Custom Built						
SUNBEAM RADIO SALES CORP.	1925	Akradyne	75.00	C	3	5	S/E	TRF - 2 - 2
		"	90.00		2	5	S	TRF - 2 - 2
		"	110.00		2	5	S	TRF - 2 - 2
		"	150.00		2	5	S	TRF - 2 - 2
		"	175.00		2	5	S	TRF - 2 - 2
		"	215.00		2	5	S	TRF - 2 - 2
		"	475.00		2	7	S	TRF - 3 - 3

MANUFACTURER	YEAR	MODEL NO. & NAME	PRICE	STYLE	D	T	P	CIR. & STAGES
SUNBEAM RADIO SALES CORP. (cont.)		Akradyne	975.00		2	5	S	TRF - 2 - 2
		"	1475.00		2	7	S	TRF - 3 - 3
		Pink-A-Tone	18.50		2		B	Rfx TRF
		" "	28.50		2		B	Rfx TRF
		" "	34.50		3		B	Rfx TRF
SUPER ANTENNA CO.	1922	FRL Super	240.00	T	2	5	S	TRF - 2 - 2
	1923	Gem	120.00					RF
		Super	210.00					RF
	1924	Gem						RF
		Super			3		E	RF 3 - - 2
	1925	Super	210.00	C	3		E	RF
SUPERIOR COIL CO.	1924	K.D. (Short Wave)			1	2		DA - - - 1
	1925	Superior		T	1	2		
SUPERIOR RADIO CO.	1922	Portable	35.00	Por	2		B	
SUPEROLA RADIO CORP.	1925		49.50	T	3	6	S	TRF - 2 - 3
			69.50	T	3	6	S	TRF - 2 - 3
SUPERTONE RADIO CO.	1925	SCR4 201A	100.00	T	3	4	E	NonReg. - - 3
		199	100.00	T	3	4	E	NonReg. - - 3
	1926	SCR4 201A	100.00	T	3	4	E	NonReg. - - 3
		199	100.00	T	3	4	E	NonReg. - - 3
SYCO RADIO PRODUCTS CORP.	1924	Superhet.						
SYLFAN	SEE	Baker-Smith Co. Inc.						
SYPHER MANUFACTURING CO.	1924	Super Reflex	60.00	Kit		3		Rfx
		KD "	42.33	T	2	4	S	RF 1 - - 2
	1925	Super Reflex	60.00		2	4	E	RF 1 - - 2
	1926	Super Selector V. T.	75.00					
TANNER CO., C. D.	1926	Neutroflex.						Rfx
TAYLOR ELECTRIC CO.	1924	Radioclear	2.90			3		C - - - -
			29.00			3	E	DAA - - - 2

MANUFACTURER	YEAR	MODEL NO. & NAME	PRICE	STYLE	D	T	P	CIR. & STAGES
TAYLOR ELECTRIC CO.	1925	Radioclear	2.90				C	- - -
	1926							- - -
TEC ELECTRIC CO.	1923	Tec	125.00					
			175.00					
TECHNICAL ENGINEERING CO.	1924		125.00					
			175.00					
TELEFONE COMPANY OF AMERICA	1925	T	225.00	C	2	5	S	TRF - 2 - 2
		RF-5	60.00	T	2	5	S	TRF - 2 - 2
TELEPHONE MAINTENANCE CO. (Telmaco)	1921	TRD-1	25.00	T	3	1		D - - -
	1923	Telmaco						Reg.
	1924	Acme P-1						Rfx
	1925	"	125.00	Por	1	4	B	Rfx - 3 - 3
		P-1	147.00	Por	1	4	B	Rfx - 3 - 3
		P-1	85.00	Kit	1	4	B	Rfx - 3 - 3
	1926	P-1	125.00	Por				Rfx - 3 - 3
		P-1	80.00	Kit	1	4	B	Rfx - 3 - 3
TELERADIO ENGINEERING CORP.	1926	VT						RF
TELETONE COMPANY OF AMERICA	1924			C				
TELETONE CO.	1925	RF	75.00		3		E	TRF - 2 - 2
			90.00		2			TRF
		Tudor	200.00		2		E	TRF
			225.00			5		TRF
TEMPLE CORP.	1929	8-60	149.00	C	1	9	A	TRF 1 3 - 2*
		8-80	189.00	C	1	9	A	TRF 1 3 - 2*
		8-16	149.00	C	1	9	A	SG 1 3 - 2*
		8-81	189.00	C	1	9	A	SG 1 3 - 2*
		8	109.00	C	1	8	B	TRF 1 3 - 2*
		8-90	289.00	RP	1	9	A	TRF 1 3 - 2*
		8-91	289.00	RP	1	9	A	SG 1 3 - 2*
		Radio Phono						
		5-60	110.00	C	1	8	B	TRF 1 3 - 2*
		7-60	149.00	C	1	8	A	TRF 1 3 - 2*

MANUFACTURER	YEAR	MODEL NO. & NAME	PRICE	STYLE	D	T	P	CIR. & STAGES		
TEMPLE CORP. (cont.)	1930	7-80	189.00	C	1	8	A	TRF	- 4 - 2	
		8-91		Ch						
		8-61		Ch	1	9	A	SG	- 4 - 2	
TEREY ELECTRIC & MFG. CO.	1925	Ten-co-Dyne	100.00	T	3		E		- 2 - 2	
	1926		250.00		3		E		- 2 - 2	
TERLEE ELECTRIC MFG. CO.	1925	Acme Reflex	165.00	T	2	4	S	RF	4 - - 3	
		L-5 Acme Reflex	150.00		2	4	E	RF	4 - - 3	
		A-6 "	65.00		2		E	RF	1 - - 2	
		A-2	55.00		2		E	RF	1 - - 2	
TERMINAL ELECTRIC CO.	1927	C-3 Powerola	115.00	T		5	D	TRF	- 2 - 2	
		6-150	155.00	T		6	A	TRF	- 2 - 2	
		C-3	165.00	T		5/6	D/A	TRF	- 2 - 2	
TERRIS RADIO MANUFACTURING CO.	1925		60.00	T	3	5	S	TRF	- 2 - 2	
TERRY ELECTRIC CO.	1925	Terry Neutrodyne	125.00	T	1	5	E	Neut.	- 1 - 3	
T. F. RADIOPHONE CO.	1924	VT Titan-o-Tone		Kit D						
THERMIODYNE RADIO CORP.	1925	TF-6	140.00	T	1	6	E	TRF	- 3 - 2	
		TF-5	100.00	T	1	5	S	TRF	- 2 - 2	
		TF-6	150.00	T	1	6	S	TRF	- 3 - 2	
		CTF-6	275.00	C	1	6	S	TRF	- 3 - 3	
	1926	TF7		T	1	7	S	TRF	- 3 - 3	
THOMPSON MANUFACTURING CO., R. E.	1923	5B						Reg.		
	1924	5-A						Reg.		
	1925	S70 Concert Grand	150.00	T	3	5	S	Neut.	- 2 - 2	
		S60 Parlor Grand	180.00	T	3	5	S	Neut.	- 2 - 2	
		V50	145.00	T	3	5	S	Neut.	- 2 - 2	
		PI1	125.00	Por	3	5	B	Neut.	- 2 - 2	
		PI2	115.00		3			Neut.		
		5C						Neut.		
		5M Minuet						Neut.		
		K40 Lafayette						Neut.		
		C61 Super Duo Tone	360.00					Neut.		

MANUFACTURER	YEAR	MODEL NO. & NAME	PRICE	STYLE	D	T	P	CIR. & STAGES
THOMPSON MANUFACTURING CO., R. E. (cont.)		R81 Super Duo Tone	150.00				Neut.	Neut.
		Minuet	150.00				Neut.	Neut.
THOMPSON, R. E. CO.	1924	Neutrodyne	150.00	T	3	5	S	Neut. - 2 - 2
THOROLA	SEE	Reichmann Co.						
TIDMARSHS RADIO SUPPLY	1927	TRS Super 4	85.00	C		7	B	TRF - 3 - 3
TILMAN RADIO CORP.	1925	T-18	49.50	T	3	5		TRF
	1926	T-18	49.50	T	3	5		TRF
		Challenger	49.50	T	3	6		TRF
TIFFANY TONE	SEE	Horn, H. H.						
TORODYNE	1925	Torodyne		T	3	5	S	TRF
TRANSFORMER CORP. OF AMERICA "TCA"	1930	Clarion Jr. AC-60	47.50	M	1	6	A	SG - 2 - 1*
		AC-51	109.00	LB	1	8	A	SG - 3 - 2*
		AC-53	129.00	HB	1	8	A	SG - 3 - 2*
		AC-55 Comb.	199.00	RP	1	8	A	SG - 3 - 2*
		AC-25-51	109.00	LB	1	8	A	SG - 3 - 2*
		AC-25-53	129.00	HB	1	8	A	SG - 3 - 2*
		AC-25-53 Comb.	199.00	RP	1	8	A	SG - 3 - 2*
TRAV-LER MANUFACTURING CORP.	1925	Trav-Ler	75.00	Por	1	5	B	RF - 2 - -
	1926	"	65.00	Por	1	5	B	RF - 2 - -
	1927	Standard	65.00	Por	1	5	B	RF - 2 - -
	1928	T	57.50	Por	1	5	B	RF - 2 - -
	1929	A	59.50	M	1	6	A	TRF - 2 - 2*
	1930	A-DC	59.50	M	1	6	D	TRF - 2 - 2*
		B	59.50	M	1	6	A	TRF - 3 - 1
		# 6 Standard	65.00	Por	1	4/5	B/A	SG - 1 - 2
		# 7 DeLuxe	75.00	Por	1	4/5	B/A	SG - 1 - 2
		# 10 Arist	100.00	Por	1	4/5	B/A	SG - 1 - 2
TREGO RADIO MANUFACTURING CO.	1923		33.75	T	2		E	Reg.
	1924		45.00	T	3	5	E	TRF - 2 - 2
	1925		45.00	T	3	5	E	TRF - 2 - 2
	1926		45.00	T	3	5	E	TRF - 2 - 2

MANUFACTURER	YEAR	MODEL NO. & NAME	PRICE	STYLE	D	T	P	CIR. & STAGES
TRESCO (Davenport, Iowa)	1922	Super-Universal DeLuxe	125.00	T	3	1	B	D - - - -
TRESCO ATCHISON	SEE	Steinite Labs						
TRESCO SALES, INC.	1925	1 Trescola	22.50	T	2	1	E	Reg. - - - -
		2 "	22.50	T		3	E	Reg. - - - 2
		3 "	50.00	T	2	3	E	Reg. - - - 2
		4 "	60.00	T	2	6	S	TRF - - 2 - 3
		5 "	60.00	T	2	5	S	TRF - - 2 - 2
TRIANGLE ELECTRIC CO.	1926	Apollo-dyne						D
TRI-CITY RADIO SUPPLY CO.	1923	Tresco	125.00	Box	3	1	E	Reg. - - - -
		Woc-Tresco	25.00	Por	2	1	E	Reg. - - - -
		" " X	37.50		2	1	E	Reg. - - - -
		"	10.00	Box	2	1	E	Reg. - - - -
		"	12.50	Box	2	1	E	Reg. - - - 2
		Simple Simon	72.50	Box		3	E	Reg. - - - -
		SS1	15.00	Box		1	E	Reg. - - - -
		TT DeLuxe	18.50	Box		2	E	Reg. - - - 1
		Y Audio Unit	35.00	T		3	E	AA - - - 2
		SU						
	1924	Reg. Tuner	12.50	Box	2	1	E	Reg. - - - -
			25.00	Box	2	1	E	Reg. - - - -
			37.50	Box	2	1	E	Reg. - - - -
			12.50	Box	2	1	E	Reg. - - - -
TRINITY RADIO	SEE	Beacon Mfg. Co.						
TRUE TONE RADIO MFG. CO.	1923		8.00				C	- - - -
	1924						C	- - - -
TRUETONE SALES CO.	1929	Philharmonic		MT	1	7	A	TRF 1 3 - 2
TUSKA CO., C. D.	1922	222	63.00	T	2	1	E	Reg. - - - -
		224	35.00	T	2	1	E	Reg. - - - -
		227		T	2	3	E	Reg. - - - 2
	1923	RT-225	59.50	T	2	3	E	Reg. - - - 2

MANUFACTURER	YEAR	MODEL NO. & NAME	PRICE	STYLE	D	T	P	CIR. & STAGES	
TUSKA CO., C. D. (cont.)		RT-224	31.50	T	2	1	E	Reg.	- - - 2
		225	75.00		2	3	E	Reg.	- - - 2
	1924								
		Tuska Superdyne	120.00	T	3	4	E	TRF	- 1 - 2
	1925	228 "	350.00	T	2	4	E	Reg.	
		305 Superdyne		Desk	2	4	E	TRF	- 1 - 2
		305 "	275.00	T	3	3	E	TRF	- 1 - 2
		301 Jr. "	85.00				E	Rfx	
TUSTIN RADIO & ELECTRIC CO.	1926	VT							
20th CENTURY RADIO CO.	1925	Air King	90.00	CT	3	5		TRF	
TWITCHELL RADIO CO., S. A.	1924	Reinartz	15.00					Reinartz	
			25.00					"	
			45.00					"	
			100.00					"	
			175.00					"	
	1925	Reinartz R-2	90.00	T				"	
TYME SON RADIO CO.	1926	Mell-O-Tone							
TYRMAN (Also made "Tyrman Ten" Superhet about 1926)	1928	60	69.50	Kit			S		
		Shielded-Grid 7	98.50	Kit	2	7	S	SH	- - 2 2
		72	153.50	Kit			A		
		Imperial 80	199.50	Kit	2	10	A	SH	- - 3 2
U-FLEX MANUFACTURING CO.	1927	U-Flex	125.00	T		5	S	TRF	- 2 - 2
ULTRADYNE	SEE	Phenix Radio Corp.							
UNCLE AL'S RADIO SHOP	1925	Miracle	12.75	T	2	0	-	C	- - - 1
		"		T	2	1	E	Cry-A	- - - 1
UNION CONSTRUCTION CO.	1923				5	3		DAA	- - - 2
UNION SERVICE CO.	1926	Super 5	75.00	T	3	5	S	TRF	- 2 - 2
UNIRADIO MFG. CO.	1924	Super-Unidyne	16.00	Kit	4	7	E	SH	- 2 1 2

MANUFACTURER	YEAR	MODEL NO. & NAME	PRICE	STYLE	D	T	P	CIR. & STAGES
UNITED AIR CLEANER CORP.	1928		31.00	Ch	1	7	A	TRF - 3 - 2
			33.00	T	1	7	A	TRF - 3 - 2
	1929	440			1	7	A	SG - 2 - 2*
		444			1	7	A	SG - 3 - 2
		445	55.00	T	1	7	A	SG - 3 - 2
		550			1	8	A	TRF 13 - 2*
		555			1	8	A	TRF 13 - 2*
		666	99.50	C	1	9	A	SG 13 - 2*
		666-C	149.00	RP	1	9	A	SG - 3 - 2*
	1930	8	99.50	HB	1	8	A	SG - 3 - 2*
		9	149.50	RP	1	8	A	SG - 2 - 2*
		10	127.00	LB	1	7	A	SG - 2 - 2*
		11	130.00	LB	1	7	A	SG - 2 - 2*
		12	180.00	RP	1	7	A	SG - 2 - 2*
		15	137.50	C	1	7	A	SG - 2 - 2*
		16	150.00	C			A	SG - 2 - 2*
UNITED AMERICAN BOSCH CORP.	SEE	American Bosch Magneto Corp.						
UNITED ELECTRIC CO. OF CHICAGO	1926	A-2 Superior	100.00	T	3	5		TRF - 2 - 2
		A-2-C	140.00	C	3	5		TRF - 2 - 2
		Superior DeLuxe	220.00	HB	3	5		TRF - 2 - 2
UNITED ENGINE CO.	1925	K Radio Lark	60.00	T	3	5	S	TRF - 2 - 2
		M Lan Sing		T	3	5	S	TRF - 2 - 2
		W " "			3	5	S	TRF - 2 - 2
		Lan Sing Phono		RP	3	5	S	TRF - 2 - 2
		" " Console		C	3	5	S	TRF - 2 - 2
	1926	United Lan Sing		T			B	- 3 - 2
	1927	" " 90-28						
		160-28	90.00	C			B	- 3 - 2
		225-28	160.00	C			B	- 3 - 2
		275-28	225.00	C			A	- 3 - 2
		205-28	285.00	T			A	- 3 - 2
		340-28	340.00	C			A	- 3 - 2
	1928	50-301	99.50	L	1	8	A	SG - 3 - 2*
	1929	50-302	109.00	HB	1	8	A	SG - 3 - 2*
	1930	50-303	110.00	HB	1	8	A	SG - 3 - 2*

MANUFACTURER	YEAR	MODEL NO. & NAME	PRICE	STYLE	D	T	P	CIR. & STAGES
UNITED MANUFACTURING & DISTR. CO.	1924	Unidyne	75.00	T	2	4	E	TRF - 1 - 2
	1925	IV Unidyne	130.00	T	2	4	E	TRF - 1 - 2
		V Super Unidyne	125.00	T	3	5	E	TRF - 2 - 2
		Super Unidyne		T	3	5	E	TRF - 2 - 2
UNITED METAL STAMPING CO.	1924	Midget	2.00					C - - -
		Travellers	3.00					C - - -
		Diamond	4.00					C - - -
		L. R. D.	4.90					C - - -
	1925	1 Paraflex	35.00		2		S	Rfx
		2 "	45.00		2		S	Rfx
		3 "	70.00		3		S	Rfx
		6 Flyn	120.00		4		S	TRF
		5 "	90.00		3		S	TRF
	1926	Paraflex	25.00					
		Aristocrat	80.00					
		"	125.00					
UNITED RADIO & MFG. CO.	1926	Chummy	15.00	T	1	1	E	D - - -
		Rover	32.50	T	1	3	E	DAA - - 2
		Air Scout	60.00	T	3	5	E	TRF - 2 - 2
		Hamoney	80.00	T	3	5	E	TRF - 2 - 2
		International	85.00	T	1	4	E	Rfx TRF - 2 - 2
		Majestic	150.00	T	2	8	A	- 4 - 2
		" DeLuxe	300.00	C	2	8	A	- 4 - 2
	1927	"	185.00	T	1		A	
		" DeLuxe	295.00	C	1		A	
UNITED RADIO CORP.	1926	Peerless						
UNITED REPRODUCERS CORP. (Tube count was one higher than shown when not using dynamic speaker.)	1929	21	195.00	C	1	9	A	SG - 3 - 2*
		22	245.00	C	1	9	A	SG - 3 - 2*
		23	245.00	C	1	9	A	SG - 3 - 2*
		24	375.00	RP	1	9	A	SG - 3 - 2*
		25		T	1	9	A	SG - 3 - 2*
	1930	65	85.00	C	1	8	A	SG - 3 - 2*
		651	140.00	C	1	8	A	SG - 3 - 2*
		652	165.00	C	1	8	A	SG - 3 - 2*
		653	165.00	C	1	8	A	SG - 3 - 2*
		K71	149.50	C	1	8	A	SG - 3 - 2*
		K72	169.50	C	1	8	A	SG - 3 - 2*

MANUFACTURER	YEAR	MODEL NO. & NAME	PRICE	STYLE	D	T	P	CIR. & STAGES
UNITED SALES INC.	1926		50.00					TRF
UNITED SCIENTIFIC LAB.	1926	Pierce-Airo	42.50	Kit	1	6	S	TRF - 2 - 3
	1927	B " "	45.00	Kit	1	6	B	TRF - 2 - 3
	1928	B " "		Ch	1	6		TRF - 2 - 3
UNIVERSAL RADIO & RESEARCH CO.	1923	V-310	95.00		1			RF
UNITY CO.	1926	5 Orpheus	25.00		3	5		TRF
U-S-L RADIO INC.	1925	RC-5	80.00	T	2/3	4	S	TRF - 1 - 3
	1926	Broadcast Receptor	80.00	T	1	6	S	TRF - 2 - 2
	1927	DC6	69.50	T	1	6	S	TRF - 3 - 2
		DC6	69.50	C	1	6	S	TRF - 3 - 3
		DC7	90.00	T	1	7	S	TRF - 3 - 3
		DC7	90.00	C	1	7	S	TRF - 3 - 3
		AC7	95.00	T	1	8	A	TRF - 3 - 3
		AC7	95.00	C	1	8	A	TRF - 3 - 3
U. S. RADIO & TELEVISION CORP. U. S. Electric Corp. also built sets with overlapping model numbers (e.g. model 37 8-tube battery TRF).	1928	20		C	1	4	A	TRF - 1 - 1
	1929	21		T	1	6	S	TRF - 3 - 2
		22		T	1	6	S	TRF - 3 - 2
		36	37.95	C	1	7	A	TRF 12 - 2
		37	49.95	C	1	7	A	TRF 12 - 2
		80		C	1	9	A	TRF 13 - 2*
		46	119.95	T	1	9	A	SG - 2 - 2*
		47		C	1	7	A	SG - 2 - 2*
		48		C	1	7	A	SG - 3, 2*
		49		T	1	5	B	SG - 3 - 2*
		26, 27		C	1	5	A	SG - 2 - 1
		50	79.95	C	1	7	A	SG 12 - 2
		55	74.95		1	2	A	TRF - 3 - 2
		90	89.95		1	9	A	TRF 13 - 2*
		89	89.95	T	1	7	A	TRF 12 - 2*
		60	99.95	C	1	9	A	SG 13 - 2*
		70	149.95	C	1	9	A	SG - 2 - 2*
		40	89.95	C	1	8	A	TRF - 2 - 1
	1930	28A, 29	105.00	LB	1	8	A	SG - 3 - 2*
		28AX	109.00	LB	1	8	A	SG - 3 - 2*
		31B	127.00	LB	1	8	A	SG - 3 - 2*
		31BX	131.00	LB	1	8	A	SG - 3 - 2*
		31C Comp.	175.00	LB	1	8	A	SG - 3 - 2*

MANUFACTURER	YEAR	MODEL NO. & NAME	PRICE	STYLE	D	T	P	CIR.	& STAGES
U. S. RADIO & TELEVISION CORP.(cont.)		31CX	179.00	LB	1	8	A	SG	- 3 - 2*
		31D	185.00	LB	1	8	A	SG	- 3 - 2*
		31DX	189.00	LB	1	8	A	SG	- 3 - 2*
		54	95.00	LB	1	5	S	SG	- 2 - 2
		55	58.00	T	1	5	S	SG	- 2 - 2
		27	59.50	M	1	8	A	SG	- 2 - 1
		11	130.00	C	1	8	A	SG	
		14	155.00	C	1	8	A	SG	
		115	115.00	C	1	8	A	TRF	- 3 - 2*
		140	140.00	C	1	8	A	TRF	- 3 - 2*
		160	160.00	C	1	9	A	TRF	- 4 - 2*
		240	240.00	C	1	7	A	SG	- 2 - 2*
		R-1 Radiotrope	115.00	C	1	7	A	SG	- 2 - 2*
		R-2 "	140.00	C	1	7	A	SG	- 2 - 2*
UTICA COMPRESSOR CO.	1925	UCO	125.00		3	5	S	TRF	- 2 - 2
VAGA MANUFACTURING CORP.	1929	51	58.00	Por	1	5	B	TRF	- 2 - 2
	1930	Vagabond	58.00	Por	1	5	B	TRF	- 2 - 2
VALLEY ELECTRIC CO.	1925	5 Valleytone	110.00	T	3	5	S	TRF	- 2 - 2
		Valleytone	115.00	T	3	5	S	TRF	- 2 - 2
		"	250.00	C	3	5	S	TRF	- 2 - 2
	1926	35 "	90.00	C	2	5	S/A	TRF	- 2 - 2
		52 "	85.00	T	2	5	S/A	TRF	- 2 - 2
		52 "	95.00	T	2	5	S	TRF	- 2 - 2
		71 "		T	2	5	S	TRF	- 2 - 2
VAN NUYS ELECTRIC CO.	1926	Kirk Recreatone							
VAN VALKENBURGH CO., L. D.	1925	Van	3.50	T	1			C	: - :
			4.00	T	1			C	: - :
VIBROPLEX CO. INC.	1924	VT	20.00	T	1		E	NonReg.	: - :
	1925	1 Martinola	75.00	T	2		E	RF	1 - - 2
		4 "	85.00	T	2		E	RF	2 - - 2
		5 "							
VAN SICKLE		C		T	1	6	S	TRF	1 2 - 2
VICTOREEN RADIO CO.	1928	Superhet		C					

MANUFACTURER	YEAR	MODEL NO. & NAME	PRICE	STYLE	D	T	P	CIR. & STAGES
VICTOREEN RADIO CO. (cont.)	1930	345	345.00	LB	1	11	A	SH - 1 3 2
		395	395.00	HB	1	11	A	SH - 1 3 2
		595	595.00	RP	1	11	A	SH - 1 3 2
VICTOR TALKING MACHINE CO.	SEE	R. C. A. Victor Co., Victor Division						
VICTORY RADIO ELECTRIC CO.	1923	Grantone	102.00					
	1924	"	102.00					
VIKING RADIO LABS.	1925		29.50	T	3	5	E	TRF - 2 - 2
	1926							
	1927		25.00	T	1	6	B	TRF - 2 - 3
	1928		50.00	T	1	7	A	TRF - 2 - 3
VITANOLA TALKING MACHINE CO.	1924		220.00	C	3	5	S	TRF - 2 - 2
	1925							
VOISOMETER MANUFACTURING CO.	1923		55.00					
			75.00					
VOLOTONE	1926							
VOLTAMP ELECTRIC MFG. CO.	1923		160.00					
	1924							
WAKEM & CO., HAROLD R.	1923	Zanaford	17.50					
		Sensitone	95.00					
WALBERT MANUFACTURING	1924	R				5		
		K				4		
	1925	Isofarad Jr.	150.00	T	3	5	S	TRF - 2 - 2
		"	150.00	T	3	6	S	TRF - 3 - 2
		Penetrola	200.00	T	1	1	S	
		"	35.00	Kit	1	1	S	
	1926	5 Isofarad	15.00	T	3	5	S	TRF - 2 - 2
		6 "	140.00	T	4	6	S	TRF - 3 - 2
		6 "	180.00	T	2	6	A	TRF - 3 - 3
		7 "	200.00	T	2	7	S	TRF - 3 - 3
			350.00					

MANUFACTURER	YEAR	MODEL NO. & NAME	PRICE	STYLE	D	T	P	CIR. & STAGES
WALBERT MANUFACTURING CO. (cont.)		Penetrola	35.00	T	1	1	S	
		"	15.00	Kit	1	1	S	
		Isofarad	75.00	Kit	3	5		
		"	125.00	Ch	3	5	S	TRF -2-2
	1927	"	165.00	Ch	4	6	S	TRF -2-2
		47-T Isofarad	180.00	T		7	A	TRF -3-3
		26 "	215.00	T		7	A	TRF -2-3
		26P-T "	250.00	T		7	A	TRF -2-3
WALLACE CO., K. J.	1925		40.00		2			
			50.00		2			
			75.00		3			
			100.00		3			
WALTHAM RADIO CORP. LTD.	1930	31	59.50	M	1	6	A	SG -3-1
WARE RADIO CORP. (See Sonora, Music Master and Ware Manufacturing Co.)	1922	AD2	110.00	T	1	4	S	RF 3 - - -
	1924	T	65.00	T	2		B	
		TU	150.00	C	1		B	
		X	150.00	T			B	
		XU	275.00	C	3	5	B	Neut. -2-2
		W	175.00	T	3	5	B	Neut. -2-2
		WU	300.00	C	3	5	B	Neut. -2-2
		L						
WARE MANUFACTURING CO.	1929	Bantam B1 Ampico		Ch	1	6	A	SG -2-2
		" B2 "		Ch	1	6	A	SG -2-2
	1930	5MW		Desk	1	7	A	SG -2-2*
		Trainon	135.00	T	1	7	A	SG -2-2
		10	275.00	HB	1	7	A	SG -2-2
		Byron	235.00	HB	1	7	A	SG -2-2
		Desk	400.00	Desk	1	7	A	SG -2-2
WASHBURN BURNER CO.	1925		90.00		3	5		TRF
WASMUTH GOODRICH CO.	1924		300.00	RP	1	4	S	TRF -1-2
			240.00	RP		4	S	
			395.00	RP	3	5	S	TRF -2-2

MANUFACTURER	YEAR	MODEL NO. & NAME	PRICE	STYLE	D	T	P	CIR. & STAGES
WASMUTH GOODRICH CO. (cont.)								
		15	220.00	RP	1	4	S	TRF - 1 - 2
			280.00	RP	2	4	S	Reg. - 1 - 2
			150.00	RP	1	3	E	TRF - 1 - 2
			185.00	RP	2	4	S	Reg. - 1 - 2
			240.00	RP	1	3	E	TRF - 1 - 2
			300.00	RP	2	4	S	Reg. - 1 - 2
			220.00	RP	2	3	S	TRF - 1 - 2
		Verdi		RP	3	4	S	Neut. - 1 - 2
		"	150.00	RP	1	5	S	TRF - 1 - 2
		Mozart		RP	3	4	S	Neut. - 2 - 2
		"		RP	1	5	S	TRF - 1 - 2
		Wagner		RP	3	5	S	Neut. - 2 - 2
WAUGH ELECTRIC MFG. CO.	1925	Echo	90.00	T	3	5	E	TRF - 2 - 2
WAVE MASTER	SEE	Kellogg Switchboard & Supply Co.						
WEBSTER ELECTRIC CO.	1923	2A	30.00	Box	1	1	S	D - - -
		3B	27.50	Box	0	2	S	AA - - - 2
		$30. to $119.						
WELLS-GARDNER & CO. (Became a division of Gulbransen Co. in 1930.)	1929	60 Arcadia	45.00	T	1	6	B	Neut. - 3 - 2
		70	56.00	T	1	7	B	Neut. - 4 - 2
		72	92.00	C	1	7	B	Neut. - 4 - 2
		92	134.00	C	1	9	A	Neut. - 4 - 2
		94	155.00	C	1	9	A	Neut. - 4 - 2
		9-C	150.00	C	1	9	A	Neut. - 13 - 2 *
		9-C	136.00	C	1	7	A	SG - 13 - 2 *
		72AC		C	1	8	A	SG - 2 - 2 *
		82AC						- 3 - 2 *
WELLS MANUFACTURING CO.	1925	24	70.00	T	1	4	B	RF - 1 - 2
		23	90.00	T	3	5	B	TRF - 2 - 2
	1926	25	65.00	T	1	4	B	RF - 1 - 2
		25	55.00	T	3	6	S	TRF - 2 - 2
		27	75.00	T	2	5	S	TRF - 2 - 2
		35	100.00	T	3	6	S	TRF - 2 - 3
		45	175.00	C	3	6	S	TRF - 2 - 3

MFR.	YEAR	MODEL NO. & NAME	PRICE	STYLE			S		CIR. & STAGES
WELLS PARK WONDER HORN MFG. CO.	1925		150.00						- 2 - -
WELLS RADIO MANUFACTURING CO.	1925	Bear Cat	110.00	Por	3	5	B	RF	2 - - 2
		50 Bear Cat	95.00	T	3	5	B	RF	2 - - 2
		5 " "	110.00	T	3	5	B	RF	2 - - 2
		500 " "	110.00	Por	3	5	B	RF	2 - - 2
		V " "	110.00		3	5	B	RF	2 - - 2
		55	160.00	C	3	5	B	RF	2 - - 2
WELLSTON RADIO CORP.	1927	Ford Radio Marvel	50.00	T		6	B	TRF	- 3 - 2
		Wonder	50.00	T		7	A	TRF	- 3 - 2
		FR-8	150.00	T		8	B	TRF	- 4 - 3
		FRA-8	150.00	T		9	A	TRF	- 4 - 3
		FRC-8	225.00	C		9	A	TRF	- 4 - 3
WELTY CO., THE WM.	1926	Monarch of the Air W-6	125.00	C		6	B	TRF	- 3 - 2
	1927	A-C-7	175.00	C		8	A	TRF	- 3 - 3
WESTARK RADIO INC.	1930	Knight			1	8	A	SG	1 2 - 2*
WESTBURR INC.	1924	Six		Por	1/2	6	B	RF	3 - - 2
	1925	Six	165.00	Por					
WESTERNER	1929	A	49.50	LB		5	A		
		AA	59.50	C		5	A		
		B	54.50	M		5	A		
		C	99.50	C		7	A		
		H	114.50	HB		7	A		
WESTERN AIR PATROL	1924		110.00	T		5			
	1925		148.50	T		6			
	1926		168.50	T		6			
		100	225.00	C		6			
	1927	100	225.00	LB		7			
	1928	AC100	167.50	LB		7			
		80	232.50	HB		7	A		
	1929	100	98.50	T		7	A		
		80	129.75	LB		7	A		
		80	189.50	C		8	A		
		90							

MANUFACTURER	YEAR	MODEL NO. & NAME	PRICE	STYLE	D	T	P	CIR. & STAGES
W. E. SUPPLY & SERVICE CO.	1923	A Aerial	25.00					
WESTERN COIL & ELECTRICAL CO.	1923	WC 5	80.00	T	3	4	E	TRF - 1 - 2
	1924	Radiodyne	150.00	T	2	4	S	TRF - 1 - 2
	1925	WC-12 Radiodyne	250.00	C	3	6	B	TRF - 2 - 3
		WC-5B "	80.00	T	2	4	E	RF - 1 - 1
		WC-11	250.00	C	3	6	S	RF - 3 - 2
		WC-11B "	150.00	T	3	6	S	RF - 3 - 2
		WC-12B "	150.00	T	3	4	B	RF - 2 - 3
		WC-14A "	65.00	T	2	4	S	RFx TRF - 2 - 2
		WC-17A "	75.00	T	2	5	S	TRF - 2 - 2
		WC-15 "	39.50	T	3	5	E	TRF - 2 - 2
		WC-14B "	85.00	T	2	5	S	TRF - 2 - 2
		WC-18B "	100.00	T	3	5	B	TRF - 2 - 2
		WC-12B "	100.00	T	3	5	S	TRF - 2 - 2
		WC-14C "	185.00		3	5	S	TRF - 2 - 2
		WC-12C "	200.00	C	2	5	S	TRF - 2 - 2
		WC-18C "	110.00		3	5	B	TRF - 2 - 2
		Radiodyne	210.00		3	5	S	TRF - 2 - 2
		"	185.00		2	5	B	TRF - 2 - 2
		"	215.00		2	5	B	TRF - 2 - 2
	1926	WC-15 Jr. Radiodyne	49.50	T	2	5	S	TRF - 2 - 2
		WC-15 Jr. "	85.00	C	2	5	S	TRF - 2 - 3
		WC-19E "	110.00	T	2	6	S	TRF - 2 - 3
		WC-19E "	120.00		2	6	S	TRF - 2 - 3
		WC-19E "	125.00		2	6	S	TRF - 2 - 3
		WC-19E "	140.00		2	6	S	TRF - 2 - 3
		WC-19E "	195.00		2	6	S	TRF - 2 - 3
		WC-19E "	210.00		2	6	S	TRF - 2 - 3
		WC-70G Super	485.00	T	2	9	S	TRF - 2 - 3
		WC-20F	225.00	C	2	9	S	TRF - 2 - 3
		"Other models up to $595."	320.00					
WESTERN ELECTRIC CO.	1923 1926	48 6004-C		MT	2		SH	
WESTINGALE ELECTRIC CO.	1926		57.00 47.00	T T	1 2	5 5		

MANUFACTURER	YEAR	MODEL NO. & NAME	PRICE	STYLE	D	T	P	CIR. & STAGES	
WESTINGALE ELECTRIC CO. (cont.)	1927		57.00	T	1	5			
			47.00	T	2	5			
			85.00	C	1				
			87.00	C	1	6			
		"Also 21 other models up to $72."							
WESTINGHOUSE ELECTRIC MFG. CO. (RCA was sole sales agent for Westinghouse until 1930. See RCA.)	1921	RA Reg. Tuner	65.00	T	1			PT	- - 2
		RC Receiver	125.00	T	0	3	B	DAA	- 3 - 1*
	1930	WR44	110.00	LB	1	8	A/D	SG	- 1 2 1*
		WR 5	142.00	LB	1	9	A	SH	
		WR 6	179.00	HB	1	9	A	SH	
		WR 7	275.00	LB	1	9	A	SH	- 1 2 1*
WEST PENN RADIO CO.	1924	Fireside							
	1925	Fireside							
	1926								
WHEELER MANUFACTURING CO.	1925	A Aertone	75.00		3	5	S	TRF	- 2 - 2
		B "	95.00		3	5	S	TRF	- 2 - 2
WHEELOCK MANUFACTURING CO.	1925	5 Mayflower	60.00	T	3	5	S	TRF	- 2 - 2
WHITE BEAUTY ELECTRIC CO.	1925	C-119	75.00	T	3	6	S	TRF	- 3 - 2
	1926		65.00	T	3	6	S	TRF	- 3 - 2
WHITE MANUFACTURING CO.	1923	Martian Big Four	7.50		2			C	- - - -
WHOLESALE RADIO SERVICE CO. "LAFAYETTE"	1929	Preselector			1	7	A	SG (PT)	- 2 - 2
		Duo Symphonic			1	9	A	TRF	1 3 - 3
	1930	AC524				5	A	SG	- 2 - 1
WILCOX LABORATORIES	1923		80.00						
	1924	10H Hexair Coil	100.00	T	3	5	S	TRF	- 2 - 2
	1925	DeLuxe Hexair Coil	250.00	C	3	5	S	TRF	- 2 - 2
		Hexair Coil	88.00		3		S	TRF	
	1926		140.00		2		S	TRF	
		J Cathedral	80.00	T	1	5	E	TRF	- 2 - 2
		Grand Cathedral	150.00	T	1	6	E	TRF	- 3 - 2

MANUFACTURER	YEAR	MODEL NO. & NAME	PRICE	STYLE	D	T	P	CIR.	STAGES
WILCOX LABORATORIES (cont.)	1927	VIII	110.00	MT	1	7	A	TRF	- 3 - 2
	1928	VIII	120.00	T	1	7	A	TRF	- 3 - 2
WILKINS RADIO CO.	1926	Crystal Artay	5.00					C	- - -
		A Artay	27.50		2	2	E	Rfx	- 1 - 2
		C	45.00		3	5	E	TRF	- 2 - 2
		D	50.00	Por	1	6	E	RF	3 - - 2
		B	85.00	C	2	2	E	Rfx	- 1 - 2
WITHERBEE CO., T. S.	1926	Shielded Knight	65.00	T		6	B	TRF	- 3 - 2
	1927	665 " "	65.00						
WINDSOR RADIO CO.	1925	XI Magnadyne	75.00		3	5	S	TRF	- 2 - 2
		XII	110.00		3	5	S	TRF	- 2 - 2
		XIII	175.00		3	5	S	TRF	- 2 - 2
		XV	175.00		3	5	S	TRF	- 2 - 2
	1926	A-1		T	3	5	S	TRF	- 2 - 2
		A-2		T	3	5	S	TRF	- 2 - 2
		A-3		C	3	5	S	TRF	- 2 - 2
		B-1		T	1	6	S	TRF	- 2 - 3
		B-2		T	1	6	S	TRF	- 2 - 3
		B-3		C	1	6	S	TRF	- 2 - 3
WIPPLE RAINE CO.	1925	Five	88.00	T	3	5	S	TRF	- 2 - 2
	1926	W-R-88	88.00	C	3	5	S	TRF	- 2 - 2
		7	175.00	C	3	5	S	TRF	- 2 - 2
		22	195.00	C	3	5	S	TRF	- 2 - 2
		16	250.00	C	3	5	S	TRF	- 2 - 2
WIRED WIRELESS	1923							RF	
WIRELESS CORP. OF AMERICA	1926								
WIRELESS EQUIPMENT CO. (ABC)	1921	Receiving Unit, VT Detector, Two-Step Amp	86.00	3Box	1	3	E		- - 2
WIRELESS IMPROVEMENT CO.	1922	178		Box	1	-	-	C	- - -
WIRELESS SHOP, THE (A. J. Edgcomb)	1923	Perflex	75.00						

MANUFACTURER	YEAR	MODEL NO. & NAME	PRICE	STYLE	D	T	P	CIR. & STAGES
WIRELESS SHOP, THE (cont.) (A. J. Edgcomb)								
	1924	Detector Unit	105.00					
			130.00					
			4.00					
	1925	Perflex	170.00	C	2	2	A	Rfx - 1 - 2
		"	145.00					
WIRELESS SPECIALTY APPARATUS CO. (Sold thru RCA after 1920.)	SEE	RCA						
W. K. ELECTRIC CO.	1925	5 Oriole	90.00		2	5	S	RF 2 - - 2
		6 "	100.00		2	5	S	RF 2 - - 2
		7 " Special	150.00		2	5	S	RF 2 - - 2
		8 "	65.00		2	5	S	RF 2 - - 2
		60 "	120.00		2	5	S	RF 2 - - 2
	1926	7-D"	125.00		2	5	S	RF 2 - - 2
		7-D"	145.00		2	5	S	RF 2 - - 2
		7-D"	210.00					
		78	270.00					
		70	125.00			6		
		75	150.00					
WOLVERINE RADIO CO.	1925	25B Combidyne	100.00	T	3	4	E	TRF - 1 - 2
		Combidyne	75.00		3	4	E	TRF - 1 - 2
WORK RITE MANUFACTURING CO.	1923	Work Rite Neut.	70.00	Kit	3	5	S	Neut. - 2 - 2
	1924		25.00	Kit	3	5	S	Neut. - 2 - 2
		Work Rite Neut.	80.00	T	3	5	S	Neut. - 2 - 2
		Neutro-Grand						
		Chum	65.00	CT	2	3	B	Rfx Neut. - 1 - 2
		Air Master	160.00	T	3	5	E	Neut. - 2 - 2
		Radio King	220.00	T	3	5	E	Neut. - 2 - 2
		Aristocrat	350.00	CT	3	5	E	Neut. - 2 - 2
		Winner Five	80.00	C	3	5	S	Neut. - 2 - 2
	1926	Air Master Six	125.00	T	3	6	S	Neut. - 2 - 3
		Radio King Six	170.00	T	3	6	S	Neut. - 2 - 3
		Aristocrat Six	275.00	C	3	6	S	Neut. - 2 - 3
		16	80.00	T	2	6	S	Neut. - 2 - 3
		26	145.00	C	2	6	S	Neut. - 2 - 3

MANUFACTURER	YEAR	MODEL NO. & NAME	PRICE	STYLE	D	T	P	CIR. & STAGES
WORK RITE MANUFACTURING CO. (cont.)		36	270.00	Desk C	2	6	S	Neut. - 2 - 3
		Air Master 5	120.00		3	5	S	Neut. - 2 - 2
		Neut. Kit		Kit	3	5	S	Neut. - 2 - 2
	1927	17	95.00	Kit	1	6	S	TRF - 2 - 3
		26	160.00	T	1	6	S	TRF - 2 - 3
		37	160.00	C	1	8	S	TRF - 4 - 3
	1928	18	128.00	T	1	7	A	TRF - 3 - 2
		28	195.00	T	1	7	A	TRF - 3 - 3
		38	160.00	C	1	9	A	TRF - 4 - 3
		48	250.00	T	1	9	A	TRF - 4 - 3
		58	75.00	C	1	7	A	TRF - 3 - 2
	1929	33	165.00	Ch	1	8	A	TRF
		35	175.00	LB	1	8	A	TRF
		37	195.00	LB	1	8	A	TRF
		39	195.00	HB	1	8	A	TRF
		40	295.00	HB	1	8	A	TRF, 1SG
		24		RP	1	8	A	TRF
		27		Ch	1	8	A	TRF
WORLD ELECTRIC CO.	1925	Plug In	150.00		2		A	- 1 - 1
WORLD RADIO CORP.	1926	Compact	29.50	T	3	5		TRF - 2 - 2
	1927	Standard	45.00	T	3	5		TRF - 2 - 2
		D-5	24.50	T	3	5		TRF
WORLD WIRELESS CORP.	1924			Por	2			RF
	1925	Super Four	65.00		2		S	TRF - 1 - 2
WRIGHT ELECTRIC CO.	1920		50.00		2	1	E	Reg. - - -
	1921	BA	80.00		2	3	S	Reg. - - 2
	1922	B	130.00		3	4	S	Reg. - - 3
WRIGHT RADIO MANUFACTURING CO.	1924	RF	50.00	Por		4		- 2 - 2
		ARF	70.00			1		- 2 - 2
	1925	Acme Special	23.00		3	5	B	TRF
		5A	160.00					
		III W	60.00					- 1 - 2
		IV D	85.00					- 1 - 4
		VI	100.00		2		B	RF 1 - - 4
		VI Wright DeCoster	125.00	C	2		B	RF 1 - - 4
		VIC "	250.00		2		R	Reg. - - -
		Acme Special	23.00		2	1		Reg. - - -
		A Wright	50.00		2	2	E	NonReg. - - - 1

MANUFACTURER	YEAR	MODEL NO. & NAME	PRICE	STYLE	D	T	P	CIR. & STAGES
WRIGHT RADIO MANUFACTURING CO. (cont.)	1927	B Wright	50.00	T		7	B	Reg. - 1 - -
		7	165.00			7	B	TRF - 3 - 3
		7A	185.00			7	B	TRF - 3 - 3
WURLITZER CO., THE RUDOLPH	1924	5D	85.00	T	3	5		TRF
	1925							
	1926	MF5	210.00	C		5		
		5C	185.00	T		5		
		5C	195.00	C		5		
	1927	3D	149.50	C		6		
	1928	AC	149.50	C		7		
		T4	79.50	T		4		
	1929	7A	135.00	T		7		
		9A	165.00	T		9		
		7B	150.00	C		7		
		9B	175.00	C		9		
		7C	175.00	HB		7		
		9C	232.00	HB		9		
	1930	840	149.50	HB		8	A	SG
		850	165.00	HB		8	A	SG
X L RADIO CO.	1925	XL-Three Way Radio	8.75		1	-	-	C - - - - -
YALE RADIO & ELECTRIC CO.	1925	Yale Premier	50.00	T	3		E	TRF
		"	105.00	T	3		E	TRF
		"	150.00	T	3		E	TRF
		Thor-O-Dyne	85.00	Por	2		S	TRF
ZANEY-GILL CORP.	1930	Clarion	49.50	M	1	6	A	SG - 3 - 1
		Clarionette	49.50	M	1	6	A	SG - 2 - 1*
ZENITH AUTOMOTIVE MFG. CO.	1927	$29. and Up.		T		6		
				T		7		
		$42. and Up.		C		6		
				C		7		
ZENITH RADIO CORP. (Chicago Radio Lab. prior to 1923.)	1920	CRL Reg.	65.00	T	2	-	-	Reg. PT
		Z-Nith Long Distance		T	2	-	-	Reg. PT
	1921	Z-Nith Regenerator		T	3	1	E	Reg. - - - 3
	1922	1R, M		2T		4		DAAA - - - 3
	1923	3R	175.00	T	2	4	E	DAAA - - - 3

MANUFACTURER	YEAR	MODEL NO. & NAME	PRICE	STYLE	D	T	P	CIR. & STAGES
ZENITH RADIO CORP. (cont.)	1924	4R	100.00	T	2	4	E	DAAA	- - - 3
			150.00	P	2	4	E	DAAA	- - - 3
		Super Portable	224.00	Por	2	6	B	TRF	- - 2 - 3
		VII Super	240.00	T	2	6	A/S	TRF	- - 2 - 3
		VIII "	260.00	Desk	2	6	A/S	TRF	- - 2 - 3
		IX "	355.00	Desk	2	6	A/S	TRF	- - 2 - 3
		X "	550.00	T	2	6	A/S	TRF	- - 2 - 3
	1925	Spanish	2000.00	HB	2	6	A/S	TRF	
		Italian DeLuxe	1100.00	LB	1	10	A	TRF	
		Chinese	1500.00	LB	1	10	A	TRF	
		English	750.00	LB	1	10	A	TRF	
	1926	Colonial DeLuxe	650.00	C	1	10	A	TRF	
		English "	800.00	C	1	10	A	TRF	
		Italian "	1250.00	C	1	6	S	TRF	- 3 - 2
		Chinese "	1700.00	C	1	6	S	TRF	- 3 - 2
		Spanish	2500.00	C	1	6	S	TRF	- 3 - 2
	1927	11	100.00	T	1	6	A	TRF	- 4 - 3
		12	110.00	T	1	6	A	TRF	- 2 - 3
		14	185.00	C	1	6	A	TRF	- 3 - 2
		15	185.00	T	1	8	A	TRF	- 3 - 2
		16	300.00	C	1	8	A	TRF	- 4 - 3
		17	175.00	T	1	10	A	TRF	- 2 - 3
		11E	255.00	C	1	7	A	TRF	- 3 - 2
		14E	285.00	T	1	7	A	TRF	- 3 - 2
		15E	300.00	C	1	9	A	TRF	- 4 - 3
		15EP			1	9	A	TRF	- 4 - 3
		16E	450.00	C	1	9	A	TRF	- 2 - 3
		16EP		T	1	10	A	TRF	- 3 - 2
		17E	350.00	T	1	6	S	TRF	- 3 - 2
	1928	31	100.00	LB	1	6	A	TRF	- 3 - 2
		32	180.00	T	1	7	A	TRF	- 3 - 2
		33	150.00	T	1	7	D	TRF	- 3 - 2*
		33X	150.00	T	1	7	A	TRF	- 3 - 2
		333	150.00	LB	1	7	A	TRF	- 3 - 2
		34	230.00	C	1	8	A	TRF	- 3 - 2
		34P	250.00	HB	1	7	A	TRF	- 3 - 2
		35	270.00	C	1	7	A	TRF	- 3 - 2
		35A	325.00	C	1	8	A	TRF	- 3 - 2
		35AP (352AP)	385.00	C	1	8	A	TRF	- 3 - 2
		35P (352P)	330.00	C	1	8	A	TRF	- 3 - 2

(- - 2 Versions are 25 cycle power)

MANUFACTURER	YEAR	MODEL NO. & NAME	PRICE	STYLE	D	T	P	CIR. & STAGES
ZENITH RADIO CORP. (cont.)		353A	325.00	C	1	7	D	TRF - 3 - 2*
		362 (342, 352)	165.00	T	1	7	A	TRF - 3 - 2
		36X			1	7	A	TRF - 3 - 2
		35 PX (352 PX)	330.00	C	1	9	A	TRF - 3 - 3
		35 APX (352 APX)	405.00	C	1	9	A	TRF - 3 - 3
		37A (8 & 9 Tube)	625.00	RP	1	8/9	A	TRF - 3 - 2
		39 (392)	450.00	LB	1	10	A	TRF - 4 - 3
		39A (392A)	510.00	C	1	10	A	TRF - 4 - 3
		Super			1	6	s	TRF - 2 - 3
		Super 27			1	7	A	TRF - 2 - 3
	1929	40A	850.00	RP	1	10	A	TRF - 4 - 3
		41	100.00	T	1	7	A	TRF1SG1 2 - 2
		42	175.00	C	1	7	A	TRF1SG1 2 - 2
		52 (522)	275.00	C	1	9	A	SG - 2 - 3**
		53 (532)	395.00	C	1	9	A	SG - 2 - 3**
		54 (542)	250.00	C	1	9	A	SG - 2 - 3**
		563		C	1	11	D	TRF - 3 - 2*
		57	495.00	C	1	8	A	SG - 2 - 3**
		55	700.00	C	1	8	A	SG - 2 - 3**
		60 (602)	188.00	LB	1	9	A	SG - 2 - 3**
	1930	61 (612)	155.00	LB	1	9	A	SG - 2 - 3**
		613			1	9	A	SG - 2 - 3**
		62 (622)	235.00	LB	1	9	A	SG - 2 - 3**
		64 (642)	370.00	LB	1	9	A	SG - 2 - 3**
		67 (672)	545.00	Auto	1	9	A	SG - 2 - 3**
		71 (712)	185.00	LB	1	9	A	SG - 2 - 3**
		72 9722)	210.00	LB	1	9	A	SG - 2 - 3**
		73 (732)	265.00	LB	1	9	A	SG - 2 - 3**
		75	375.00	RP	1	9	A	SG - 2 - 3**
		77 (777)			1	9	A	SG - 2 - 3**
		74	315.00	LB	1	9	A	SG - 2 - 3**
		70			1	9	A	SG - 2 - 3**

1931-1932 TABULATION

INTRODUCTION. The catalogue for 1931 and 1932 is published separately in an effort to give far more complete information than was available for the earlier years, and because the last two years mark fundamental changes in the industry, including the swing to superheterodyne, the introduction of a large number of new tubes, and advent of the small models, and the rapid downward trend of prices. The tabulation is presented in a new form, and many new symbols have been used. The symbols used in the earlier listing have been retained, but are repeated below for convenience.

ARRANGEMENT. Manufacturers are listed alphabetically with a heading giving the manufacturers name, the trade name, the location of the factory, the number of chasses and models, and the range of prices and number of tubes, for the two year period. Column headings are given at the top of each page. A heavy vertical line divides chassis information, on the left, from model information, on the right. Models are listed below the chassis they employ. No ditto marks are used, the data on each line applying to subsequent lines, until otherwise shown. Single dashes indicate that no information was available. Double dashes indicate that the receiver does not have the particular tube or feature.

COLUMNS. The first three columns give type of power supply, number of tubes, and type of circuit. The next six columns, between the double rules, show the type and position of all tubes. Where tube positions are not known, the tube list is given in parenthesis. The next three columns give the tuning range, the control arrangements, and the indicators. Model information, to the right of the black line, includes number and name, first advertised Eastern list price, type of cabinet, type and number of loud speakers, and references to notes giving other features of each receiver, as listed below.

COLUMN HEADINGS - ABBREVIATIONS - SYMBOLS - NOTES

P - POWER; A-AC (60 cycles); U - Universal, AC or DC; B -.Battery: C-DC
    Star means 25 cycle model is also available
T - Number of tubes, (excluding ballast tube)
C - CIRCUIT: N - Neutrodyne REG - Regenerative
    SH - Superheterodyne
    TRF - Tuned Radio Frequency

TUBES - Underlining means two tubes are used
RADIO - Number and type of RF amplifier tubes
D - Type of 1st Detector
O - Type of Oscillator (Star means function is performed by 1st Detector)
IF - Number and type of IF amplifier tubes
2nd - Type of 2nd Detector (W - Wunderlich)
1st - Type of 1st AF amplifier tube
OUT. - Number and type of AF Output Tubes (In Push-Pull unless otherwise noted)
RECT. - Type of Rectifier tube
AVC - Type of tube used for AVC (Star means function if performed by 2nd Detector)
NS - Type of tube used for noise suppression

R - RANGE;
B - Broadcast	200 -	550 m.
L - Long Wave	550 -	2000 m.
P - All Police & Television,	75 -	200 m.
p - One Police Band	150 -	200 m.
S - Short Wave	15 -	200 m.

CONT. - CONTROL
A - Automatic tone compensation
N - Automatic noise suppression
R - Remote Control, electrical or mechanical
T - Manual tone control
U - Automatic selectivity adjustment
V - Automatic Volume Control

TUNING: D - Vernier Drive Dial
G - Four dials in one.
M - Resonance Indicator
Q - Full Vision Dial
S - Hair-line Shadow Dial
    Suffix 3 or 4, 3 or 4 gang condenser

MODEL NUMBER AND NAME: Star preceding number means chassis is available in different cabinets.
PRICE: First advertised Eastern price with tubes. Star indicates price is without tubes.

CAB. - CABINET STYLE

A. - Automobile Radio
BB - Book-Back Table Model
BC - Bookcase with Clock
BR - Bar and Radio
C - Console
ch - Chassis only
CL - Consolette
CM - Console or Midget
CN - Column
CP - Compact
CT - Console Table
D - Desk-type Floor Cabinet
GC - Grandfather Clock
HB - Highboy
HT - Home Talkie
K - Kit
LB - Lowboy
LP - Portable Lowboy
M - Mantle or Midget
m - Metal
NC - Mantle or Midget with Clock
ML - Metal Locker
Mn - Miniature.
MP - Midget Radio Phonograph
MS - Midget or Chest
PA - Portable and Automobile
PN - Radio Piano
Pr - Portable
R - Rack
RP - Radio Phonograph Combination
SS - Smoking Stand
St - Chest
T - Table Model

SPKR. - TYPE AND NUMBER OF LOUD SPEAKERS

D - Dynamic
M - Magnetic
D-M - Dynamic or Magnetic
PD - Permanent Magnetic Dynamic
Number indicates number of speakers
Star indicates speaker costs extra

NOTES.

a   Price less batteries or power pack
b   Phonograph optional at extra cost

---

d   Class B amplification
e   Early model
f   Late model
g   Phonograph Pick-up connection
h1   Also has one '24 type tube in RF amplifier
h2   "   "   "   '27 "   "   " RF   "
h3   "   "   "   '57 "   "   " AF   "
h4   "   "   "   '24 "   "   " IF   "
h5   "   "   "   '36 "   "   " IF   " *
h6   "   "   "   '56 "   "   " AVC
h7   additional '24 short-wave detector,
     '35 untuned RF and '27 oscillator.
h8   "   one '37 type tube in RF amplifier.
h9   "   a voltage regulator tube
lh   "   one '80 type tube in rectifier
2h   "   one '827 type tube in AF amplifier
3h   One RF amplifier stage is untuned
4h   Also has one '58 type tube in oscillator,
     '58 in 1st AF, and '80 in rectifier.
5h   "   one '27 type tube in oscillator
6h   "   "   '57   "   "   as 1st Detector
7h   "   "   '58   "   "   in 4th RF stage
8h   "   "   '56   "   "   as voltage regulator.
9h   "   "   '58   "   "   as phase changer
ha   "   "   '35   "   "   in AVC
hb   "   "   '27   "   "   "
hc   "   "   '56   "   "   as harmonic generator
hd   Has four untuned RF stages
he   Also has two '56 type tubes in AF Amplifier
hf   Early models use two '45 tubes in AF output.
j   Uses one or more Spray-shield tubes
k   AF output tubes are two in parallel
l   Interchangeable with "24" series at $7.50 extra.
n   Automatic Phonograph
pa   Police-automotive
pl   AF output tubes in parallel push-pull
ps   Police station type
q   Converter
ql   Adapter
r   Local-Distance switch
s   Single Band-Selector switch
tr   Television Receiver
ts   Television Scanner only
trs Television receiver and scanner
u   For use with headphones
v   Tuner only

REPRODUCED DIRECTLY FROM RALPH H. LANGLEY'S ORIGINAL LISTING.

P	T	C	RADIO	INTERMEDIATE D	O	IF	AUDIO D	1st	OUT.	RECT.	AVC	NS	R	CONT	TUNING	MODEL NUMBER AND NAME	PRICE	CAB.	SPKR.	NOTE

ACME MFG. CO. — MIAMISBURG, OHIO — "ACME" (1932)
1 Chassis — 2 Models — 5 to 6 Tubes — $ -- to $ --

P	T	C	RADIO	D	O	IF	D	1st	OUT.	RECT.	AVC	NS	R	CONT	TUNING	MODEL NUMBER AND NAME	PRICE	CAB.	SPKR.	NOTE
B	5	--	--			1-56,1-57		1-41,	2-44				B	V		Moto Midget	--	A	--	-
B	6	--	--			1-56,1-57		2-41,	2-44				B	VR		DeLuxe	--	A	--	-

ADVANCE ELEC. CO. — LOS ANGELES, CAL. — "FALCK" (1931)
1 Chassis — 1 Model — 4 Tubes — $ --

P	T	C	RADIO	D	O	IF	D	1st	OUT.	RECT.	AVC	NS	R	CONT	TUNING	MODEL NUMBER AND NAME	PRICE	CAB.	SPKR.	NOTE
A	4	TRF	(1-24,1-51			1-47,1-80)							B	--	--	E	--	M	M	-

ADVANCE RADIO CORP. — CHICAGO, ILL. — "ADVANCE" (1931)
1 Chassis — 1 Model — 6 Tubes — $69.00

P	T	C	RADIO	D	O	IF	D	1st	OUT.	RECT.	AVC	NS	R	CONT	TUNING	MODEL NUMBER AND NAME	PRICE	CAB.	SPKR.	NOTE
B	6	TRF	(4-24,1-27,1-112)										B	R	--	Auto Radio	69.00	A	D	-

ALL AMERICAN MOHAWK CORP. — NORTH TONAWANDA, N.Y. — "LYRIC"
20 Chasses — 31 Models — 5 to 13 Tubes — $32.50 to $139.50

P	T	C	RADIO	D	O	IF	D	1st	OUT.	RECT.	AVC	NS	R	CONT	TUNING	MODEL NUMBER AND NAME	PRICE	CAB.	SPKR.	NOTE
A	6	TRF	3-24	--	--	--	24	--	1-45	80	--	--	B	--	--	J-3	69.50	M	D	o
A	6	TRF	3-24	--	--	--	24	--	1-47	80	--	4	B	T	--	J-8	89.50	CL	D	o
A	6	SH	--	24	27	1-35	24	--	1-47	80	--	--	B	T	--	J-3	69.50	M	D	f
B	6	SH	1-32	32	30	1-32	32	--	1-33	--	--	--	B	T	--	J-8	89.50	CL	D	f
A	6	SH	--	24	27	1-35	24	--	1-47	80	--	--	B	T	--	P-4	69.50	M	CL	-
																P-8	89.60	CL	D	-
B	7	TRF	1-35	24	27	(5-32 or 30)	24	--	2-31	80	--	--	B	--	--	P-9	99.50	O	A	-
A	7	SH	1-35	24	27	1-35	24	--	1-47	80	--	--	B	T	--	S-6	49.50	M	A	-
A	8	SH	1-35	24	27	1-35	27	--	2-47	80	--	--	B	T	--	B7	72.50	M	A	-
A	9	SH				(1-24,2-27,3-35)			2-47	80	--	--	B	VT	--	B34	99.50	LB	-	-
										80	--	--	B	VT	--	S-61	69.50	C	D	-
										80	--	--	B	VT	--	S-62	89.50	GC	--	-
A	10	SH	--	--	--	--	--	--	2-47	80	--	--	B	--	--		--	M	PD	-
-		SH	--	--	--	--	--	--	--	--	--	--	B	--	--	S-7	69.50	M	A	-
														T		S-8	99.50	M	A	-
														T		S-9	119.50	O	A	-
																S-9	139.50	O	A	-
																S-10	139.50	O	A	-
																	--	PN	--	-
A	5	SH	--	--	--	--	--	--	--	--	--	--	B	T	--	S-50	32.50	M	D	-
A	5	SH	--	--	--	--	--	--	--	--	--	--	B	T	--	S-51	42.50	O	D	-

													Model	Price		
A	6	SH	1-58	57	*	--	1-47	80	*	--	B	VT	SA-65	42.50	M D	--
D	6	SH	1-39	36	*	--	2-33	--	--	--	B	VT	SA-66	49.95	LB D	--
D	7	SH	1-36	36	37	--	2-33	--	--	--	B	--	DC65	47.50	M --	--
D	8	SH	1-34	32	30	30	2-30	--	--	--	F	T	DC65	49.50	-- M	--
A	8	SH	--	57	56	57	1-47	80	--	--	BS	--	DC57	*89.50	LB HB	--
A	9	3H	1-58	57	56	56	2-47	80	*	--	B	VT	B-57	84.50	HB D	--
A	13	SH	1-58	57	56	56	2-58	2-47	82	57	B	VTN	SW-80	69.50	HB D	--
													SA-90	74.50	C D	--
													SA-91	139.50	C D2	--
													SA-130			

ALLIED RADIO CORP. — (1931) 3 Models   CHICAGO, ILL.   3 Chasses

											Model	Price		
A	5	TRF	--	--	--	--	--	--	B	--	Roemer	34.75	M K	--
A	5	TRF	--	--	--	--	--	--	B	--		48.25	C K	--
A	--	--	--	--	--	--	--	--	B	--		49.95	A oh	--

$34.75 to $49.95

ALLIED ENGINEERING INSTITUTE "FIND-ALL" (1931) 3 Models   NEW YORK CITY   2 Chasses   5 to 8 Tubes   6 to 7 Tubes

											Model	Price		
A	6	--	--	(5-24,1-45,1-80)	--	--	--	--	P	--	FA	49.50	K tr.	--
A	7	--	--	--	--	--	--	--	P	--	FA	69.50	oh tr.	--

$49.50 to $69.50

AMERICAN RADIO & TELEVISION CO. (1932) 2 Models   LOS ANGELES, CAL.   1 Chassis   4 Tubes

									Model	Price		
4	--	(1-47,1-57,1-58,1-82)	--	--	--	--	B	--	61	14.95	st tr.	--
							BP	--	62 Music Box	17.50	st --	--

$14.95 to $17.50

ANSLEY RADIO LABS. "ANSLEY UNIVERSAL" 2 Models   NEW YORK CITY   2 Chasses   4 and 8 Tubes

										Model	Price		
U	4	TRF	3-24	--	--	24	27	2-45	80	B	T	U-1	89.50	C D
U*	8	SH	1-39	39	37	1-39	85	2-89	80	*	VN	U-9	79.50	Pr. D

$79.50 to $89.50

ARTLIN CO., THE (1932) 1 Model   NEW YORK CITY   1 Chassis   7 Tubes

						Model	Price		
--	7	TRF	(3-24,1-27,2-45,1-80)	--	--	779	16.00	ch D	--

$16.00

ATCHISON RADIO MFG. CO. — ATCHISON, KAN. — Price not known. (1931) Tubes not known.

1 Chassis — 1 Model

P	T	C	RADIO	D	O	IF	D	1st	OUT.	RECT.	AVC	NS	R	CONT	TUNING	MODEL NUMBER AND NAME	PRICE	CAB.	SPKR.	NOTE
A	-	TRF	-	-	-	-	-	-	-	-	-	-	B	-	-	-	-	M	-	-

ATLANTIC RADIO CORP. — BROOKLYN, N.Y. — $16.00 to $31.00 (1931) 5 and 7 Tubes

3 Chasses — 5 Models

P	T	C	RADIO	D	O	IF	D	1st	OUT.	RECT.	AVC	NS	R	CONT	TUNING	MODEL NUMBER AND NAME	PRICE	CAB.	SPKR.	NOTE
A	5	TRF	-	-	-	-	-	-	-	-	-	-	B	-	T	3LAC	16.00	N	D	-
A*	5	TRF	2-35	24	-	-	24	-	1-47	80	-	-	B	-	T	-	31.00	GC	D	-
A	7	TRF	-	-	-	-	-	-	-	-	-	-	B	-	-	-	18.00	M	D	-

"ATWATER KENT" — ATWATER KENT MFG. CO. — PHILADELPHIA, PA. — $41.25 to $159.00 — 4 to 12 Tubes

27 Chasses — 49 Models

P	T	C	RADIO	D	O	IF	D	1st	OUT.	RECT.	AVC	NS	R	CONT	TUNING	MODEL NUMBER AND NAME	PRICE	CAB.	SPKR.	NOTE
A	6	SH	--	24	27	1-24	24	--	1-47	80	--	--	B	--	E	84 - Golden Voice	69.50	Cp	D	e
A	6	SH	--	35	27	1-35	24	--	1-47	80	--	--	B	--	E	84 - Golden Voice	69.50	Cp	D	f
A*		SH	--		37		36	37	1-33		--	--	B	--	E	83	89.00	LB	D	-
D	6	SH	--	36	27	1-36	24	--	1-47	80	24	--	B	--	VT	80	62.80	M	-
A*	7	SH	--		30		32	30	1-33		--	--	B	--	VT	82-D	74.80	M	D	-
B	7	SH	1-32	32	30	1-33	32	30	1-33	--	--	--	B	--	VT	82	69.80	M	D	-
B	7	TRF	3-36	32	30	2-32	32	30	1-33	--	--	--	B	--	E	82-P	69.80	M	D	-
B	7	SH	1-36	36	-i	1-36	37	58	2-38	--	37	--	B	--	V	85	99.00	LB	D	-
D	8	SH	1-35	55	37	1-35	36	--	2-33	--	37	--	B	--	VT	82-Q	94.80	M	PD	-
A	9	SH	1-35	35	27	1-33	24	--	1-47	80	24	--	B	--	T	84-Q	94.50	M	PD	-
A*	10	SH	1-35	35	27	1-35	27	27	2-47	80	24	--	B	--	VT	85-Q	121.00	LB	D	-
A		SH											B		VT	81	89.50	A	D	-
A*	7	SH											B			87-D	-	-	D	-
A*	7	SH											B		--	86	99.00	HB	D	-
A*	7	SH											B		--	87	115.00	LB	D	-
A*	7	SH											B		--	87	125.00	HB	D	-
A	8	SH											B		--	89	132.00	HB	D	-
A		SH											B		--	89-P	169.00	RP	D	-
A*	7	SH	--	35	27	1-35	24	--	1-47	80	24	--	B	--	VT	82	74.50	T	D	-
A*	7	SH	--	35	27	1-35	24	--	1-27	80	--	--	B	--	E	90	49.50	Cp	D	-
A*	7	SH											B		E	94	69.00	LB	D	-
A*	7	SH											B		E	94	79.00	M	D	-
A*	7	SH	1-58	58	56	1-58	55	--	1-47	80	*	--	B	--	T	567	49.50	M	D	r
A*	7	SH											Bp	Q4	VT	627	53.90	Cp	D	-
A	8	SH	1-35	35	27	1-35	24	--	1-47	80	27	--	B	--	VT	92	59.50	Cp	D	r

AUDIOLA RADIO CO.   CHICAGO, ILL.

"AUDIOLA"

15 Chasses   25 Models   4 to 11 Tubes $26.50 to $119.50

	Tubes	Type	Det						Out			B	VT	Model		Price	Code	
A	4	TRF	1-35	--	--	24	--	--	1-47	80	--	B	--	416	--	37.50	M	-
A	5	TRF	2-35	--	--	24	--	--	1-47	80	--	B	--	506	--	43.95	M	-
A	6	TRF	2-35	--	--	24	27	27	1-47	80	--	B	--	610	--	*48.00	LB	-
A	7	SH	1-35	24	27	24	1-35	--	1-47	80	24	Bp	VT	612	--	*60.00	M	-
A	8	SH	1-35	24	27	24	1-35	--	1-47	80	--	B	--	710	--	54.50	M	-
														712		69.95	LB	-
A	9	SH	1-35	24	27	24	1-35	27	1-47	80	27	Bp	--	714	--	79.95	M	-
														810		*57.00	LB	-
B	5	TRF	--	--	--	(1-36,1-37,2-39,2-39,1-85,1-89,1-BR)			--	--	--	--	--	812	--	*69.50	M	-
B	7	SH	--	--	56	56	--	--	--	--	*	SB	--	814	--	89.00	LB	-
A	8	SH	1-58	57	56	1-58	56	56	1-47	80	--	B	VT	914	--		C	-
A	10⁻¹	SH	--	24	27	1-27	--	--	--	80	--	SB	--	67-10AW (All Wave)	--	89.50	C	-

		Price	Code
416		37.50	M
506		43.95	M
610		*48.00	LB
612		*60.00	M
710		54.50	M
712		69.95	LB
714		79.95	M
810		*57.00	LB
812		*69.50	M
814		*76.50	LB
914		89.00	C
517		29.95	SB
867		69.50	C
811		49.95	M
843		56.50	HB
868		64.50	C
67-10AW (All Wave)		89.50	SB

(continued)

P	T	C	RADIO	INTERMEDIATE			AUDIO			RECT.	AVC	NS	R	CONT	TUNING	MODEL NUMBER AND NAME	PRICE	CAB.	SPKR.	NOTE
				D	O	IF	D	1st	OUT.											
			(Audiola)																	
A	10	SH	1-58	57	58	2-58	56	56	2-47	80	*	--	B	--	V	1011	56.50	M	D	--
A	11	SH	--	--	--	--	--	--	--	--		--	B	--	V	1050	56.50	LB	D	--
A	11	SH	--	--	--	--	--	--	--	--		--	B	--	V	1068	77.50	HB	D	--
A	-	-	--	--	--	--	--	--	--	--		--	B	--	VT	11300DN	109.50	HB	D2	--
													B	--	V.	1168	99.50	LB	D	--
													B	--	V	11200D	119.50	HB	D2	--
													S	--	--	22	26.50	T	--	q

AUTOCRAT RADIO CO., 7 Models   CHICAGO, ILL. $13.95 to $34.50

6 Chasses   (1932)   4 to 6 Tubes

P	T	C	RADIO	INTERMEDIATE			AUDIO			RECT.	AVC	NS	R	CONT	TUNING	MODEL	PRICE	CAB.	SPKR.	NOTE
A	4	-	-	--	--	--	--	--	--	--	--	--	B	--	--	2413G	13.95	K	--	--
A	4	TRF		(2-24,1-47,1-80)							--	--	B	--	--	24-CT	18.75	M	A	--
A	4	-		(1-47,1-57 1-58,1-80)							--	--	B	--	--	57	19.75	M	A	--
A	5	-		(1-47,3-57,1-80)							--	--	B	--	--	80	20.50	-	A	--
A	5	-		(3-24,1-47,1-80)							--	--	B	--	--	25-KS	22.50	-	A	--
B	6	TRF		(1-36,1-37 2-58,2-39)							--	--	B	R	H	-	21.50	A	•	--
																	34.90			

AUTOMATIC RADIO MFG. CO.   "TOM THUMB"   BOSTON, MASS. $29.50 to $79.50

9 Chasses   12 Models   4 to 6 Tubes

P	T	C	RADIO	INTERMEDIATE			AUDIO			RECT.	AVC	NS	R	CONT	TUNING	MODEL	PRICE	CAB.	SPKR.	NOTE
A	5	TRF	1-35	--	--	--	24	--	1-47	80	--	--	B	--	--	J25	29.50	M	A	--
A	5	-	--	--	--	--	(3-24,1-47,1-80)			--	--	--	-	--	--	P-55	39.50	M	A	s
U	5	TRF	--	--	--	--	(4-SG,1-45,1-80)			--	--	--	BL	--	--	*Universal	-	M	A	-
B	6	-	--	--	--	--	27	--	2-12A	--	--	--	-	--	--	JR	79.50	CL	-	h2
B	6	TRF	2-24	--	--	--	24	--	2-47	--	--	--	B	--	--	SR	74.50	A	-	--
B	6	TRF	3-24	--	--	--	24	--	1-47	80	--	--	B	--	--	V45	79.50	A	D	--
A	6	TRF	3-35	--	--	--					--	--	--	--	--	P45	59.50	A	D	--
																	68.50	MC	-	--
A	4	TRF	1-35	--	--	--	24	--	1-47	80	--	--	B	--	--	P25	29.50	M	D	--
A	5	-	--	(1-24,2-35 1-47,1-80)							--	--	-	--	--	P-35	34.50	M	D	--
A	6	TRF	3-35	--	24	--	--	--	1-47	80	--	--	B	--	--	V45	39.50	M	D	--
A	6	-	--	(1-47,1-57 3-58,1-80)							--	--	B	--	--	P-45	44.50	M	D	--

AZTEC RADIO CO.   "AZTEC" (1931)   6 Models   ATCHISON, KAN. $39.90 to $84.50

3 Chasses   5 to 9 Tubes

P	T	C	RADIO	INTERMEDIATE			AUDIO			RECT.	AVC	NS	R	CONT	TUNING	MODEL	PRICE	CAB.	SPKR.	NOTE
A	5	TRF	2-24	--	--	24	--	1-47	80	--	--	--	B	--	--	50	39.90	M	D	-

	No	Type														Model	Price			
A	7	SH	1-35	24	27	1-35	24	--	1-47	80	--	--	B	--	55	54.00	LB	D	
A	9	SH	1-35	24	27	2-35	27	--	1-47	80	27	--	B	--	70	54.50	M	D	
													B	--	75	72.00	HB	D	
													B	VT	90	69.50	M	D	
													B	VT	95	84.50	LB	D	

BALDER RADIO CORP. — 2 Chasses — 4 Models
"BALDER, KNICKERBOCKER" (1931) NEW YORK CITY $43.00 to $49.50 6 Tubes

	No	Type														Model	Price			
D	6	TRF	2-36	--	--	36	37	2-33	--	--	--	--	B	--	633C	43.00	ch	D	
A	6	TRF	2-35	--	--	--	--	1-47	80	--	1-47	80	B	--	633A	43.50	M	D	
															635C	43.00	ch	D	hl
															635A	49.50	M	D	

BALKEIT RADIO CO. — 9 Chasses — 9 Models
"BALKEIT" CHICAGO, ILL. $24.50 to $99.75 4 to 10 Tubes

	No	Type														Model	Price			
A	4	TRF	1-24	--	--	--	--	1-47	80	--	--	--	B	--	M	39.50	M		
A	5	TRF	2-24	--	--	--	--	1-47	80	--	--	--	B	--	KP	49.50	M	A	
A	6	TRF	2-24	--	--	--	--	2-47	80	--	--	--	*	--	DP	59.50	M	D	
A	6	SH	1-24	24	*	1-24	--	--	1-47	80	--	--	B	--	L	69.50	LB	D	
A	8	TRF	4-27	--	--	--	--	2-47	80	--	--	--	B	▷	Super C	--			
A	4	--	(1-47,1-57,1-58,1-80)										B	--	42E	24.50	M	A	
A	5	SH	(1-47,1-55,2-58,1-80)										B	--	52	29.50	L	-	
A	5	SH	(1-47,2-57,1-58,1-80)										B	▷	55	34.50	C	D	
A	10	SH	(3-58,56)	55	2-45	82	*						B		742	99.75	D	D	

BALTIMORE RADIO CORP. — 1 Chassis — 1 Model
(1932) NEW YORK CITY $13.35 5 Tubes

	No	Type								Model	Price		
A	5	TRF	(1-24,2-35)	1-47,1-80		B	--		R239	13.35	M	D	

BELMONT RADIO CORP. — 18 Chasses — 18 Models
"FRESHMAN-BELMONT" CHICAGO, ILL. $13.95 to $-- 4 to 11 Tubes

	No	Type														Model	Price			
-	4	TRF	1-35	--	--	24	--	1-47	80	--	--	--	B	--	40 (Series)	15.95	M	D	A
-	5	TRF	--	--	--	--	--	--	--	--	--	--	B	E	--	--	--	--	
-	6	TRF	--	--	--	--	--	--	--	--	--	--	B	E	--	--	--	--	
-	7	SH	--	--	--	--	--	--	--	--	--	--	B	E	--	--	--	--	
-	9	SH	--	--	--	--	--	--	--	--	--	--	B	E	--	--	--	--	
A	4	TRF	1-58	--	--	57	--	1-47	80	--	--	--	B	--	41-A	19.95	M	D	

(continued)

P	T	C	RADIO	INT D	INT O	INT IF	AUD D	AUD 1st	AUD OUT	RECT.	AVC	NS	R	CONT	TUNING	MODEL NUMBER AND NAME	PRICE	CAB.	SPKR.	NOTE
																(Belmont)				
D	4	TRF	1-39	--	--	--	36	37	1-38	--	--	--	B	--	--	45	24.50	M	D	-
A	5	SH	--	57	*	1-58	57	--	1-47	80	--	--	B	--	--	51-C	27.95	M	D	-
D	5	-	--	--	--	--	--	--	--	--	--	--	--	--	--	58	-	-	-	-
D	7	-	--	--	--	--	--	--	--	--	--	--	--	--	--	55-A	-	M	-	-
A	7	SH	1-58	57	56	1-58	55	--	1-47	80	*	--	B	VT	H	71-A	39.95	M	D	-
D	7	-	--	--	--	--	--	--	--	--	--	--	B	V	--	78	-	-	-	-
A	8	SH	1-36	39	36	1-39	W	57	38	BR	*	--	B	V	H	70-B	69.50	A	D	-
B	8	-	--	--	--	--	--	--	--	--	--	--	--	V	--	80-A	-	A	-	-
B	8	-	--	--	--	--	--	--	--	--	--	--	BS	V	--	80-B	-	C	D	-
A	10	SH	1-58	57	56	58	56	56	2-47	80	--	--	B	--	H	100-A	59.95	C	D	-
-	10	SH		(4-56,1-57,2-58,2-59,1-83)							--	--	B	--	IQ	1000-	-	C	D	-
-	11	SH	--	--	--	--	--	--	--	--	--	--	--	VT	--	110-B	-	LB	D2	-

BREMER-TULLY MFG. CO.   NEW YORK CITY   (1931)   7 Tubes

1 Chassis   1 Model $34.50

P	T	C	RADIO	INT D	INT O	INT IF	AUD D	AUD 1st	AUD OUT	RECT.	AVC	NS	R	CONT	TUNING	MODEL	PRICE	CAB.	SPKR.	NOTE
D	7	TRF	3-32	--	--	--	32	50	2-31	--	--	--	B	--	--	80	34.50	C	D	-

BROWN & MANHART   LOS ANGELES, CAL.   "ROAMER" (1931)   4 to 8 Tubes

4 Chassis   4 Models $29.50 to $69.50

P	T	C	RADIO	INT D	INT O	INT IF	AUD D	AUD 1st	AUD OUT	RECT.	AVC	NS	R	CONT	TUNING	MODEL	PRICE	CAB.	SPKR.	NOTE
A	4	TRF	1-51	--	--	--	24	--	1-47	80	--	--	B	--	--	50	29.50	M	D	-
A	5	TRF	2-51	--	--	--	24	--	1-47	80	--	--	B	--	--	55	39.50	M	D	-
A	6	TRF	2-51	--	--	--	24	27	1-47	80	--	--	B	V	--	44	69.50	T	D	-
B	8	TRF	3-36	--	--	--	37	37	2-38	--	37	--	S	--	--	-	69.50	A	-	-

BRUNSWICK RADIO CORP.   CHICAGO, ILL.   "BRUNSWICK" (1931)   5 to 11 Tubes

5 Chasses   11 Models $39.50 to $265.00

P	T	C	RADIO	INT D	INT O	INT IF	AUD D	AUD 1st	AUD OUT	RECT.	AVC	NS	R	CONT	TUNING	MODEL	PRICE	CAB.	SPKR.	NOTE
A	5	TRF	2-51	--	--	--	24	--	1-47	80	--	--	B	--	--	10	39.50	M	A	·
A*	7	TRF	3-24	--	--	--	24	--	2-45	80	--	--	B	--	--	15	139.50	LB	A	k
A*	7												B	T	--	42	265.00	C	A	1k
A*	7	SH	1-51	24	24	1-51	24	--	1-47	80	--	--	B	T	--	11	79.50	M	A	·
A*													B	T	--	12	99.50	HB	A	·
													B	T	--	16	119.50	LB	A	f
													B	T	--	18	-	-	A	·
A	9	SH	1-51	24	24	1-51	24	--	2-47	80	27	--	B	T	--	33	169.50	RP	A	·
													-	VT	--	17	149.50	LB	A	·
													BS	VT	--	24	169.50	HB	A	k
-	11	SH		(5-24,2-47,2-$1,5-54,1-80)							--	--		VT	--	25	225.00	HB	-	·

200

CAPEHART CORP. — FORT WAYNE, IND. — $169.50 to $1,123.
10 Chasses — 7 to 14 Tubes — 19 Models

	Tubes															Model	Price	Op	Cp
																2			
	7	TRF	3-24				2-45									5 Junior	225.00	RP	pl
A	8	SH	1-51	27	27		2-47	80	56	57	B				15	262.00	RP	pl
A	13	SH	1-51	27	27	2-45	4-45	80	56	57	B	E			20	275.65	RP	pl
A	13	SH	1-51	27	24	4-47	80				B	E			21	1125	RP	pl
												E			400	1123	RP	pl
															400	1023	RP	pl
															401	973.45	RP	pl
															402			
A	9	SH	58	57	2-58	2-47	80	56	57	BS	V		1		169.50	LB	D
A	10	SH	58	57	2-58	2-47	80	57		BS	VN		10 Combinaire		234.50	RP	
										BS	VN		11 Combinaire		234.50	RP	
										BS	VN		12 Combinaire		279.50	RP	
A	11	SH	1-58	58	1-58	2-47	80	56		B	VN	M	14		299.50	RP	
										B	VN		200		495.00	RP	
										B	VN	M	300		675.00	RP	
A	14	SH	1-58	58	2-58	4-75	80	56	57	B	VN	M	400			RP	
										B	VN	M	400-A	895.00	RP	
										B	VN	M	402-A	875.00	RP	

CARDINAL RADIO MPG. CO. — "CARDINAL" (1931) — LOS ANGELES, CAL. — $59.50 to $105.50
7 Chasses — 5 to 9 Tubes — 8 Models

	Tubes							Model	Price	Op	Cp
A	5	TRF	2-35	--	--	1-47	80	B	82	--	
A	5	SH	--	--	--	--	--	B	E	--	
A	6	SH	(2-24,1-27,1-47,1-51,1-80)					B	66	59.50	M	D
A	6	SHP	--					B	72	105.50	RP	D
A	8	TRF	(4-24,1-27,1-45,1-80)					B	91	69.50	M	D
A	9	SH	(3-24,3-27,2-45,1-80)					B	60	74.50	M	D
A	9	--						B	71	99.50	MP	D

CARTERET RADIO LABS. — "CARTERET" (1931) — NEW YORK CITY — $ -- to $ --
3 Chasses — 6 Tubes — 3 Models

	Tubes									Model	Op
B	6	TRF	2-37	--	--	36	37	2-33	B	AR35	A
A	6	TRF	2-35	--	--	24	--	1-47	80	B	635	M
D	6	--	1-36	36	36	37	--	2-38	B	638	M

Ca

P	T	C	RADIO	INT. D	INT. O	IF	AUD. D	1st	OUT.	RECT.	AVC	NS	R	CONT.	TUNING	MODEL NUMBER AND NAME	PRICE	CAB.	SPKR.	NOTE
																CENTURY RADIO PRODUCTS CO. CHICAGO, ILL.				
																"CENTURY" 4 to 7 Tubes	$ -- to $ --			
																9 Chasses				
◄	4	TRF	1-24	--	--	--	24	--	1-47	80	--	--	B	--	--	4-47	22.50	M	A	--
◄	5	TRF	2-24	--	--	--	24	--	1-47	80	--	--	B	--	--	4-47C	-	MC	A	--
D	5	TRF	2-24	--	--	--	27	--	2-47	--	--	--	B	--	--	5-47	30.00	M	A	--
B	5	TRF	2-35	--	--	--	36	57	1-58	--	--	--	-	--	--	5-47	42.50	M	A	--
																A-5	45.00	A	A	--
																A-6	55.00	A	A	--
◄	4	TRF	1-58	--	--	--	57	--	1-47	1-47	--	--	B	--	--	4-78	--	M	A	--
◄	5	TRF	2-24	--	--	--	24	--	1-47	80	--	--	B	--	--	5-47	--	M	A	--
													BP			5-47-SW	--	M	A	--
D	5	TRF	2-59	--	--	--	33	--	2-38	--	--	--	B	--	--	5-58	--	M	A	--
◄	6	TRF	3-58	--	--	--	55	--	1-47	80	--	--	B	--	--	6-55	--	M	A	--
B	7	TRF	3-59	--	--	--	37	57	2-38	--	--	--	-	--	--	7-58	--	A	A	--
																CIAGO RADIO CORP. CHICAGO, ILL.				
																"MAYFLOWER" (1931) 6 to 8 Tubes	$34.50 to $69.50			
																3 Chasses				
◄	6	SH	--	24	27	1-35	27	--	1-47	80	--	--	B	--	--	61	34.50	M	A	--
◄	7	SH	1-55	24	27	1-55	27	--	1-47	80	--	--	B	--	--	67	44.50	LB	A	--
◄	8	SH	1-35	24	27	1-35	27	--	2-47	80	--	--	B	--	--	72	44.50	M	A	--
													--			73	54.50	LB	A	--
													--			84	64.50	HB	A	--
													--			95	89.50	HB	A	--
																COLONIAL RADIO CORP. BUFFALO, N.Y.				
																"COLONIAL" 5 to 12 Tubes	$31.95 to $99.50			
																15 Chasses				
◄	5	TRF	2-24	--	--	--	24	--	1-45	80	--	--	B	--	--	39	49.95	M	A	--
◄	6	TRF	2-24	--	--	--	24	--	2-45	80	--	--	B	--	--	36C	*69.50	MC	A	--
													B	--	T	41C	99.50	GC	A	--
A*	6	SH	--	24	27	1-35	24	--	1-47	80	--	--	B	--	T	44	59.95	M	A	--
◄	8	SH	1-35	35	27	1-35	24	--	2-47	80	--	--	B	--	T	47	79.95	LB	A	--
													B	--	T	47H	*99.50	HB	A	--
													B	--	T	47L	*69.95	LB	A	--
													B	--	T	47M	*84.50	HB	A	--
													B	--	T	48	49.95	M	A	--
													B	--	T	48A	*54.50	A	A	--
◄													B	--	--	220	31.95	M	-	--

COLUMBIA PHONOGRAPH CO. INC. "COLUMBIA" NEW YORK CITY $38.50 to $325.00

18 Chasses — 25 Models — 5 to 12 Tubes

Grp	Tubes	Type									B	T		Model	Code	Price	D	d
A	5	SH	2-51	--	--	--	--	24	--	1-47	80	B	T	--	399	M	34.50	D	--
A	6	SH	1-51	--	--	--	--	24	--	1-47	80	B	V	--	C-599	C	39.90	D	--
A	6	SH	--	--	--	--	--	--	--	--	4-39	B	I	--	C-495	M	49.50	D	--
A	8	--	--	--	--	--	--	36	37	--	--	B	V	--	240	C	41.95	D	--
A	9	SH	--	--	--	--	--	--	--	--	--	B	I	--	C-595	C	59.52	D	--
A	10	SH	--	--	--	--	--	--	--	--	--	B	V	--	280	-	52.95	D	--
A	12	SH	--	--	--	--	--	--	--	--	--	B	I	--	C-495	C	69.50	D	--
A	12	SH	--	--	--	--	--	--	--	1-53	1-47	B	V	--	280	C	73.95	D	--
A	12	SH	--	--	--	--	--	--	--	--	--	B	--	--	C-995	C	99.50	D	--

Grp	Tubes	Type									B	T		Model	Code	Price	D	g
A	5	TRF	2-51	--	--	24	--	1-47	80	--	B	T	--	C-31	M	--	D	--
A	7	SH	1-51	51	27	24	--	1-47	80	--	B	T	--	C-32	C	67.50	D	--
D A	8	TRF	2-36	--	--	36	37	4-39	--	--	B	T	--	C-33	LB	87.50	D	--
A	8	--	--	--	--	--	--	--	--	--	B	--	--	C-34	C	89.50	D	--
A	8	--	--	--	--	--	--	--	--	--	B	--	--	+		145.00	D	--
A	8	--	--	--	--	--	--	--	--	--	B	--	--	C-20	LB	185.00	D	--
A	6	SH	--	--	--	--	--	--	--	--	--	B	--	--	C-21	HB	235.00	D	--
A	6	SH	--	--	--	--	--	--	--	--	--	B	--	--	939	RP	--	D	--
A	6	SH	--	--	--	--	--	--	--	--	--	BS	--	--	991	RP	325.00	D	--
A	6	SH	1-32	32	30	32	--	1-32	--	--	B	VT	--	C-53	Cp	44.95	D	--
A	7	SH	1-58	58	56	55	--	1-58	--	--	B	VT	M	C-59	LB	59.95	D	--
B A	8	SH	1-58	58	56	4	--	1-58	--	--	B	VT	S	C-54	LB	84.95	D	--
A										All Wave		VT	--	C-559	RP	84.95	D	--
A											B	T	M	C-125	C	99.80	D	--
A											B	VTN	M	C-103	IB	99.80	D2	9h
A											B	VTN	M	C-81	Cp	49.80	D	9h
A											B	T	--	C-83	LB	54.50	D	9h
A	9	SH	--	--	--	--	--	--	--	--	--	B	--	--	C-84	HB	66.00	D	9h
A	11	SH	1-58	58	56	4	--	1-58	82	57	B	--	--	C-85	RP	88.00	D2	--
A											B	--	--	C-256	LB	108.00	A	--
A	12	SH	--	--	--	--	--	--	--	--	--	B	--	--	C-93	LB	84.50	A	--
A											S	--	--	C-93	HB	89.50	A	--
A											--	--	C-95	HB	89.50	--	--
A											--	--	C-223	HB	139.00	--	--
A											--	--	C-12	RP	890.00	D2	--
												--	--	--	-	38.50	--	--

COMMONWEALTH RADIO MFG. CO. "AJAX" CHICAGO, ILL. $-- to $79.50

9 Chasses — 15 Models — 5 to 12 Tubes

Grp	Tubes	Type									B			Model	Code	Price	A	
B	5	TRF	2-24	--	--	--	--	01A -- 2-12A (continued)	--	--	B	--	--	--	A	--	79.50	A	--

P	T	C	RADIO	INTERMEDIATE D	O	IF	AUDIO D	1st	OUT.	RECT.	AVC	NS	R	CONT	TUNING	MODEL NUMBER AND NAME	PRICE	CAB.	SPKR.	NOTE
			(Commonwealth)																	
A	6	TRF	3-24	--	--	--	24	--	1-45	80	--		B		--	13	--	M	D	.
A	6	TRF											B		--	14	--	C	D	.
A	6	TRF											B		--	51	--	LB	D	.
A	6	TRF											B		--	53	--	RP	D	.
A	6	SH	--	24	27	1-35	27	--	1-47	80	--	--	B		--	16	49.75	M	D	.
				(4-24,2-27,1-80)									B			91	--	EB	D	.
A	9	SH											B		--	92	--	HB	D	.
													B		--	93	--	RP	D	.
A	9	SH	1-35	24	27	1-35	27	--	2-47	80	--	--	B		--	19	84.50	M	D	.
A	12	SH											B		--	29	84.50	LB	D	.
A	-	-											B	▷	--	Super Master	67.50	C	D	.
A	-	-											B	T	--	The Mars	55.70	M	D	.
													B		--	Cub Midget	49.75	M	D	.
A	8	SH		(1-24,3-27,2-35,1-47,1-80)									B	T		The Roosevelt	-	M	D	.

CONSOLIDATED RADIO MFG. CO. — 3 Chasses — 3 Models
"MISSION" (1931) LOS ANGELES, CAL. 4 to 6 Tubes $23.50 to $49.50

A	4	TRF	--	--	--	--	--	--	1-45	80	--	--	B		--	--	29.50	M	D	--
A	6	SH	--	--	--	--	--	--	--	--	--	--	B	T	--	--	44.50	M	D	--
-	-	-	--	--	--	--	--	--	--	--	--	--	3		--	Mission (converter)	49.50	M	-	q

CORDONIC MFG. CO. — 2 Models
"GENEVA" (1931) HOLLAND, MICH. 7 Tubes $69.50 to $84.50

1 Chassis

A	7	TRF		(4-24,1-27,1-80)					1-45,1-80							38	69.50	M	D	
																	84.50	GL	D	

CORONADO MFG. CO. — 2 Models
"CORONADO" (1932) ST. PAUL, MINN. 5 Tubes $36.00

1 Chassis

A	5	TRF	2-35	--	--	--	24	--	1-45	80	--	--	B		--	Three Star	36.00	M	D	--
													B			Treasure Chest	36.00	M	D	--

COSMOTONE INC. — 1 Model
"COSMOTONE" (1931) NEW YORK CITY 7 Tubes $295.00

1 Chassis

CRESCENT RADIO MFG. CO. "CRESCENT" MINNEAPOLIS, MINN. $59.50 to 398.00

7 Chasses   11 Models   6 and 7 Tubes

														Car Electric			
U 6	TRF	3-24	--	--	--	--	24	--	1-71A	80	B	--	--	--	69.50	PA	--	--
U 7	TRF	3-24	--	--	--	--	24	27	1-71A	80	B	--	--	--	59.50	PA	--	--
B 7	TRF	4-32	--	--	--	--	30	30	1-33	--	B	--	--	--	78.00	M	--	--
											B				79.50	LB	--	--
											B				98.00	LB	--	--

														Car Electric			
U 7	TRF	3-24	--	--	--	--	24	27	1-47	80	BP	--	--		59.50	PA	--	--
B 7	TRF	3-24	--	--	--	--	32	30	2-30	80	B	--	--	M-2	59.50	M	--	--
D 7	TRF	3-32	--	--	--	--	32	30	2-33	--	B	--	--	2-70	79.50	LB	D	D
											B			32-70	88.00	LB	D	D
											B			M-32	73.00	M	D	D

CROSLEY RADIO CORP. CINCINNATI, OHIO $19.99 to $199.50

38 Chasses   80 Models   2 to 12 Tubes

A 5	TRF	2-24	--	--	--	24	--	1-45	80	B	--	Elf	37.50	M	D	--
A* 5	TRF	2-35	--	--	--	24	--	1-47	80	B	--	Buddy Boy	59.50	M	D	--
										B	--	Buddy	64.50	HC	D	--
A* 5	SH	--	24	*	24	--	1-47	80	B	3	Pal	74.50	T	D	1
										B	--	Mate	79.50	C	D	--
B 6	TRF	2-32	--	--	38	31	2-31	--	B	--	New Classmate	85.50	C	D	--
A 7	TRF	2-24	--	--	24	27	2-45	80	B	--	Wight	39.50	M	D	--
										B	--	Johnny Smoker	47.50	SS	D	--
D 7	SH	1-36	1-36	37	37	--	2-71A	--	B	T	59 Show Boy	49.50	M	D	--
A* 8	SH	1-24	1-24	27	27	--	2-45	80	B	--	59 Sonneteer	59.50	C	D	--
										B	--	59 Songster	79.50	M	D	--
										B	--	59 Oracle	99.50	GC	D	--
A* 8	SH	1-35	1-35	24	24	--	2-47	80	B	V	125-N Litlfella	36.36	LB	D	--
A* 8	SH	1-35	1-35	27	27	--	2-47	80	B	V	125 Litlboy	48.50	M	D	--
										B	V	28-N	47.50	M	D	--
										B	--	Director	107.59	C	D	--
										B	T	New Administrator	112.50	C	D	--
										B	T	Arbiter	137.50	ch	D	--
										B	T	126-1 -	Note			--
										B	T	120 Sup.-Administrator	109.50	C	D	--
										B	T	120 Super-Rondeau	119.50	C	D	--
										B	T	120 Super-Sondo	189.50	C	D	--
										B	T	123 Super Buddy Boy	65.00	M	D	--
										B	--	123 Musicale	94.50	C	D	--
										B	--	124-H Play Boy	49.75	M	D	--

(continued)

P	T	C	RADIO	INTERMEDIATE			AUDIO			RECT.	AVC	NS	R	CONT	TUNING	MODEL NUMBER AND NAME	PRICE	CAB.	SPKR.	NOTE
				D	O	IF	D	1st	OUT.											
			(Crosley)																	
A*	8	SH	1-35	24	27	1-35	27	--	2-47	80	--	--	B	H	--	124-J Cheerio	65.00	HB	D	--
													B	H	--	124-K Merry Maker	75.00	HB	D2	--
													B	H	--	124-L Announcer	85.00	HB	D2	--
A*	10	SH	1-35	24	24	1-35	27	27	2-47	80	27	--	B	H	--	124-M Playtime	95.00	GC	D	--
													B	VT	--	121-A Minstrel	129.50	HB	D	--
A*	10	SH	2-35	35	24	1-24	27	27	2-47	80	*	--	B	VT	--	121-A Troubadour	199.50	HB	D	--
													B	VT	--	121-IC Minstrel	129.50	HB	D	--
A*	10	SH	1-35	35	27	1-35	27	27	2-47	80	*	--	B	VT	--	121-ID Troubadour	199.50	RP	D	--
B	5	TRF	2-24	--	--	--	24	12A	1-12A	--	--	--	B	VT	M	127 Tenstrike	69.50	M	D	h4
B	6	TRF	2-36	--	--	--	36	57	1-71	--	56	--	B	VT	M	127 Happy Hour	99.50	C	D2	h4
A	3	-		--	--	(1-24,1-70,1-80)							B	V	M	127-1 Happy Hour	109.50	O	D	h4
													B			92 Roamio	59.50	A	--	--
													B			Roamio	49.00	A	--	--
													S			7-IF Adapter		-	--	g1
U	4	TRF			(1-36,1-38,1-39,1-R)		--	--	--	--	--	--	B			Totem	19.99	Pr	A	--
A	4	SH			--	--	--	--	--	--	--	--	B			Pup	25.00	Cpm	A	--
A	4	SH		*	--	--	--	--	--	--	--	--	B			131 Tynamite	28.75	M	A	--
A	4	SH			(1-24,1-35,1-47,1-80)		--	--	--	--	--	--	B			Bonniboy	39.75	LB	A	--
A	5	SH		24	*	1-58	57	--	1-47	80	--	--	B	V		Vagabond	29.25	Stm	A	--
													B			141 Nomad	32.50	St	A	--
A	5	SH		24	*	1-58	57	--	1-47	80	--	--	B	E		141 Bigfella	43.49	C	A	--
													B	E		141 Playtime Jr.	79.75	GC	A	D2
A	5	SH		58	*	1-58	57	--	1-42	80	--	--	B	E		148 Fiver	19.99	M	A	--
													B	E		148 Fiver Lowboy	29.99	C	A	--
													Bp	E		Book Case	34.75	BB	A	--
													Bp	E		Jewel Case	34.95	CT	A	--
A	6	SH		24	*	1-58	57	--	2-42	80	--	--	Bp	E	D	Sextet	34.95	M	A	--
													Bp		S	129 Sextet Lowboy	38.50	M	A	--
													B		SD	129-1 Alderman	39.95	LB	A	--
													B		SD	129-2 Judge	46.50	St	A	--
													BS		SD3	158 Septet	48.95	C	A	--
													B		SD3	158 Septet Lowboy	29.99	M	A	--
													B			Forty Five	39.99	C	A	--
													B		s	Discoverer	45.00		A	--
													B			Caroler	77.50	C	A	--
													B			Playtime	59.75		A	D2
A	8												Bp			128-2-EA	95.00	M	A	--
B	8		1-32	32	30	1-32	30	30	2-31	82		--	Bp	VT	SDM4	128-1-LC	59.95	C	A	D2
													Bp	VT	SDM4	146 Mayor	73.50	M		D2
A	9	SH	1-58	57	*	1-58	58	89	2-46	82	56	--	Bp	VT		146 Congressman	49.95	St	D2	d
																146 Senator	57.75	C	D	d

A	10	SH	--	58	56	2-58	56	56	2-42	80	--	--	BS	VT	SDM	136-1	Secretary	75.00	St	D2	d
													BS	VT	SDM	136-1	Governor	89.50	C	D2	d
A	10	SH	--	--	--	--	--	--	--	--	--	--	B	VT	-	-	Tenace	39.99	M	D	-
													B	VT	-	-	Tenace	49.99	LB	D	-
A	12	SH	--	--	--	--	--	--	--	--	--	--	BS	VT	-	-	Adventurer	119.50	C	D	-
A	12	SH	1-58	58	56	2-58	56	42	2-46	82	56	--	B	VT	SDM4	132-1	Symphony	89.50	C	D2	d
													B	VT	SDM4	132-1	Commissioner	99.50	C	D2	d
													B	VT	SDM4	132-1	Ambassador	119.50	C	D2	d
													B	VT	SDM4	132-1	Chief	139.50	C	D2	d
B	6	SH	--	36	*	1-39	37	37	1-41	--	*	--	B	V		95	Roamio	37.50	A	D	ch5
B	6	SH	1-39	36	*	2-39	85	--	1-89	--	*	--	B	-	-	96		39.50	A	-	-
-	2	-	--	36	37	--	--	--	--	--	--	--	S	-	-	9-2-FF		22.50	St	-	q

DAVISON-HAYNES MFG. CO. "ANGELUS" (1931) LOS ANGELES, CAL.

3 Chasses 8 Models 7 to 9 Tubes $49.50 to $89.50

A	7	SH	1-51	24	27	1-51	27	--	1-47	80	--	--	B	-	-	751		49.50	M	D	-
													B	-	-	752		59.50	LB	D	-
													B	-	-	753		69.50	HB	D	-
A	8	SH	1-51	24	27	1-51	27	--	2-47	80	--	--	B	-	-	81		59.50	M	D	-
													B	-	-	82		69.50	LB	D	-
													B	-	-	83		79.50	HB	D	-
A	9	SH	1-51	24	27	2-51	27	--	2-47	80	--	--	B	-	-	92		79.50	LB	D	-
													-	-	-	93		89.50	HB	D	-

DELCO RADIO CORP. "DELCO" DAYTON, OHIO

6 Chasses 6 Models 5 to 8 Tubes $ -- to $ --

B	5	TRF		(3-24,1-112A,1-pentode)									P	-	-	-		-	A	-	pa
-	-	-	--	--	--	--	--	--	--	--	--	--	P	-	-	-		-	M	-	ps
-	-	-	--	--	--	--	--	--	--	--	--	--	-	-	-	-		-	M	-	-
D	6	TRF	3-36	--	--	--	36	--	2-38	--	--	--	B	T	-	-		-	C	D	-
B	-	-	--	--	--	--	--	--	--	--	--	--	-	-	-	-		-	LB	-	-
B	8	SH	--	--	--	--	--	--	--	--	--	--	-	-	-	-		99.95	A	-	-

DE PREE SALES CO. -- (1931) SOUTH BEND, IND.

2 Chasses 2 Models 5 and 7 Tubes $ -- to $ --

A	5	-	--	--	--	--	--	--	--	--	--	--	B	-	-		Wren	-	M	D	-
A	7	-		(3-vari-mu,1pent,1-24,1-27,1-80)									B	-	-		Lark	59.50	M	D	-

P	T	C	RADIO	INTERMEDIATE D	O	IF	AUDIO D	1st	OUT.	RECT.	AVC	NS	R	CONT	TUNING	MODEL NUMBER AND NAME	PRICE	CAB.	SPKR.	NOTE
			DETROLA RADIO CORP.							"DETROLA" (1932)						ECORSE, MICH.				
			1 Chassis								1 Model							$26.50			
B	5	TRF		(1-36,1-37 | 2-39,1-41)								B			-		26.50	A	-	-
			DUBILIER CLOCK CORP.							"DUBILIER" (1931)							NEW YORK CITY				
			5 Chasses							6 Models				5 to 7 tubes			$ -- to $ --				
A	5	- TRF		(2-24,1-27,1-80,1-pentode)								B	T		-		-	-	M	D	-
A	5	- TRF		(1-27,1-47,2-51,1-80)								-	-		-		-	-	Pr	D	-
A	6	2-35		--	24	--	2-45	--	--			-	-		-		5	34.50	M	D	-
-	6	- TRF		(3-SG,1-27,1-45,1-80)								-	-		-		501	44.50	Pr	D	-
-	7	3-35		--	24	--	2-45	80	--			-	-		-		6	44.50	M	D	-
																		44.50	M	D	-
			DUMONT ELECTRIC CO. INC.							"DUBILIER" (1932)							NEW YORK CITY				
			6 Chasses							8 Models				4 to 9 Tubes			$29.50 to $49.50				
A	4	TRF		(1-24,1-35,1-47,1-80)								B	-		-		-	29.50	M	D	-
A	5	TRF		--	27	--	--	--	--			B	-		-		-	-	ch	D	-
A	6	-		--	--	--	--	--	1-47			Bp	-		-		400	29.50	M	D	-
A	6	3-35		--	27	24	--	2-47				Bp	-		-		503	39.50	M	D	-
												Bp	-		-		600	49.50	MP	D	-
A	9	TRF		(2-27,4-35,2-47,1-80)								-	-		-		-	49.50	ch	D	-
A	9	-		(1-24,2-27,3-35,2-47,1-80)								BL	-		-		904	49.50	ch	D	-
			ECHOPHONE RADIO MFG. CO.							"ECHOPHONE"							WAUKEGAN, ILL.				
			11 Chasses							24 Models				4 to 12 Tubes			$24.75 to $245.00				
A	4	TRF	1-35	--	--	24	--	1-47	80	--			B	-		-		40 Echoette	32.75	M	D	-
A	7	SH	1-35	--	27	1-35	24	--	1-47	80	--		B	T		-		60	53.75	M	D	-
D	7	-	--	--	27	--	--	2-47		--			B	-		-		65	53.75	LB	D	-
A	8	SH	1-35	1-35	27	24	--	2-47	80	--			B	T		-		70	59.50	M	D	-
													B	-		-		80	69.50	M	D	-
													B	T		-		90	89.50	LB	D	-
A	4	TRF	1-58	--	--	57	--	1-47	80	--			R	-		-		4	24.75	M	D	-
A	5	SH	--	57	1-58	57	--	1-47	80	--			R	-		-		44	24.75	M	D	-
													R	-		-		12	32.75	M	D	-
A				(1-24,1-27,2-35,1-47,1-80)								R	E		-		50	39.75	M	D	-

(Continued from preceding page)

Grp	Tubes	Type										Model	Price $			
A	6	SH	1-58	57	*	1-58	55	1-47	80	--	--	55	49.75	LB	D	g
A	8	SH	1-58	58	57	1-58	55	2-47	80	--	*	5	39.75	X	D	--
												14	46.50	M	D	--
												10	59.50	M	D	--
												16	59.50	M	D2	--
												15	69.50	M	D	--
												17	69.50	LB	D2	--
												18	89.50	LB	D2	--
												20	89.50	C	D2	--
												25	89.50	C	D2	--
												25	99.50	C	D2	--
A	12	SH	1-58	58	*	1-58	56	2-58	80	--	--	30	159.50	LB	D2	d
												35	159.50	--	D2	d
A	-	-	1-58	--	--	--	--	--	--	--	--	35 DeLuxe	245.00	--	D	tsr

ELECTRIC AUTO-LITE CO. "AUTO-LITE" (1932) — TOLEDO, OHIO
2 Models — 2 Chasses — 7 Tubes — $ -- to $ --

Grp	Tubes	Type								B	VTR	Model	Price $		
B	7	TRF	1-39	36	(2-27,3-36,1-37,1-47)	55	1-47	80	--	B	V	3722	89.50	A	D
B	7	SH	1-39	*	1-39;37,39	2-41	2-46	80	*	B	V	--	--	A	--

ELECTRICAL RESEARCH LABS. "ERLA" — CHICAGO, ILL.
12 Models — 3 Chasses — 3 to 7 Tubes — $ -- to $ --

Grp	Tubes	Type								B/R/S	Model	Price $		
A	4	TRF	1-35	--	--	24	--	1-47	80	B	21P	29.75	M	D
D	4	TRF	1-3	--	--	36	--	2-39	--	B	22P	39.50	MC	D
D	4	TRF	1-36	27	--	36	--	2-38	--	B	336	--	M	D
D	5	SH	1-35	24	27	24	--	1-47	80	R	41	--	M	--
A	6	SH	1-35	24	27	24	--	1-47	80	B	62P	--	M	D
A	7	SH	1-35	24	27	24	1-35	1-47	80	B	61P	--	M	D
										B	81P	--	M	--
										B	82P	--	C	D
B	7	SH	1-32	32	30	30	1-32	1-33	--	B	30-248	--	C	D
										B	67P	--	M	--
-	3	-	--	--	--	--	--	--	--	S	90P	12.50	C	--

ELGIN RADIO & TELEVISION CORP. "ELGIN" (1931) — DALLASTOWN, PA.
7 Models — 7 Chasses — 5 to 8 Tubes — $39.95 to $84.50

Grp	Tubes	Type					B/T	Model	Price $		
U*	5	TRF	--	--	--	1-47	B	--	38.95	--	--
U	5	TRF	--	--	--	1-47	T	--	79.50	GC	--
D*	6	TRF	--	--	--	--	B	--	43.95	--	--

(continued)

E

P	T	C	RADIO	INT D	INT IF	AUD D	AUD 1st	AUD OUT	RECT	AVC	NS	R	CONT	TUNING	MODEL NUMBER AND NAME	PRICE	CAB	SPKR	NOTE
			(Elgin)																
-	6	TRF	--	--	--	--	--	2-47	--	--	--	B	T	--	Air Column	54.50	GC	D	-
U*	7	TRF	--	--	--	--	--	--	--	--	--	B	-	--		47.95	-	-	-
U*	8	TRF	--	--	--	--	--	--	--	--	--	B	-	--		49.95	-	-	-
U*	9	TRF	--	--	--	--	--	--	--	--	--	B	T	--		-	-	-	-

ELREY RADIO MFG. CO., LOS ANGELES, CALIF. "EL REY" (1932)
2 Chasses   2 Models   5 and 6 Tubes $39.50 and $49.50

P	T	C	RADIO	INT D	INT IF	AUD D	AUD 1st	AUD OUT	RECT	AVC	NS	R	CONT	TUNING	MODEL	PRICE	CAB	SPKR	NOTE
B	5	TRF	3-39	57	--	36	--	1-41	--	--	--	B	--	--	40	49.50	-	-	-
A	6	SH	--	56	1-58	56	--	1-47	80	--	--	Ep	--	--	Garset	39.50	F	D	-

EMERSON RADIO & PHONO. CORP., NEW YORK CITY "EMERSON"
22 Chasses   30 Models   4 to 10 Tubes $13.75 to $79.50

P	T	C	RADIO	INT D	INT IF	AUD D	AUD 1st	AUD OUT	RECT	AVC	NS	R	CONT	TUNING	MODEL	PRICE	CAB	SPKR	NOTE
A	8	SH	--	(3-24,1-27,2-35,1-47,1-80)								BS	VT		-	59.50	N	D	-
A	8	SH	--									B	VT		E70	-	C	D	-
A	8	SH	--									B	VT		B30	79.50	C	D	-
A	4	TRF	--	--	--	--	--	--	--	--	--	B	--	--	T-51	19.50	M	A	-
A	4	TRF	--	--	--	--	--	--	--	--	--	BS	--	--	TS-51	24.50	M	A	-
A	4	TRF	1-58	--	--	57	--	1-47	80	--	--	B	--	--	L-458	16.75	Cp	A	-
												B			LR-458	-	Cp	A	-
D	4	TRF	2-39	--	--	36	--	1-33	--	--	--	B	--	--	L-460	22.50	M	A	-
												B			LR-460	-	M	A	-
U*	4	-	--	--	--	--	--	--	--	--	--	B	--	--	L-457	27.50	N	A	-
A	5	SH	--	--	--	--	--	--	--	--	--	B	--	--	L-557	27.50	M	A	-
A	5	SH	--	--	--	--	--	--	--	--	--	B	--	--	L-456	29.50	M	A	-
A	5	SH	--	--	--	--	--	--	--	--	--	B	--	3	L-459	34.50	St	A	-
A	5	SH	--	--	--	--	--	--	--	--	--	R	--	--	C-52	25.00	Kn	A	-
A	5	SH	--	--	--	--	--	--	--	--	--	BS	--	--	C3-52	32.00	M	A	-
A	5	SH	--	--	--	--	--	--	--	--	--	B	--	--	J-53	34.00	M	K	-
A	5	TRF	2-58	--	--	57	--	1-47	80	--	--	RS	--	--	JS-53	34.00	M	A	-
												B			J-54	36.00	C	A	-
												BS			JS-54	44.50	C	A	-
												B			L-556	49.50	O	A	-
												B			L-556	29.50	Cp	A	-
A	6	SH	--	24	1-58	24	--	1-47	80	--	--	BSL	--	--	L-559	27.50	St	A	-
A	7	SH	--	--	--	--	--	--	--	--	--	-	T	--	L-557	34.50	M	A	-
A	8	SH	--	--	--	--	--	--	--	--	--	B	--	--	L-559	55.00	M	A	-
															AW-55	39.50	M	D	-
															M-755	64.50	C	D	-
															K-70				

ESSEX RADIO CORP.   SPRINGFIELD, MASS.   (1932)

3 Chasses — 2 Models — 4 and 10 Tubes — $ -- to $ --

								Model							Price		
A 8	SH	--	--	--	--	--	--	--	KS-70				C	D	--	69.50	
A 8	SH	--	--	--	--	--	--	--	K-80				C	D	--	74.50	
A 8	SH	--	--	--	--	--	--	--	KS-80				C	D	--	79.50	
A 10	SH	--	--	--	--	--	--	--	B-10				oh	D2	d	--	

EXCELLO PRODUCTS CORP.   CHICAGO, ILL.

4 Chasses — 4 Models — -- Tubes — $ -- to $ --

								Model							Price	
A 4	--	--	--	--	--	--	--	--			B		CP	D	--	
A 10	--	--	--	--	--	--	--	--					C	D	--	

FADA RADIO & ELECTRIC CORP.   (FADA)   LONG ISLAND CITY, N.Y.

13 Chasses — 32 Models — 5 to 11 Tubes — $39.50 to $175.00

								Model							Price	
A 4	TRF	--	--	--	--	--	--	--	R279		B		RP	D	--	
A 4	--	--	--	--	--	--	--	--	--		B		M	D	--	
A 5	SH	. --	--	--	--	--	*	--	R-369		B		RP	D	--	
													MC	D	--	

32 Models

	circuit				47	80		Model					Price	
A 5	TRF	2-35	--	24	--	1-47	80	--	61	B	T	M	84.50	D	--
A 7	TRF	2-24	--	24	27	2-45	80	--	66	B	T	LB	69.50	D	--
A* 7	SH	1-35	1-35	24	--	1-47	80	--	43	B	T	M	89.50	D	--
A* 8	SH	1-35	27	27	--	2-47	80	--	51	B	--	LB	159.50	D	--
A 9	TRF	3-24	--	--	27	2-45	80	*	53	B	T	LB	112.50	D	--
									57	B	VT	C		D	--
A* 10	SH	1-35	2-35	27	27	2-47	80	*	45	B	VT	--	--	D	--
									42	B	VT	--	--	D	--
									44	B	VT	--	--	D	--
									46	B	VT	RP	124.50	D	--
		(1-24,2-35,	1-47,1-80)						47	B	VT	LH	147.50	D	--
A 5	TRF	--	57	--	*	1-47	80	--	65	BL	T	C	175.00	D	--
A* 5	SH	--	56	55	--	1-47	80	*	48	B	--	LB	39.50	D	--
A* 7	SH	1-58	1-58		27				49	B	VT	T	49.50	D	--
									63	BL	VT	LB	62.50	D	--
									55	BL	VT	LR	--	D	--

(continued)

P	T	C	RADIO	D	O	IF	D	1st	OUT.	RECT.	AVC	NS	R	CONT	TUNING	MODEL NUMBER AND NAME	PRICE	CAB.	SPKR.	NOTE
																(Peda)				
D	8	-	--	--	--	--	--	--	--	--	--	--	B	--	--	171	72.50	T	-	-
													B	--	--	173	92.50	LB	-	-
A	9	SH	1-58	58	56	1-58	56	56	2-47	80	*	--	B	VT	M	74	79.50	C	D	-
													B	VT	M	76	89.50	LB	D	-
													B	VT	M	83	-	LB	D	-
													B	VT	M	87	73.00	C	D	-
													B	VT	M	88	-	LB	D	-
													B	VT	M	89	-	HB	D	-
													RS	V	-	97	73.00	LB	D	-
A	10	SH	1-35	24	27	1-35	27	35	1-47	80	*	--	B	VTN	M	66 Round-The-World	99.50	C	D	h7
A	11	SH	1-58	58	56	2-58	56	56	2-47	80	*	57	B	VTN	M	78 DeLuxe	125.00	LR	D	-
																79 DeLuxe	135.00	HB	D	-

FEDERAL RADIO CORP.   "FEDERAL ORTHO-SONIC" (1931) LOS ANGELES, CAL. $59.50 to $89.50

2 Chasses   5 Models   8 and 9 Tubes

P	T	C	RADIO	D	O	IF	D	1st	OUT.	RECT.	AVC	NS	R	CONT	TUNING	MODEL NUMBER AND NAME	PRICE	CAB.	SPKR.	NOTE
A	8	SH	1-35	24	27	1-35	27	--	2-47	80	--	--	B	--	--	F81	59.50	N	D	-
													B	--	--	F82	69.50	LB	D	-
A	9	SH	1-51	24	27	2-51	27	--	2-47	80	--	--	B	--	--	F83	79.50	HB	D	-
													B	--	--	F92	79.50	LB	D	-
													B	--	--	F93	89.50	HB	D	-

FEDERATED PURCHASER   "ACRATONE"   NEW YORK CITY $13.50 to $42.50

9 Chasses   23 Models   5 and 6 Tubes

P	T	C	RADIO	D	O	IF	D	1st	OUT.	RECT.	AVC	NS	R	CONT	TUNING	MODEL NUMBER AND NAME	PRICE	CAB.	SPKR.	NOTE
A	5	TRF	TRF	(3-SQ,1-47,1-80)			--	--	--	--	--	--	B	--	--	--	35.00	M	D	-
A	6	-	--	--	--	--	--	--	--	--	--	--	B	--	--	--	*23.50	M	-	-
A	5	TRF	2-51	24	27	--	27	--	1-47	80	--	--	-	--	--	6 (110v.)	*13.50	K	D	-
D	-	--	--	--	--	--	--	--	--	--	--	--	B	--	--	23 (220v.)	*18.50	M	-	-
D	-	--	--	--	--	--	--	--	--	--	--	--	B	--	--	24	*14.75	K	D	-
D	-	--	--	--	--	--	--	--	--	--	--	--	BL	--	--	32	*16.25	M	D	-
D	-	--	--	--	--	--	--	--	--	--	--	--	BL	--	--	27	*19.50	M	D	-
A	5	TRF	2-58	58	--	--	57	--	1-47	80	--	--	BL	--	--	30	*39.50	MP	D	-
A*													BL	--	--	33	*42.50	MP	D	-
A													B	--	--	38	*41.50	M	D	-
A*													B	--	--	39	*14.75	M	D	-
A*													BL	--	--	41	*16.25	M	D	-
A*													BL	--	--	42	*15.75	M	D	-
																43	*21.50	M	D	-

(continued)

										Tube	Price			
A	6	SH	1-58	56	*	1-57	55	--	*	46	*19.50	M		D
A*										47	*33.50	NP		D
A										48	*37.50	MP		D
A										49	*41.00	MP		D
A						1-47	80			91	*15.25	MP		D
A*										92	*16.75	M		D
A										17	*19.50	M		D
										84	*20.50	M		D

FERGUSON RADIO CORP. NEW YORK CITY

"FERGUSON" (1932) $ -- to $
9 Models 4 to 8 Tubes
8 Chasses

										Model					
A	4	TRF	1-58	--	--	1-47	80	--	--	F-4-AC	B	--	M	--	D
D	4	TRF	1-39	--	37	1-89	--	--	--	F-4-DC	B	--	M	--	D
A	5	TRF	2-59	--	37	1-47	80	--	--	F-5-AC	B	--	M	--	D
D	5	TRF	2-39	--	37	1-89	--	--	--	F-5-DC	BP	--	M	--	D
A	6	SH	1-58	56	--	1-47	80	--	--	S-6	BP	V	M	--	D
A	6	TRP	3-35	--	24	1-47	80	--	--	BL-60	B	V	M	--	D
A	8	SH	1-35	35	27	1-35	24	1-47	80	27	BL-61	BL-	VT	M	--	D	hB
A	8	SH	(1-24,1-27,3-35,2-47,1-80)						27	CB-81	B	I	M	--	D	g

FINK INDUSTRIES LANSING, MICH.

"IMPERIAL" (1931) $24.95 to $159.50
8 Models 4 to 9 Tubes
4 Chasses

								Tubes	Price				
A	4	TRF	1-51	--	--	1-47	80	4	24.95	B	M	--	D h1
A	5	TRF	1-51	--	--	1-47	80	5	34.95	B	M	--	D
A	7	SH	1-51	27	1-51	1-47	80	7	40.95	B	M	--	D
								7	59.95	C	--	D
								7	99.50	GC	--	D
								9	139.50	RP	--	D h9
A	9	SH	1-51	24	27	2-47	80	9	84.95	C	--	D h9
								9	159.50	RP	D	

FLEETWOOD RADIO CORP. FLEETWOOD, PA.

"FLEETWOOD" (1932) $169.50 to $197.50
4 Models 6 to 14 Tubes
4 Chasses

											Model			Price			
B	6	SH	1-39	36	39	37	1-41	--	*	GF-106	Gov.Winthrop	B	A	--	D h6
A	10	SH	1-58	58	56	56	2-47	80	56	57	VN	GF-110	Gov.Winthrop 169.50	B	D	--	D
A	11	SH	1-58	56	56	56	2-42	82	57	-VN	GF-111	Gov.Winthrop 189.50	B	D	--	D
A	14	SH	1-58	58	56	56	4-42	80	58	55	VN	GF-114	Gov.Winthrop 197.50	B	D	--	D

213

F1

P	T	C	RADIO	D	O	IF	D	1st	OUT.	RECT.	AVC	NS	R	CONT TUNING	MODEL NUMBER AND NAME	PRICE	CAB.	SPKR.	NOTE
						INTERMEDIATE		AUDIO											

FLINT RADIO CO. INC.   LOS ANGELES, CAL.   (1931) -- Tubes

| | | | 1 Chassis | | | | | | | | | | | | 1 Model | | $ -- | | |

FORDSON RADIO MFG. CO.   DETROIT, MICH.   (1932) - Tubes

| B | | | 1 Chassis | | | | | | | | | | | | 1 Model | 49.50 | A | | |

FRANKLIN RADIO CORP.   DAYTON, OHIO   "FRANKLIN"   3 to 6 Tubes

6 Chasses   10 Models

P	T	C	RADIO	D	O	IF	D	1st	OUT.	RECT.	AVC	NS	R	CONT	MODEL	PRICE	CAB.	SPKR.	NOTE
3			(1-24,1-27,1-90)	--	--	--	--	--	--	--	--	--	S	--	Rembert	29.75	M		q
A	4	TRF	1-35	--	--	--	35	--	1-47	80	--	--	B	--	101	--	M	D	
A	4	TRF	1-35	--	--	--	24	--	1-47	80	--	--	B	--	105	--	M	D	
A	5	SH	--	--	*	1-35	24	--	1-47	80	--	--	B	--	102	--	M	D	
A	5	TRF	2-35	--	--	--	24	--	1-47	80	--	--	B	--	106	--	M	D	
													BL		104	--	M	D	
A	6	SH	--	24	27	1-35	24	--	1-47	90	--	--	BL	--	108	--	M	D	
													BL		103	--	M	D	
B	6	SH	--	36	*	1-36	36	37	2-38	--	--	--	B	--	107	--	M	D	
															100	--	A	D	

FREED TELEVISION & RADIO CORP.   LONG ISLAND CITY, N.Y.   "FREED-EISEMANN"   4 to 11 Tubes

13 Chasses   18 Models

P	T	C	RADIO	D	O	IF	D	1st	OUT.	RECT.	AVC	NS	R	CONT	MODEL	PRICE	CAB.	SPKR.	NOTE
A	4	TRF	1-51	--	--	--	24	--	1-47	80	--	--	B	--	FE94	34.50	M	D	
A	5	TRF	--	--	--	--	--	--	--	--	--	--	B	--	Mighty Miniature	--	M	D	
A	7	TRF	2-36	(2-24,2-27,1-45,1-51,1-90)	--	37	4-38	--	--	--	--	--	P	--		84.00	K		tr
D	8	TRF	2-36	36	--	37	(4-36,4-38)	--	--	--	--	--	P	--	FE96	69.50	M		
D	8	TRF	1-51	24	27	1-51	24	--	2-47	90	--	--	B	--	FE97	69.50	M		
A	8	SH	1-51	24	27	1-51	24	--	2-47	90	--	--	B	--	FE98	64.50	M	D	
D	5	TRF	2-39	36	--	--	36	--	2-43	--	--	--	B	--	51 52 53	--	M St T ch	D	
A	5	TRF	2-58	57	--	--	57	--	1-47	80	--	--	B	--	63 54 56	31.50	T M D	D	

214

														Model	Price				
A	5	SH	--	57	*	58	--	--	--	1-47	80			58			B	M	ch
A	7	SH	1-58	58	56	55	--	--	--	1-47	80			72			B	ch	D
A	8	SH	1-58	58	56	56	--	--	2-46	80				-			B	ch	D	d
A	9	SH	1-58	58	56	55	--	--	2-46	80		V		90			B	ch	D	d
A	11	SH	1-58	58	56	55	--	--	2-46	82		V		120			B	ch	D	dh3

FRENCH, JESSE MFG. CO.   "JESSE FRENCH" (1931) NEWCASTLE, IND.
2 Chasses — 5 and 7 Tubes — $54.50 to $129.50

													Model	Price			
A	5	TRF	2-51	--	--	--	1-58	58	--	1-47	80		Tudette	54.50	B	M	f
													Combination	129.50	B	RP	f
													Devon	69.50	B	M	
A	7	SH	1-35	24	27	1-35	24	--	1-47	80	T	Tudor	89.50	B	C	
												T	Tudor	129.50	B	RP	

FROST-MINTON CORP.   "FROST-MINTON" (1931) NEW YORK CITY
2 Chasses — 4 Models — $29.50 to $36.50

												Model	Price			
A	4	TRF	1-24	--	--	--	24	--	1-45	80		FM-4	29.50	B	BP	D
												-	32.50	B	BP	D
												FM-5	36.50	B	BP	D
A	4	TRF	1-24	--	--	--	24	--	1-47	80		4-FW	34.50	B	M	

GALVIN MFG. CORP.   "MOTOROLA"
9 Chasses — 9 Models — 5 to 8 Tubes — $49.50 to $94.00

												Model	Price			
E	5	TRF	2-24	--	--	24	01A	38	1-71A	--		5W71 Standard	59.50	B	A	D
B	6	TRF	3-24	--	--	01A	--	2-12A	--		6T12 FL	84.50	B	A	D
B	7	TRF	3-35	--	--	37	2-33	--		7T38A DeLuxe	79.50	B	A	D
B	5	SH	--	37	--	--	85	--	--		Standard	49.50	B	A	
B	6	SH	1-36	--	--	1-36	--	1-41	--	VR	61 Super DeLuxe	59.50	B	A	D
A	7	SH	--	--	--	--	--	BR		Super DeLuxe	94.00	B	V	D
D	8	SH	1-36	39	--	1-36	85	37	2-38	BR	88 Super DeLuxe	74.95	B	VR	
B	-		--	--	--	--	--	--		Super DeLuxe	62.50	B	A	

GENERAL ELECTRIC CO.   BRIDGEPORT, CONN.
25 Chasses — 43 Models — 4 to 12 Tubes — $37.50 to $354.90

										Model	Price			
A	4	TRF	1-24	--	24	--	1-47	80		T12	37.50	B	M	D
D	4	TRF	1-36	--	36	--	2-38	--		T12D	45.00	B	M	D
(continued)

(General Electric)

P	T	C	RADIO	D	O	IF	D	1st	OUT.	RECT.	AVC	NS	R	CONT	TUNING	MODEL NUMBER AND NAME	PRICE	CAB.	SPKR.	NOTE
D	7	SH	1-35	24	27	1-35	27	—	2-45	—	—	—	B	—	—	S22D	77.50	M	D	—
D	7	TRF	3-24	—	—	—	24	—	2-45	80	—	—	B	—	—	S42D	94.50	LB	D	—
A	8	SH	1-35	24	27	1-35	27	—	2-45	80	—	—	B	—	—	T-41 Studio LB	*112.50	LB	D	g
A	6	SH	1-35	24	27	1-35	27	30	1-47	80	27	—	B	T	—	S-22 GE Junior	72.50	M	D	g
B	8	SH	1-32	32	30	1-32	30	30	2-30	—	—	—	B	T	—	S-22 GE Junior	84.50	MC	D	g
A*	9	SH	1-24	24	27	2-24	27	—	2-45	80	27	—	B	T	—	S-22 GE Junior	89.50	C	D	—
A	9	SH	1-35	24	27	1-35	27	—	2-47	80	27	—	B	VT	—	S-43	89.50	LR	D	—
A	10	SH	1-35	24	27	2-35	27	—	2-47	80	—	—	B	T	—	J-85 New Junior	89.95	C	PD	—
													B	—	—	S-42B	99.50	LR	D	—
A	7	SH	1-35	24	27	1-35	27	—	1-47	80	—	—	B	—	—	H-51 The Lowboy	*142.50	HB	D	—
A	7	SH	1-55	24	27	1-55	27	—	1-47	80	*	—	B	VT	—	H-51 The Highboy	*179.50	RP	D	—
B	8	SH	1-32	32	30	1-32	30	30	2-30	—	27	—	B	VT	—	H-71	285.00	LB	D	—
B	8	SH	1-34	32	30	1-34	34	30	2-30	—	56	—	B	VT	—	K-62 Popular C.	124.75	GC	D	—
A	8	SH	—	—	—	—	—	—	—	80	—	—	B	VT	—	K-82 Georgian	179.00	LB	D	n
A	8	SH	1-35	24	27	1-35	27	—	1-47	80	27	—	B	VT	—	H-52 DeLuxe	164.50	GC	D	n
A	8	SH	1-58	58	56	1-58	56	56	1-47	80	56	—	B	VT	—	H-72 DeLuxe	345.00	RP	D	—
A	9	SH	1-35	24	27	2-35	27	—	2-47	80	27	—	B	VT	—	H-91 Longfellow	285.00	GC	D	—
A	10	SH	1-35	24	27	1-55	27	—	2-47	80	27	—	B	VT	—	H-91LR	254.90	GC	D	—
A	10	SH	1-58	58	56	1-58	56	56	2-46	82	56	—	B	VT	—	J-70	48.75	T	D	—
A	12	SH	1-58	58	56	1-58	56	56	2-46	82	58	—	B	VTA	—	J-75	66.50	LB	D	—
B	9	—	—	—	—	—	—	—	—	—	—	—	B	VT	—	J-72	47.50	T	D	—
B	6	SH	1-36	36	37	1-36	37	37	2-12A	—	37	—	B	V	—	2-42-B	99.50	LB	D	d
													B	V	—	A-31	81.50	Pr	D	d
													B			J-83	59.50	MC	D	d
																J-80	59.95	T	D	dh6
																J-85	79.50	LB	D	—
																J-82	59.50	T	D	—
																J-86	72.95	RP	D	—
																J-87	79.50	C	D	—
																J-88	124.75	RP	D	—
																K-82	179.00	GC	D	—
																H-72	345.00	RP	D	—
																H-91	285.00	GC	D	—
																J-100	73.75	T	D	—
																J-105	93.50	LB	D	—
																J-107	104.50	LB	D	—
																J-109	269.50	RP	D	—
																J-125	147.50	LR	D	—
																Convention	139.50	A	A	—
																A-60	49.95	A	—	—
																A-90	76.75	A	—	—

GENERAL MOTORS RADIO CORP.   "GENERAL MOTORS" (1931)   DAYTON, OHIO $39.50 to $270.00

8 Chasses   26 Models   2 to 10 Tubes

Full complement note: (2-24, 1-27, 2-35, 1-47, 1-80)

Chassis / tube data

Prefix	Grp	Chassis	Tube data	B	Det
A	6	SH	3-24, 24, 2-35, 1-47, 80	B	T
A	6	TRF	3-32, 30, 2-31, 80	B	T
B	7	TRF	27, 80	B	T
A*	7	SH	35, 27, 1-35, 1-47, 80, 27	B	T
A*	7	SH	24, 27, 2-35, 1-47, 80	B	T
A*	8	SH	24, 27, 2-35, 1-47, 80, 27	B	T
A*	8	SH	3-24, 2-45, 80, 27	B	VT
A*	8	TRF	—	B	—
A*	10	SH	1-35, 24, 27, 2-35, 2-45, 80, 27	B	VT
U	2	—	36, 37	SW	R

Models

Model	Name	Price			
MA	Little Corporal	39.50	M	D	—
170	Pioneer	74.60	M	D	—
201		136.00	LB	M	—
—		129.50	LB	D	—
—	Warwick	95.00	T	D	—
216	Tudor	95.00	T	D	—
217	Standish	95.00	T	D	—
219		79.50	T	D	—
220	Salem	69.50	C	D	—
250	Little General	69.50	M	D	—
251	Valere	99.50	C	D	—
	Hepplewhite	136.00	—	D	—
	Sheraton	152.00	—	D	—
	Little Italian	172.00	RP	D	—
	Queen Anne	198.00	RP	D	—
	Georgian	270.00	C	D	—
252	Cosmopolitan	129.50	C	D	—
253	Imperial	149.50	LB	D	—
254	Queen Anne	175.00	LB	D	—
255	Louis XV	185.00	T	D	—
256	Cromwell	160.00	HB	D	—
257	Winslow	225.00	LB	D	—
258	Abbey	165.00	LB	D	—
290	Queen Anne	250.00	RP	D	n
291	Louis XV	350.00	RP	D	n
281		49.75	Pd	D	—

GENERAL TELEVISION & RADIO CORP.   "GENERAL" (1932)   KINGSTON, PA $—

1 Model   1 Chassis   11 Tubes

Prefix	Grp	Chassis			Price		
—	11	—	—	—	$—	—	—

GILBERT, R. W.   "GILBERT" (1931)   LOS ANGELES, CAL. $59.50

1 Model   1 Chassis   6 Tubes

Prefix	Grp	Chassis	Tube data	Model	Price		
A	6	TRF	(4-24, 1-45, 1-80)	70	59.50	M	D

P	T	C	RADIO	D	O	IF	D	1st	OUT.	RECT.	AVC	NS	R	CONT	TUNING	MODEL NUMBER AND NAME	PRICE	CAB.	SPKR.	NOTE

GILFILLAN BROS. "GILFILLAN" LOS ANGELES, CAL. $79.50 and $89.50

P	T	C	RADIO	D	O	IF	D	1st	OUT.	RECT.	AVC	NS	R	CONT	TUNING	MODEL	PRICE	CAB.	SPKR.	NOTE
A	8	5 Chasses	TRF 2-35	35	27	--	35	--	2-47	80	--	--	B	--	8 Tubes	200	79.50	LB	D	--
																250	89.50	LB	D	--
A	5		SH 1-58	57	--	--	55	--	1-47	80	*	--	BP	V		5	51.95	M	D	--
A	6		TRF 2-58	57	--	--	55	--	1-47	80	*	--	BP	V		7-M	47.50	C	D	--
A	7		TRF 2-58	57	--	--	56	--	2-47	80	*	--	BP	V		7-C	59.50	C	D	--
A	12		SH 1-58	57	56	2-58	55	56	2-46	82	*	57	BS	VN		12	99.50	C	D	d

GLOBE TELEVISION & PHONE CORP. "GLOBE" (1932) NEW YORK CITY

P	T	C	RADIO	D	O	IF	D	1st	OUT.	RECT.	AVC	NS	R	CONT	TUNING	MODEL	PRICE	CAB.	SPKR.	NOTE
A	8	1 Chassis	TRF 2-24	--	--	--	27	24	2-45	80	--	--	P	--	8 Tubes	- Television Set	--	M	--	2h
													P	--		--	--	C	--	2i

GOLD SEAL ELECTRIC CO. "GOLD SEAL" (1931) NEWARK, N.J.

P	T	C	RADIO	D	O	IF	D	1st	OUT.	RECT.	AVC	NS	R	CONT	TUNING	MODEL	PRICE	CAB.	SPKR.	NOTE
A	7	1 Chassis	- 2-35	--	--	27	27	27	1-46	80	--	--	P	-	7 Tubes	SW50 Television Set	45.50	K	--	2h

GRAND RAPIDS RADIO MFG.CO. "GYPSY" (1931) GRAND RAPIDS, MICH.

P	T	C	RADIO	D	O	IF	D	1st	OUT.	RECT.	AVC	NS	R	CONT	TUNING	MODEL	PRICE	CAB.	SPKR.	NOTE
B	6	1 Chassis	TRF 2-36	--	--	--	37	37	2-38	--	--	--	B	--	6 Tubes	1200	69.50	A	--	--
													B	--		P1200	69.50	A	--	--
													B	--		Tottler	69.50	A	--	--

GRAYBAR ELECTRIC CO. "GRAYBAR" NEW YORK CITY $37.50 to $285.00

P	T	C	RADIO	D	O	IF	D	1st	OUT.	RECT.	AVC	NS	R	CONT	TUNING	MODEL	PRICE	CAB.	SPKR.	NOTE
A	4	9 Chasses	TRF 1-24	--	--	--	24	--	1-47	80	--	--	B	B	4 to 10 Tubes	GB-4	37.50	M	D	--
A	7		TRF 3-24	--	--	--	24	--	2-45	80	--	--	B	T		GB-678	*112.50	C	D	--
A	8		SH 1-35	24	27	1-35	27	--	2-45	80	--	--	B	T		GB-8	78.10	M	D	--
A	9		SH 1-35	24	27	1-35	27	--	2-47	80	--	--	B	T		GB-8A	69.50	M	D	--
A*	9		SH 1-24	24	27	2-24	27	--	2-45	80	--	--	B	T		GB-700	*142.50	HB	D	--
																GB-770	*179.50	HB	D	--
																GB-900	*285.00	RP	D	--
A	9		SH 1-35	24	27	1-35	27	--	2-47	80	27	--	B	Vf		GB-9	119.00	C	D	--

													Name	Price		
														478.00	HB	D
A*	7	SH	1-35	24	27	--	1-35	27	--	1-47	80	--	GT-7	46.75	LB	D
A*	8	SH	1-35	24	27	--	1-35	27	--	1-47	80	27	GC-13	66.50	c	D
													GT-8	59.95	c	D
													GC-14	79.50	c	D

GRAY-DANIELSON MFG. CO. — 1 Chassis — 1 Model — (1931) — SAN FRANCISCO, CAL.

													Model	Price		
A	7	TRP	3-24	--	--	27	--	--	--	2-45	80	--	160	*160.00	LB.	D
A	7	SH	1-35	24	27	--	1-35	24	--	1-47	80	--	M-1	59.75	-	D
A	8	SH	1-35	24	27	--	1-35	27	--	2-47	80	--	M-2	79.75	LB	D
													M-3	99.75	HB	D
													M-4	129.75	HB	D

GREBE, A.H. & CO. — 3 Chasses — 5 Models — "GREBE" (1931) — RICHMOND HILL, L.I., N.Y. $59.75 to $160.00 — 7 and 8 Tubes

GRIFFIN-SMITH MFG. CO. — 1 Chassis — 1 Model — (1931) — LOS ANGELES, CAL.

													Model	Name	Price		
A*	5	SH	--	24	*	1-51	24	--	1-51	--	1-47	80	--	151	Havenwood	44.50	M	D
														153	Ellswood	59.50	LB	D
														154	Fyfewood	64.50	T	D
														155	Castlewood	109.00	RP	D
															Sherwood	84.50	GC	D
A	6	TRP	2-24	--	--	--	--	--	2-45	80				31		79.50	M	D
B-	6	SH	1-32	32	30	1-32	32	--	1-33	--				121		99.50	c	D
A*	8	SH	1-51	51	27	1-61	27	--	2-45	80				-		69.50	M	D
A*	9	SH	1-51	51	27	1-51	27	--	2-47	80					Tudor	119.50	LB	D
														251	Cheltenwood	79.50	HB	D
														251	Cheltenwood	79.50	HB	M
														253	Brentwood	99.50	LB	D
														253	Brentwood	99.50	LB	D
														254	Bruewood	129.50	GC	D

GRIGSBY-GRUNOW CO. — 25 Chasses — 40 Models — "MAJESTIC" — CHICAGO, ILL. $18.45 to $290.00 — 3 to 12 Tubes

(continued)

P	T	C	RADIO	D	O	IF	D	1H	OUT.	RECT.	AVC	NS	R	CONT	TUNING	MODEL NUMBER AND NAME	PRICE	CAB.	SPKR.	NOTE
			(Grigsby-Grunow)																	
A*	9	SH	1-51	51	27	1-51	24	--	2-45	80	24	--	B	VT	-	254 Brycewood	129.50	GC	D	-
A*	10	SH	1-51	51	27	2-51	27	--	2-47	80	--	--	R	VT	M	351 Hepplewhite	149.50	HB	D	-
B	7	TPF	3-56	--	--	--	37	37	2-38	--	*	--	R	VT	-	353 Collingwood	165.00	LB	D	n
													P	VT	-	110 Abbeywood	290.00	RP	D	-
		TPF		37	--	--	37	37	2-38	--	--	--	P	VR	-	110 Motor Majestic	87.50	A	-	-
A	3	SH	--	--	--	--	--	--	--	--	--	--	B	--	-	11	38.50	T	-	g
I	4	TRF	(1-G-57,1-G-58AS,1-G89,1-G84)										B	--	-	Pirate Chest	18.45	St	D	j
A	6	SH	(1-24,1-248,1-27,1-47,1-51,1-80)										P	--	-	56 Ardmore	44.50	T	D	j
A	6	SH					55	--	1-47	80	--	58	BS	T	-	57 Berkshire	59.50	LB	D	j
A	7	SH	1-58	58	56	1-59	55	--	1-47	80	*	--	B	VT	-	33 Viking	84.50	T	D	j
A	8	SH	--	58	--	--	--	--	--	--	--	--	B	VT	-	311 Chippendale	69.50	LB	D	j
A	8	SH	--	--	--	--	--	--	--	--	--	--	B	--	-	314 Sheffield	59.50	M	D	-
A	8	SH	--	--	--	--	--	--	--	--	--	--	B	--	-	Fairfax	60.50	LB	D	-
A	9	SH	1-58	58	56	1-58	4	57	1-47	82	*	58	B	VTN	-	204 Explorer	94.50	LB	D	j
A	10	SH	--	--	--	--	--	--	--	--	--	--	B	VTN	-	291 Madison	59.50	T	D	-
A	10	SH	--	--	--	--	--	--	--	--	--	--	B	V	-	293 Adams	69.50	LB	D	-
A	10	SH	--	--	--	--	--	--	--	--	--	--	B	V	-	211 Whitehall	89.50	HB	D	-
A	11	SH	1-58	58	56	1-58	4	57	2-47	82	57	--	B	VT	-	214 Stratford	99.50	-	D2	j
A	12	SH	1-58	58	56	1-58	4	57	1-47	82	*	--	B	VT	-	215 Croydon	119.50	HB	D2	19h
A	12	SH	1-58	58	56	1-58	4	57	2-47	82	57	58	BS	VTN	-	307 Gothic	89.50	LB	D2	19h
D	6	SH	1-39	38	*	1-39	85	--	2-38	--	*	--	B	VT	-	304 Jacobean	99.50	C	D	•01h
A	3	-	--	24	35	--	--	--	--	80	--	--	S	VNR	-	294 Monroe	14.50	LR	D2	19h
															-	324 Anniversary	149.50	A	D	-
															-	114	--	-	-	g
															-	10	--			

15 Chassis   GULBRANSEN CO.   26 Models   CHICAGO, ILL. $39.50 to $148.50

"GULBRANSEN"   5 to 12 Tubes

P	T	C	RADIO	D	O	IF	D	1H	OUT.	RECT.	AVC	NS	R	CONT	TUNING	MODEL NUMBER AND NAME	PRICE	CAB.	SPKR.	NOTE
B	5	SH	1-32	32	*	1-32	32	--	1-33	--	--	--	B	--	-	926	49.50	C	-	-
A*	6	TRF	3-24	--	--	--	24	--	1-45	80	--	--	B	T	-	330	48.00	M	-	3h
A*	7	SH	1-35	27	27	1-35	24	--	1-47	80	--	--	B	T	-	130	58.00	C	D	o
													B	T	-	135	66.00	M	D	o
A*	7	SH	1-51	24	27	1-51	24	--	1-47	80	--	--	B	T	-	130	58.00	C	D	f
													B	VT	-	135	68.00	M	D	f
A*	10	SH	1-35	35	27	2-35	27	27	2-47	80	*	--	B	VT	-	235 DeLuxe	97.50	C	D	-
													B	VT	-	236 Twin Voice	148.50	C	D2	-
													B	VT	-	237 Twin Voice	118.50	HB	D2	-
B	5	SH	(4-32 1-33)	35									B			925		LR		

HALSON RADIO MFG. CO. — 9 Chasses

		Type													Model		to $		
A	6	SH	---	57		1-58	57	*	1-58	57	80	--	1-47	BP	2525		39.50	C	D
A	7	SH	1-58	57		1-58	57	*	1-58	57	80	--	1-47	BP	3521		39.50	M	D
A	9	SH							30	30		2-30		BP	3525		49.50	CL	D
B	9	SH	1-34	34	30	1-34	30	30	1-34	30				B	7721		49.50	M	D
A	10	SH	1-58	57	56	2-58	57	56	2-47	56	80	2-47		B	7725		69.50	LB	D2
A	12	SH	1-58	58	56	2-58	56	56	2-46	56	82	2-46		B	8726		69.50	LB	D2
A														C	535		-	C	PD
B	6	SH	1-59	36	*	1-39	37	37	1-41	39	80	1-41	*	B	2925		72.50	C	D2
B	7	SH	1-39	36	*	1-39	37	37	2-41	39	82	2-41	*	B	3925		74.50	C	PD
A													VTN	9027		79.50	C	PD
A													VTN	2225 Twin Voice		94.50	C	D
B													VR	3225		99.50	HB	D2
B														3226		129.50	HR	D2
														1622		57.50	A	
														3722		62.50	A	

"HALSON DIAMOND" 12 Models — NEW YORK CITY, 4 to 6 Tubes

		Type										Model		to $		
A	4	TRF	1-24	--	--	24	38	24	1-47	80	B	Junior		22.50	M	D
A	4	TRF	1-36	--	--	36	38	24	1-33	--	B			-	M	
A	4	TRF	2-35	--	--	24	37	01A	1-47	80	B			-	M	
A	6	TRF	2-35	--	2-35	24	38	01A	2-47	80	B	DeLuxe		39.50	M	D
D	6	TRF	2-36	--	2-35	36	37		2-33	--	B				M	
D	6	TRF	2-01A	--	2-58	01A	01A		2-71A	--	B				M	
U	4	TRF	1-58	--	--	57	--	57	1-47	80	Bp	414S		9.75	M	D
												414		10.50	M	D
												200		13.00	st	D
B	5	TRP	2-58	--	--	57	--	57	1-47	80	Bp	510		13.50	M	D
D	6	TRP	2-01A	--	--	01A	01A		1-33	--	B	615		11.50	M	D

HAMMARLUND MFG. CO. — 5 Chasses, 7 Models (HAMMARLUND) — NEW YORK CITY, 8 Tubes

		Type											Model		to $		
A	8	TRF	3-24	--	--	24	27	2-45	80	--	B		H1Q-31 The Hampton		160.40	G	D
													H1Q-31 The Chalet		175.00	RP	D
													H1Q-31		162.55	D	D
A	8	SH	--	24	27	24	27	--	80	3S	B		Comet Pro		160.40	st	
A	8	SH	--	24	27	24	27	1-47	80	3	B		Comet All Wave		175.00	C	
A	8	SH	--	57	58	57	--	1-47	80	B3	B		Comet Pro		162.55	st	
													Comet All Wave		175.00	C	

P	T	C	RADIO	INTERMEDIATE			AUDIO			RECT.	AVC	NS	R	CONT	TUNING	MODEL NUMBER AND NAME	PRICE	CAB.	SPKR.	NOTE
				D	O	IF	D	1st	OUT.											
																HARRISON RADIO CO. NEW YORK CITY				
-	-	-	1 Chassis	--	--	--	--	1 Model	--	--	--	--	3	--	-- Tubes	RP	$25.00	St	-	-
																HIGH FREQUENCY LABS. CHICAGO, ILL. $25.00 to $86.50				
			12 Chasses					"REGENT" (1931) 14 Models					4 to 11 Tubes							
A	4	TRF	--	--	--	--	24	--	1-47	80	--	--	B	--	--	400 Little Giant	25.00	M	D	-
-	4	-	2-35	--	--	--	--	--	--	--	--	--	B	--	--	Mastertone	29.50	M	D	-
A	5	TRF	--	--	--	--	24	--	1-47	80	--	--	B	--	--	5	36.50	-	-	-
-	5	TRF	2-24	--	--	--	--	--	--	--	--	--	--	--	--	Mastertone	36.50	M	-	-
-	5	TRF	--	--	--	--	24	--	1-45	80	--	--	B	--	--	5-269 Mastertone	49.95	C	B	-
A	5	TRF	--	--	--	--	--	--	--	--	--	--	B	--	--	505	49.95	M	B	-
													B			520	52.50	M	B	-
A	7	SH	1-24	35	--	1-35	24	--	1-47	80	--	--	B	--	--	7	49.50	M	B	-
A	7	SH	--	--	27	--	--	--	--	--	--	--	B	--	--	Mastertone	62.50	ch	D	-
A	7	SH	--	--	--	--	--	--	--	--	--	--	B	--	--	Mastertone	69.50	-	ch	-
A	7	TRF			(3-24,2-27,1-45,1-80)					--	--	--	B	--	--	7-292 Mastertone	79.50	M	D	-
A	9	-	--	27	4-24	24	--	2-45	80	--	--	B	--	--	840	79.50	H	D	-	
A	11	SH	--	27	--	24	--	2-45	80	--	--	B	--	--	841	86.50	ch	D	-	
													B			1931 Mastertone	-	ch	-	q
																HOODWIN CO., CHAS. CHICAGO, ILL. $6.45 to $39.50				
			12 Chasses					"AERO" 12 Models					1 to 11 Tubes							
A	5	TRF	--	--	--	(3-24,2-27,1-45)	--	--	--	--	--	--	B	--	--	--	23.75	M	D	-
B	6	TRF	--	--	--	--	--	--	--	--	--	--	B	--	--	--	39.50	A	D	-
B	1	-	--	--	--	--	--	--	--	--	--	--	BS	--	--	--	5.95	St	-	u
B	2	-	--	--	--	--	--	--	--	--	--	--	BS	--	--	--	8.95	St	-	u
-	4	-	--	--	--	--	--	--	--	--	--	--	--	--	--	--	13.85	M	-	-
-	5	-	--	--	--	--	--	--	--	--	--	--	--	--	--	--	15.65	M	-	-
-	6	SH	--	--	--	--	--	--	--	--	--	--	--	--	--	--	21.00	M	-	-
A	11	SH	--	--	--	--	--	--	--	--	--	--	BS	V	--	--	25.00	M	-	-
B	6	SH	--	--	--	--	--	--	--	--	--	--	8	R	--	--	29.75	ch	D	-
B	1	-	--	--	--	--	--	--	--	--	--	--	S	--	--	--	39.50	A	-	-
-	-	SH	--	--	--	--	--	--	--	--	--	--	--	--	--	--	6.45	-	-	-
-	-	-	--	--	--	--	--	--	--	--	--	--	--	--	--	--	12.50	-	-	q

ROAN, ANSLEY   LOS ANGELES, CAL. $-- to $--

12 Chasses   20 Models   4 to 12 Tubes

A	6	TRF	3-35	--	--	24	--	1-47	80	--	--	B		--	15M	42.50	M	D
A	8	SH	1-35	35	27	27	1-35	2-47	80	--	--	B		--	15M	46.50	M	D
				(1-24,5-27,2-47,3-35,180)											15M	69.50	M	D
A	10	SH	1-35	35	27	27	1-35	2-47	80	--	--	B		--	59	59.50	C	D
A	12														69	69.50	M	D
A	4	TRF	1-58	--	57	57	1-58	1-47	82	--	--	B		--	79	72.50	C	D
A	5	SH	--	57	*	57	--	1-47	82	27	--	B		--	99	89.50	M	D
A	6	--	1-58	57	*	55	1-58	1-47	82	--	--	B		--	109	107.50	C	D
A	6	SH	--	--	--	--	--	2-46	82	56	--	BS		--	100	129.50	O	--
A	8	SH	1-58	58	56	56	1-58	2-46	82	56	--	B		--	25		M	D
A	10	SH	--	--	--	--	--	--	--	--	--	--	15M	--	29		M	D
A	12	SH	--	--	--	--	--	--	--	--	--	BS	59	--	30		M	D
A	12	SH	1-58	--	--	--	--	--	--	--	--	B	102	--	32		LB	D
												110			15M			D
												100			59		O	D
												109			102			D
															110			D
															100			D
															109			D

HOWARD RADIO CO.   "HOWARD"   SOUTH HAVEN, MICH. $39.50 to $395.00

14 Chasses   19 Models   4 to 13 Tubes

A	5	TRF	2-35	--	--	24	--	1-47	80	--	B			10	49.50	M	D
B	6	TRF	3-24	--	--	27	--	1-45	80	--	B			SG-B Green Diamond	69.50	Cp	D
A	7	SH	1-35	27	27	27	--	1-47	80	--	B			20	69.50	Cp	D
A	8	SH	1-35	35	27	27	--	2-47	80	--	B			29	79.50	C	D
A	9	SH	1-35	35	27	27	--	2-47	80	27	B			35	89.50	LB	D
A	4	SH	1-35	24	--	--	--	--	--	--	S			40	99.50	C	D
B	8	SH	1-44	37	85	85	2-41	27	--	Bp			H	119.50	C	D
A	4	SH	1-58	56	56	56	2-42	80	57	Bp	56	VTN	45	129.50	C	D
A	10	SH	1-56	56	56	56	2-42	83	57	Bp	56	VTN	60	295.50	RP	D
A	11	SH	1-58	56	56	56	2-42	80	57	Bp	56	VTN	33	39.50	St	
A	13	SH	1-58	56	56	56	2-46	82	57	Bp	56	VTN	K --	89.50	A	
A	15	SH	2-58	56	56	56	4-42	80	57	Bp	56	VTN	Whitehouse		C	D
A	19	SH				(2-24,5-27,6-55,4-47,2-80)				BS	57	VTN	L --	109.50	HB	D2
													M	139.50	HB	D
													500 DeLuxe	365.00	C	
													501 DeLuxe	395.00	C	D2

Hy

P	T	C	RADIO	INTERMEDIATE			AUDIO			RECT.	AVC	NS	R	CONT. TUNING	MODEL NUMBER AND NAME	PRICE	CAB.	SPKR.	NOTE
				D	O	IF	D	1st	OUT.										
			HYMAN & CO. INC., C. H.												NEW YORK CITY				
			1 Chassis				12A 12A 2-12A			--		--			Washington	--	T		--
B	7	TRF	3-22	--	--	--	12A	12A	2-12A	--	--	--	B	--	7 Tubes -- (1932)	--	--	--	--
			INSULINE CORP OF AMERICA									ICA			NEW YORK CITY				
			29 Chasses				45 Models						1 to 8 Tubes		Price 1931 only-$25.50 to $475.				
D	1	--	--	--	--	--	12A	--	--	--	--	--	B	--	Companion	*25.50	Pr	--	u
A	2	--	--	--	--	--	27	--	--	27	--	--	B	--	Companion(110v)	*25.50	Pr	--	u
U	4	TRF	1-36	--	--	--	36	--	1-38	37	--	--	B	--	Companion(220v)	*26.50	Pr	--	u
A	4	TRF	1-35	--	--	--	24	--	1-47	80	--	--	R	--	Univ.Companion		Pr	--	j
A	4	TRF	1-35	--	--	--	24	--	1-47	80	--	--	B	--	Insul	*35.50	M	--	--
A	5	TRF	2-35	--	--	--	24	--	1-47	80	--	--	BLp	--	Insul	*50.00	M	--	--
A	5	TRF	2-35	--	--	--	24	--	1-47	80	--	--	BL	--		*38.50	Pr	--	--
A	5	TRF	2-35	--	--	--	24	--	1-47	80	--	--	B	--	Env.Longfellow	65.20	M.	--	--
A	5	TRF	2-35	--	--	--	24	--	1-47	80	--	--	BLp	--	Envoy	*57.50	M	--	--
A		--	--	(2-27,1-35,1-47,1-80)									-	--	Envoy	*73.50	M	D	--
A		--	--	(1-36,2-37,2-38)									BLp	--	Envoy	*99.50	MP	D	--
A	5	TRF	2-35	(2-31,1-32,2-33)			24	--	1-47	80	--	--	P	--	Envoy	*118.00	MP	D	--
A		--	--	--	--	--	--	--	--	--	--	--	--	--	1254	*200.00	-	D	tsr
A		--	--	--	--	--	--	--	--	--	--	--	--	--	1255	75.00	K	--	ts
A		TRF	2-36	--	--	--	36	--	2-33	--	--	--	T	--	1256 (Scanner&Amp.)	*99.50	K	--	ts
A		--	--	--	--	--	--	--	--	--	--	--	--	--	1257	*59.50	K	--	tr
A		--	--	--	--	--	--	--	--	--	--	--	T	--	1276	*69.50	ch	--	tr
A		--	--	--	--	--	--	--	--	--	--	--	--	--		37.50	K	--	ts
A	5	TRF	2-36	(2-24,1-35,2-38)			30		2-33	--	--	--	B	--	Envoy	*56.00	M	D	k
D		--	--	--	--	--	27	27	1-45	80	--	--	BLp	--	Envoy	*57.50	M	D	k
A	5	--	--	--	--	--	24	24	1-47	37	--	--	B	--		--	K	--	--
B	5	TRF	1-32	--	--	--	30	30	2-33	--	--	--	BL	--	Envoy	*73.50	M	D	k
B	5	TRF	1-24	--	--	--	27	27	1-45	--	--	--	BSL	--	Env.Longfellow	*109.50	MP	--	--
A	6	TRF	3-35	--	--	--	24	24	1-47	80	--	--	BSI	--	Conqueror	*128.50	MP	D	--
U	7	TRF	1-36	--	--	--	37	37	2-37	37	--	--	BS	--	Conqueror	*59.50	K	--	--
A	8	--	--	(2-24,2-50,2-51,2-81)			--	--	--	--	--	--	BS	--	Conqueror	*69.50	K	--	--
													B	--	Conqueror	*59.50	K	--	k
													B	--	Conqueror	*65.00	ch	--	--
													P	--	New Envoy	*65.00	oh	--	--
A		--	--	--	--	--	--	--	--	--	--	--	B	--	Universal	*39.50	Pr	--	3h
													B	--	1260	*475.00	-	--	tsr
A	5	TRF	2-58	--	--	--	57	--	1-47	80	--	--	B	•	Envozette	--	M	D	--

224

INTERNATIONAL RADIO CORP., ANN ARBOR, MICH.

Model	Price		
Envoyette			
Supersix			
Supersix			
Superseven			
Superseven			
Univ.Companion	Fr		
Superconqueror			
Superconqueror			
Superconqueror			

11 Chasses

INTERNATIONAL ALL WAVE RADIO CORP. "INTERNATIONAL" ANN ARBOR, MICH. $24.50 to $79.50
4 to 8 Tubes — 20 Models

Model	Price	
K95	79.50	LB
Internat'l Duo	49.95	M
Duo	69.50	M
Duo	69.50	
D-100 Duo	79.50	
K85	49.95	M
K90	69.50	LB
The Mc K & R	29.50	-
T-61	24.50	
TS-61	25.00	M
PB	35.00	M
PD	25.00	M
PM	25.00	M
PW All Purpose	25.00	St
C-62	32.00	Cp
J-63	34.00	Cp
JS-63 Kadette	36.00	
	25.00	

JACKSON-BELL CO. LTD.
20 Chasses — 30 Models

(continued)

"PETER PAN" LOS ANGELES, CAL. $29.95 to $98.50
4 to 12 Tubes

Model	Price	
84	29.95	M
69	29.95	M
87	69.50	-
87	49.95	M
	59.95	C

P	T	C	RADIO	INTERMEDIATE			AUDIO			RECT	AVC	NS	R	CONT	TUNING	MODEL NUMBER AND NAME	PRICE	CAB.	SPKR.	NOTE
				D	O	IF	D	1st	OUT											
			(Jackson-Bell)																	
▲	8	TRF	1-35	24	27	(4-24,1-27,2-45,1-80)	27	27	1-47	80	--	--	B	--	--	68	-	M	D	-
▲	8	SH									--	--	B	--	--	88	59.50	M	D	-
✱	9	SH	1-35	24	27	2-35	27	--	2-47	80	--	--	B	--	--	88	69.50	C	-	-
											--	--	B	--	--	89	69.50	M	D	-
											--	--	B	--	--	89	79.50	C	D	-
▲	5	SH	1-58	--	--	--	--	--	--	--	--	--	B	T	--	25	29.95	M	D	-
▲	5	SH	1-58	57	*	1-55	55	--	1-47	80	--	--	B	V	--	25AV	31.95	M	D	-
▲	5										--	--	B	V	--	25AV	34.95	st	D	a
B	5	6H									*	--	B	V	--	Pandora	34.95	st	D	-
B	5	SH		58	57	1-59	57	--	1-47	--	--	--	B	V	--	205AV	39.95	A	D	-
B	6	SH	--	56	*	1-58	55	--	1-47	80	*	--	B	V	--	-	54.95	A	D	-
▲	6	SH	1-58								--	--	BS	--	--	26AV	37.95	M	D	-
▲	6										--	--	BS	--	--	26AV-CB	39.98	M	D	-
B	6										*	--	BS	--	--	26	39.95	M	D	a
▲	7	SH	1-58	57	*	1-58	55	--	2-47	80	--	--	B	V	--	26SW	49.95	C	D	-
▲	8	SH	1-58	57	56	1-58	55	--	2-47	80	*	--	B	V	--	26SW	69.95	A	D	-
▲	8	SH										--	BS	V	--	206	59.95	M	D	-
▲												--	BS	V	--	27AV	46.95	C	D	-
▲												--	BS	V	--	27AV	62.50	M	D	-
▲	8	SH	1-58	58								--	B	V	--	28AV-SB	57.95	C	D	-
▲												--	BS	V	--	28AV-SB	79.95	M	D	-
▲												--	BS	V	--	38	59.95	C	D	-
▲	12	SH	1-58	58	56	2-58	55	56	2-45	83	56	--	B	V	--	212	98.50	C	D2	-

JACKSON RADIO & TELEVISION CO. CHICAGO, ILL. (1952) -- $19.75 and $27.50

2 Chasses 2 Models 4 and 5 Tubes

P	T	C	RADIO	INTERMEDIATE			AUDIO			RECT	AVC	NS	R	CONT	TUNING	MODEL NUMBER AND NAME	PRICE	CAB.	SPKR.	NOTE
				D	O	IF	D	1st	OUT											
▲	4	TRF	1-24	--	--	--	24	--	1-47	80	--	--	B	--	--	LK-447	19.75	M	D	-
▲	5	TRF	2-57	--	--	--	57	--	1-47	80	--	--	B	--	--	SF-547	25.50	M	D	-

JACKSON RESEARCH LABS. MALDEN, MASS. "JACKSON" (1931) $59.50 to $99.50

4 Chasses 4 Models 3 to 9 Tubes

P	T	C	RADIO	INTERMEDIATE			AUDIO			RECT	AVC	NS	R	CONT	TUNING	MODEL NUMBER AND NAME	PRICE	CAB.	SPKR.	NOTE
				D	O	IF	D	1st	OUT											
▲	3	TRF	--	--	27	--	--	27	--	26	--	--	S	--	--	JC	59.50	oh	D	q
▲	8	SH	2-24	24	27	2-24	24	27	1-45	80	--	--	--	--	--	NJ32	69.50	oh	D	-
▲	8	SH	1-35	24	27	2-24	24	--	1-45	80	--	--	--	--	--	NJ8	79.50	oh	D	-
▲	9	SH	1-35	24	27	2-24	27	--	2-47	80	--	--	--	--	--	R9	99.50	oh	D	-

JENKINS TELEVISION CORP. PASSAIC, N. J. $69.50 to $335.00
11 Chassis — 11 Models — — Tubes —

	Type	Tubes	Model	Price		
A	TRF		A	119.50	K	tsr
A	TRF		B	214.50	K	tsr
A	TRF		C	169.00	ch	tsr
A	TRF		D	264.00	ch	tsr
A	TRF		J-D	150.00	-	tr
A	TRF		J-DS	175.00	-	trs
A	-		E	285.00	-	trs
A	TRF 2-24	27 24 1-45,1-80	F	335.00	CT	tr2L
A 7	TRF	(4-24,1-27,2-45,1-80)	JK-20	69.50	K	-
A 8	TRF --	80 BS	JD-30	--	M	-
A 1	-		R-400 Radiovisor	--	M	ts

JEWEL MFG. CO. SALT LAKE CITY, UTAH $ --
1 Chassis — 1 Model — (1931) — — Tubes —

				B		M	

J.M.P. MFG. CO. MILWAUKEE, WIS. $12.50 to $59.50
4 Chasses — 4 Models — "AUTO-DIAL" 1 and 5 Tubes

	Type	Tubes	Model	Price		
B 5	TRF 2-24	24 27 1-38	Submariner	59.50	A	q1
B 5	TRF 1-35	24 27 1-47	48	40.00	A	h1
U 1	-			12.50	M	q1

KARADIO CORP. MINNEAPOLIS, MINN. $86.50 and $112.50
2 Chasses — 2 Models — "KARADIO" (1932) 9 and 11 Tubes

		Tubes	Model	Price		
B 9	--	(5-36,3-57,3-71)	9	86.50	A	-
B 11	--	(4-36,3-57,4-71)	11	112.50	A	-

KELLER-FULLER MFG. CO. LOS ANGELES, CAL. $49.50 to $39.50
5 Chasses — 7 Models — "RADIETTE" (1931) 5 to 9 Tubes

	Type	Tubes	Model	Price		
A 5	TRF	(5-24,1-45,1-80)	Junior	49.50	M	D
U 7	TRF	(4-36,2-39,1-71)		49.50	Pr	D
A 9	3H	-- 2-45 80	Troubadour	89.75	Pr	D
		(continued)	-	79.50	M	D

P	T	C	RADIO	D	O	IF	D	1st	OUT.	RECT.	AVC	NS	R	CONT	TUNING	MODEL NUMBER AND NAME	PRICE	CAB	SPKR	NOTE
				INTERMEDIATE			AUDIO													
																(Keller-Fuller)				
A	7	SH	—	—	—	—	—	—	2-45	80	—	—	B	TF	—	90	—	—	D	-
A	9	SH	2-35	—	—	—	—	—	2-45	80	—	—	B	TF	—		89.50	C	D	-
																KENNEDY, COLIN B. CORP. SOUTH BEND, IND. $— to $—				
																"KENNEDY" 2 to 16 Tubes 27 Models 14 Chasses				
A	—	SH	—	—	—	—	—	—	—	—	—	—	S	—	—	—	—	—	D	q
A	2	SH	—	24	27	—	—	—	—	—	—	—	B	—	—	1754 Globe Trotter	42.50	M	D	
A	5	TRF	2-35	—	—	—	—	—	1-47	80	—	—	B	T	—	Coronet	44.50	T	D	
A	7	SH	1-35	24	27	1-35	27	—	1-47	80	—	—	B	T	—	Royalette	62.50	—	D	
																Imperial	67.50	—	D	
A	7	SH	1-35	24	27	1-35	27	—	1-47	80	—	—	B	T	—	Baronet	—	M	D	
																Premier	—	LB	D	
A	8	SH	1-35	24	27	1-35	27	—	2-47	80	—	—	B	—	—	1852	49.50	M	D	
																1952	63.50	LB	D	
																1656	89.50	LB	D	
A	11	TRF	(6-24,2-27,2-45,1-80)	27	—	—	—	—	—	—	—	—	BS	T	—	Sovereign	97.50	—	D	
																826-B Double	252.00	C	D	
A	4	TRF	1-58	—	—	—	57	—	1-47	80	—	—	BP	—	—	455 Metropolitan	—	M	D	
A	5	57	—	57	*	—	55	—	1-47	80	*	—	BP	V	—	563 Cosmopolitan	—	M	D	
																1872-B	—	M	D	
A	7	SH	1-58	57	56	1-58	55	—	1-47	80	*	56	BP	V	—	68-D	—	LB	D	
															VN		62-D	—	HB	D	
A	10	SH	1-58	57	56	1-58	56	—	1-47	80	—	—	B	VN	—	164-B	—	LB	D	
																664-B	—	C	D	
																*64	—	ch	D	
A	12	SH	1-58	57	56	1-58	56	—	2-47	80	56	—	BS	V	—	*66	—	ch	D	
																266-B	—	LB	D	
																366-A	—	HB	D	
																366-B	—	HB	D	
																766-B	—	O	D	
																866-B	—	O	D	
A	16	SH	—	—	—	—	—	—	—	—	—	—	—	—	—	— DeLuxe	—	—	D2	d
																KENOLA RADIO CORP. NEW YORK CITY $87.50				
																"KENOLA" (1931) 5 Tubes 1 Model 1 Chassis				
A	5	TRF	2-35	—	24	—	—	—	1-47	80	—	—	—	—	—	Kenola	87.50	—	D	-

228

KOLSTER RADIO INC. — "KOLSTER" — NEWARK, N. J. — $59.75 to $149.50
13 Chassis — 26 Models — 3 to 10 Tubes

Code	Tubes	Type												Model	Price			
◄*	7	SH	1-35	24	27	1-35	24	--	1-47	80	--	--	B	T	K60	69.50	T	A	--
◄	8	SH	1-35	24	27	1-35	24	--	1-47	80	24	--	B	T	K62	69.50	T	A	--
◄*	9	SH	1-35	24	27	1-35	27	--	2-47	80	24	--	B	VT	K-70	99.50	HB	A	--
◄*	10	SH	2-35	24	27	1-35	27	--	2-47	80	24	--	B	VT	K-72	99.50	HB	A	--
◄													B	VT	K-80	129.50	HB	A	∞
◄*													B	VT	K-82	129.50	HB	A	∞
◄	8	SH	1-58	58	56	1-58	56	56	1-47	80	*	--	B	VT	K-90	149.50	C	A	∞
◄													B		K-92	149.50	C	A	∞
D	8	SH	1-39	39	37	1-39	37	37	2-35	--	*	--	B	VT	K-110	59.75	M	A	--
B	8	SH	1-58	58	56	1-58	56	56	2-47	AQ	*	--	B	VT	K-112	59.75	M	A	--
B	9	SH	1-34	34	30	1-34	30	30	2-30	--	--	--	B	V	K-120	74.75	C	A	--
B	9	SH	--	--	--	--	--	--	--	--	*	--	B	V	K-122	76.50	C	A	--
A	10	SH	1-39	39	37	1-39	37	37	4-38	--	*	--	B	V	K110	--	M	A	--
													B	V	K-113	66.25	M	A	--
A	10	SH	1-58	58	56	2-58	56	56	2-47	80	*	--	B	V	K-123	81.75	C	A	--
													B	V	K-130 Noiseless	99.75	C	A	--
													B	V	K-132	102.00	C	D∞	--
													B	V	K-114	--	M	A	--
													B	V	K-133	--	C	A	--
													B	V	K-130	--	C	A	--
													B	V	K-133A DeLuxe	112.25	C	A	--
													B	V	K-140	139.75	C	D	--
-	3	-	1-58	57	56	1-58	--	--	--	--	--	--	S	--	K-141	144.75	C	D	--
															K-142 DeLuxe	148.00	C		--

KRAFT, J. — "KRAFT" (1931) — NEW YORK CITY — $165.00
1 Chassis — 1 Model — Fire Place — ← Tubes →

LANG RADIO CO. — "LANG" (1932) — NEW YORK CITY — $ -- to $ --
4 Chassis — 4 Models — 5 to 7 Tubes

Code	Tubes	Type								Model		Price
◄	5	TRF	2-58	--	--	57	--	82	B	AA5	--	M
D	6	TRF	2-39	--	--	37	37	--	B	DC-6	--	M
◄	7	SH	1-58	56	1-58	55	1-58	82	B	AA-7	--	M
D	7	SH	1-39	37	1-39	85	1-39	--	B	DR-7	--	M

229

P	T	C	RADIO	INTERMEDIATE			AUDIO			RECT.	AVC	NS	R	CONT TUNING	MODEL NUMBER AND NAME	PRICE	CAB.	SPKR.	NOTE
				D	O	IF	D	1st	OUT.										
			LEE DE FOREST MFG. CO. LTD. LOS ANGELES, CAL. (1931) -- Tubes																
-- --		-- --	-- Chasses	-- --	-- --	-- --	-- --	-- --	-- --	-- --	-- --	-- --	-- --	-- --	2 Models	to $ --	--	-- --	-- --
-- --		-- --		-- --	-- --	-- --	-- --	-- --	-- --	-- --	-- --	-- --	-- --	T-E T-E		69.50	Cp M	-- --	-- --
			LEUTZ, C. R. INC. ALTOONA, PA. (1931) -- Tubes																
A			2 Chasses	-- --	-- --	-- --	-- --	-- --	-- --	-- --	-- --	-- --	B	-- --	3 Models Cub	to $ -- --	MC	-- --	-- -- --
													--		Seven Seas	-- --	--	-- --	-- -- --
D				-- --	-- --	-- --	-- --	-- --	-- --	-- --	-- --	-- --	B	-- --	Cub	-- --	MC	-- --	-- -- --
			LINCOLN RADIO CORP. (LINCOLN) CHICAGO, ILL. 10 and 12 Tubes																
B		--	6 Chasses	--	--	--	--	--	--	--	--	--	--	--	7 Models	$ -- -- to $ --	--	-- -- -- -- -- --	-- -- -- -- -- -- --
D	10	SH		--	--	(5-30,2-31,5-32)	--	--	--	--	--	--	BS	--	DC-8	80.00	ch		
D	10	SH		--	--	--	24	27	--	--	--	--	BS	--	DC-8	130.00	LB		
D	10	SH		24	27	4-24	24	27	2-45	--	--	--	BS	--	SW-8	--	ch		
A	10	SH		--	--	--	--	--	--	--	--	--	BS	--	DC-SW-10	--	ch		
															SW-31	--	ch		
															SW-32	--	ch		
A	12	SH		35	56	4-35 W	56	56	2-45	80 *	--	--	BS V	M	SW-33	--	ch	D	--
			LIJXOR RADIO MFG. CO. "LIJXOR" (1931) NEW YORK CITY 5 Tubes																
--	5	--	1 Chassis	--	--	--	--	--	--	--	--	--	--	--	NEW YORK CITY	$22.50	M	D	--
			MARQUETTE RADIO INC. "MARQUETTE" NEW YORK CITY 4 to 9 Tubes $16.50 to $49.50																
A	5	TRF	12 Chasses	-- --	-- --	-- --	-- --	37	2-38	-- --	-- --	-- --	B	T	12 Models	16.50	M	D	--
B	6	TRF	3-56	-- --	-- --	-- --	-- --	37	2-38	-- --	-- --	-- --	B	R	Motor Car	--	A	D	--

												B		*18.50	B	--
	TRF											BS		19.50	B	--
	TRF	(1-C47,1-C57,1-C58,1-C80)								B		*19.95	MC	--
	TRF	(1-24,2-35,2-47,1-80)								B		--		
	-	(4-01A,2-71A)								B		28.50	M	--
	SH	(3-56,1-57,2-38)								B	R	39.50	M	--
	SH									BS	VR	*33.50	A	--
										BS	VR	49.50	A	--

MIDWEST RADIO CORP.   "MIRACO"   CINCINNATI, OHIO $16.75 to $49.88

6 Chasses   6 Models   4 to 16 Tubes

11	SH	1-35	24	27	1-35	27	27	2-47	80	B	VT	*	37.50	ch	D
-	SH									B			49.88	C	D
4	SH	1-24	24	27				80	S		16.75	ch	
13	-	-							BS		--	q	
15	-	-							BS		--		
16	SH	1-58	58	56	3-58	55	42	2-46	82	BS	VTN	39.96	ch	D2	4h

MINERVA RADIO CO.   "MINERVA"   CHICAGO, ILL. $19.50 to $37.50

4 Chasses   4 Models   (2-36,1-37,1-38)   4 and 5 Tubes

U	TRF									-	-	26.25	M
U	TRF	1-64			64		1-68	67	Bp	M	19.50	M
B	TRF	2-36			36		1-41	-	B	-	35.00	
D	TRF	2-44			37		2-38	80	Bp	6	37.50	M

MISSION BELL RADIO MFG. CO. INC.   "MISSION" (1932)   LOS ANGELES, CAL. $ -- to $ --

5 Chasses   4 Models   4 to 6 Tubes

A	TRF	1-58	--	57	--	1-47	80	-	--	19-A	M	--
B	SH	--	57	*	1-58	--	1-51	KR	B	--	Deluxe	A	--
A	SH	1-39	56	*	1-59	--	1-47	80	-	--	5	M	--
D	SH	1-39	56	W	1-39	--	1-41	KR	B	--	17-A	Pr	--
D	TRF	3-39	--	37	--	24	1-48	KR	V	V	6-A	A	--

P	T	C	RADIO	D	O	IF	D	1st	OUT.	RECT.	AVC	NS	R	CONT	TUNING	MODEL NUMBER AND NAME	PRICE	CAB.	SPKR.	NOTE
					INTERMEDIATE			AUDIO												

MOTOROLA – SEE GALVIN MFG. CORP.

MOTOMASTER RADIO CORP.   CHICAGO, ILL.   (1932)

1 Chassis   1 Model   7 Tubes $79.50

P	T	C	RADIO	D	O	IF	D	1st	OUT.	RECT.	AVC	NS	R	CONT	TUNING	MODEL	PRICE	CAB.	SPKR.	NOTE
B	7	SH		(2-24,1-27,3-35,1-47)									B	VR	-		79.50	A	D	a

MOTORPHONE RADIO CORP. OF AMERICA   NEW YORK CITY   (1932)

1 Chassis   1 Model   6 Tubes $33.75

| B | 6 | TRF | -- | -- | -- | -- | -- | -- | -- | -- | -- | -- | B | - | - | Perfection Autofone | 33.75 | A | D | - |

MY OWN RADIO INC.   CHICAGO, ILL.   "MY OWN"

3 Chasses   3 Models   4 and 5 Tubes $8.97 to $17.50

A	4	TRF	1-24	--	--	--	24	--	27	27	--	--	B	-	-	MO	17.50	M	-	-
-	4	"	"	--	--	--	--	--	--	--	--	--	B	R	-	-	8.97	K	-	-
B	5	"	"	--	--	--	--	--	--	--	--	--	B	R	-	-	16.95	A	D	-

NATIONAL CO. INC.   MALDEN, MASS.   "NATIONAL"

23 Chasses   25 Models   1 to 8 Tubes $37.00 to $129.00

A	4	TRF	4-24	--	--	(2-35,4-45)	--	--	--	--	--	--	3	--	--	AC-SW-45	*79.50	K	-	a
A	5	TRF	4-35	--	--	27	--	--	--	--	--	--	B	--	--	MB-30	-	ch	-	v3h
A	6	TRF	1-32	--	--	27	27	--	--	--	--	--	B	--	--	MB-32	-	ch	-	v3h
A	5	TRF	1-24	--	--	24	27	--	2-27	--	--	--	BS	--	--	AC-SW-5 Thrill Box	*79.50	Tm	-	a
B	5	TRF	1-32	--	--	32	30	--	2-31	--	--	--	BS	--	--	DC-SW-5 Thrill Box	*75.00	Tm	-	-
A	5	TRF	1-35	--	--	35	27	--	2-27	--	--	--	BS	--	--	AC-SW-5	*79.50	Tm	-	-
A	5	TRF	1-35	--	--	35	--	2-45	--	--	--	--	BS	--	--	SW-5	-	T	-	-
A	1	-	--	--	--	--	--	--	--	80	--	--	--	--	--	5880-ABS	*37.00	Pm	-	-
A	3	-	--	--	--	--	--	--	--	80	--	--	BS	--	--	5800-AB	*37.00	Pm	-	-
A	3	TRF	1-35	--	--	35	27	--	--	--	--	--	BS	--	--	SW-3	*55.00	K	-	-
B	3	TRF	1-36	--	--	36	37	--	--	--	--	--	BS	--	--	SW-3	*55.00	K	-	-
A	4	TRF	1-58	--	--	58	27	--	--	80	--	--	BSL	--	--	SW-3	89.50	m	-	a
A	5	TRF	--	--	--	--	--	--	--	80	--	--	BSL	--	--	SW-3	-	ch	-	v3h
B	5	SH	1-35	1-35	27	24	30	--	--	80	--	--	3	--	--	NC-5	*75.00	Cpm	-	q
A	6	TRF	1-34	--	--	34	30	2-31	--	--	--	--	BSL	--	--	SW-34	*85.00	m	-	a
B	8	TRF	1-58	--	--	58	27	2-45	--	80	--	--	BSL	--	--	SW-58	*129.00	m	-	a
B	8	SH	--	36	36	37	--	2-58	--	--	--	--	S	--	--	-		K	-	a

A	3	SH	1-24	24	27	--	--	--	--	--	--	--	S	-	-	HFC	*39.50	-	-	q
D	3	SH	1-36	36	37	--	--	--	--	--	--	--	S	-	-	HFC	*39.50	-	-	q
D	3	-	1-36	--	--	--	36	37	--	--	--	--	BSL	-	-	SW-3	*55.00	-	-	q
A	5	SH	1-35	24	27	1-35	--	--	--	80	--	--	S	-	-	NC-5	-	ch	-	q
-	-	-	--	--	--	--	--	--	--	--	--	--	BSL	-	-	SW-45	-	ch	-	-

NATIONAL PFANSTIEHL MFG. CO. "PFANSTIEHL" (1931) WAUKEEGAN, MICH.
2 Chasses 2 Models -- Tubes $15.50 and $24.85

A	5	TRF	1-24				24		1-47	80			B	-	-	-	15.50	M	D	-
-	-	-	--	--	--	--	--	--	--	--	--	--	B	-	-	-	24.85	M	D	-

NEWARK ELECTRIC CO. "NECO" (1932) CHICAGO, ILL.
2 Chasses 3 Models 3 and 4 Tubes $20.25 to $34.50

-	3	-	--	--	--	--	--	--	--	--	--	--	-	S	-	400	29.50	M	-	q
A	4	SH		24	27					80				S		Neco	20.25	M	-	q
-	4	-	--	--	--	--	--	--	--	--	--	--	-	S	-	440	34.50	M	-	q

NORDEN-HAUCK INC. -- (1931) PHILADELPHIA, PA.
1 Chassis 1 Model 6 Tubes $ --

A	6	TRF	1-35	--	--	--	27	27	2-45	80	--	--	S	-	-	DX-5 Super	-	D	-	-

NORTH CHICAGO RADIO PRODUCTS CO. -- (1931) NORTH CHICAGO, ILL.
1 Chassis 1 Model 6 Tubes $79.50

A	6	-	--	--	--	--	--	--	--	--	--	--	-	-	-	Tablette	79.50	T	D	-

NORTHWEST SPECIALTY CO. "WALTON" (1932 WAUKEEGAN, ILL.
5 Chasses 5 Models 5 to 11 Tubes $ -- to $ --

A	5	TRF	2-58	--	--	--	57	--	1-47	80	--	--	B	-	-	5L	-	M	D	-
D	5	TRF	2-36	--	--	--	36	37	1-38	--	--	--	B	-	-	D	-	M	-	-
A	6	TRF	2-58	--	--	--	57	--	1-47	80	--	--	B	-	-	IH	-	M	-	h2
B	6	TRF	2-39	--	--	--	36	37	2-38	--	--	--	B	-	-	M	*19.50	A	D	-
A	11	TRF	3-58	--	--	--	57	27	2-47	80	*	*	B	-	-	A-16	-	C	D	7h

No

P	T	C	RADIO	INTERMEDIATE			AUDIO			RECT	AVC	NS	R	CONT	TUNING	MODEL NUMBER AND NAME	PRICE	CAB.	SPKR.	NOTE
				D	O	IF	D	1st	OUT.											
			OTTAWA FURNITURE CO.													HOLLAND, MICH.				
			1 Chassis				1 Model									(1931) 7 Tubes				
A	7	--	--	--	--	--	--	--	--	--	--	--	H	--				MC	D	-
			OZARKA INC.													CHICAGO, ILL. "OZARKA-VIKING" (1932) $65.00 to $200.00				
			4 Chasses				4 Models									6 to 16 Tubes				
A	6	SH	1-58	57	*	1-58	55	--	1-47	80	--	--	B	V		V-6	65.00	T	D	-
A	8	SH	1-58	58	56	1-58	56	56	1-47	80	56	--	B	V		V-8	100.00	C	D	-
A	10	SH	1-58	58	56	1-58	56	56	2-46	60	56	--	B	V		V-10	125.00	C	D	d
A	16	--			(7-27,4-35,3-45,2-80)								B	V		V-16	200.00	C	D2	-
			PARSONS LABS. INC.													ST. PAUL, MINN. "PARSONS" (1931)				
			1 Chassis				1 Model									7 Tubes				
B	7	TRF	3-32	--	--	--	30	30	2-31	--	--	--	B	--	1		92.50	C	--	-
			PATENT DEVELOPMENT CO.													SOUTH BEND, IND. (1931) $39.50 to $69.50				
			2 Chasses				4 Models									4 and 8 Tubes				
A	4	TRF	2-35	--	--	--	24	--	1-47	80	--	--	--	--		Wren	39.50	M	D	-
																Wren	49.50	LR	D	-
A	8	SH	2-35	24	27	1-24	24	--	1-47	80	--	--	--	--		Lark	59.50	T	D	-
																Lark	69.50	HR	D	-
			PATERSON RADIO CORP.													LOS ANGELES, CAL. (PATTERSON)				
			1 Chassis				1 Model									(1931) -- Tubes				
--	--	--	--	--	--	--	--	--	--	--	--	--	--	--		--		$	M	-
			PATTERSON RADIO CO.													LOS ANGELES, CAL. (PATTERSON) $34.50 to $79.50				
			4 Chasses				15 Models									7 to 10 Tubes				
A	8	SH	1-35	35	27	1-35	27	--	2-47	80	--	--	--	--		831	49.50	ch	D	-
																106	55.50	ch	D	-
																208	59.50	LR	D	-
A	10	SH	1-35	35	27	2-35	27	27	2-47	80	--	--	--	--		308	69.50	LR	D	-
																1031	59.50	ch	D	-

		Circuit											Model			Tubes	Price		
A	7	SH	--	57	56	2-58	55	--	1-59	82	*	--	B	VT	70		34.50	CP	--
													BS	VT	70-AW		39.50	CP	--
													B	VT	107		44.50	C	--
													BS	VT	107-AW		49.50	C	--
													B	VT	207-AW		54.50	C	--
													RS	VT	110-AW		59.50	C	d
													BS	VT	210-AW		69.50	C	d
																	79.50	D	--

PEKO INC.   CHICAGO, ILL.
1 Chassis   1 Model   "PEKO" (1931)   8 Tubes $250.00

		Circuit											Model			Tubes	Price		
A	10	SH	1-58	57	56	2-58	55	--	2-46	82	*	--			310		250.00	RP	--

PERFECTONE INC.   CHICAGO, ILL.
2 Chasses   2 Models   "PERFECTONE" (1932)   5 and 7 Tubes $18.50

													Model			Tubes	Price		
B	5	--	--	--	--	--	--	--	--	--	--	--	B	VR	Midget		18.50	A	--
B	7	--	--	--	--	--	--	--	--	--	--	--	B	VR	Standard			A	--

PHELPS RADIO CORP.   CHICAGO, ILL.
1 Chassis   1 Model   (1931)   5 Tubes $—

																	Price		
A	5	--	--	--	--	--	--	--	--	--	--	--	--	--	--	--	--	M	D

PHILCO RADIO & TELEVISION CORP.   PHILADELPHIA, PA.
31 Chasses   70 Models   "PHILCO"   3 to 11 Tubes $18.75 to $295.00

		Circuit											Model			Tubes	Price		
A	5	TRF	2-24	--	--	24	--	1-47	80	--	--	--	50 Baby Grand		--	36.50	M	--
D	6	TRF	2-14	--	--	14	17	2-71A	--	--	--	B	50		--	49.95	LP	h9
D	6	TRF	3-24	--	--	27	--	2-45	80	--	--	B	46		--	60.95	M	h9
A	7	SH	1-32	32	30	30	30	1-33	--	--	E	B	46		--	76.75	HR	--
B	7										E	B	76 or 77		--	99.50	RP	--
A*	7	SH	1-24	24	27	24	--	1-47	80	--	E	B	35		--	59.50	M	--
A*											E	B	35		--	75.00	HB	o
A*											E	B	70B.G.		--	49.75	M	o
A*											E	B	70H.B.		--	65.75	HB	o
A*											E	B	270		--	110.00	RP	o
A*	7	SH	1-35	24	*	27	35	1-47	80	*	VT	B	370 Lazyboy		--	69.50	T	o
									(continued)				70B.G.		--	49.75	M	f

P	T	C	RADIO	D	O	IF	D	1st	OUT	RECT.	AVC	NS	R	CONT	TUNING	MODEL NUMBER AND NAME	PRICE	CAB.	SPKR.	NOTE
			(Philco)																	
c*	7	SH	1-35	24	*	1-35	27	35	1-47	80	*	-	B	VT	-	70H.B.	65.75	HB	D	f
A-*													B	VT	-	270 Lazyboy	110.00	RP	D	f
A-*													B	VT	-	370	69.50	T	D	f
A-*													B	VT	-	470	89.50	GO	D	o
A*	9	SH	1-24	24	27	1-24	24	27	2-45	80	-	-	B	VT	-	90H.C.	69.50	N	D	o
													B	VT	-	90L.R.	89.75	LB	D	o
A*	9	SH	1-24	24	27	1-24	27	27	1-47	80	-	-	B	VT	4	90B.B.	109.75	HR	D	f
													B	VT	4	90L.B.	69.50	M	D	f
A*	9	SH	1-35	24	*	1-35	27	27	2-47	80	*	-	B	VT	4	90H.B.	89.75	LB	D	f
A*	11	SH	1-24	24	27	2-24	27	27	2-45	80			B	VT	4	90B.G.	109.75	HR	D	f
													B	VT	4	112	69.50	M	D	e
A*	11	SH	1-24	24	27	2-24	27	27	2-47	80	*	-	B	VT	4	112 Louis XVI	129.50	LR	D	f
													B	VT	4	212	155.00	HB	D	f
													B	VT	4	112	155.00	HB	D	f
													B	VT	4	112	295.00	RP	D	fm
													B	VT	4	212	149.50	LB	D	
													B	VT	4	112	169.50	HB	D	
													B	VT	4	212	295.00	RP	D	
													B	V	-	3	-	A		
B	7	TRF	3-24	-	-	-	71A	01A	1-71A	-	*	-	R	-	-	80B Junior	18.75	M	P	-
A	4	SH	1-36	*	-	-	36	-	1-42	90	-	-	R	-	-	52B	36.50	-	-	-
A	5	SH	1-24	*	-	1-35	24	-	1-47	80	-	-	B	-	-	52-C	39.50	Cp	D	-
A	5	SH	1-24	35	-	1-24	24	-	1-42	80	-	-	B	-	-	52-L	37.50	C	D	-
A	5	SH	-	15	*	1-32	32	30	1-19	-	-	-	B	-	-	37	60.00	MC	PD	-
B	5	SH	1-44	36	*	1-44	37	44	1-42	80	-	-	B	-	-	24-L	75.00	RP	D	d
A	7	SH	1-32	32	30	1-32	30	30	1-33	-	-	-	B	-	-	36-B	59.95	M	D	n
A	7	SH											B	-	-	36-L	69.95	LB	D	-
													B	-	-	36-D	89.50	HB	D	-
A	7	SH	(4-Pentodes,1-36,1-57,1-80)										B	-	-	71 Baby Grand	46.50	M	D	-
													B	-	-	71A	69.50	HH	D	-
													BS	-	-	71	77.95	HB	D	-
D	7	SH	-	-	-	-	-	-	-	-	-	-	B	V	-	71-R	89.50	-	-	-
A	8	SH	1-44	36	*	1-44	37	44	1-42	80	37	-	B	V	-	71-L	89.95	HB	D	-
													B	V	-	71-H	49.50	M	D	-
													B	V	-	71-D	59.50	LB	D	-
A	9	SH	1-44	36	*	1-44	37	44	2-42	80	-	-	B	VT	-	22-L	69.50	HB	PD	-
													BS	V	-	91	79.95	RP	D	D2
A	9	SH	1-44	44	37	2-44	37	44	1-42	80	37	-	BS	V	-	43-B Baby Grand	129.50	M	D	
																	68.50	-	D	
																	110.00	M	D	
																	59.95			

PHILMORE MFG. CO.   NEW YORK CITY (1932)   4 to 12 Tubes

"PHILMORE" — 35 Models, 27 Chasses

											Model	Price		
D 9	SH	1-44	36	*	37	37	2-43	--	BS	V	43-H	79.95	HH	D
									BS	V	43-X	100.00	C	D
A 9	SH	1-44	(1-24,3-27,2-35,2-47,80)						B	V	47-B	59.95	M	D
A 10	SH	1-44	36	*	37	37	2-42	80	B	V	47-D	89.95	HB	D
									B	R	47-X	100.00	C	D
									R	V	90-X	100.00	C	D
									B	V	91-B	69.50	M	D
									B	V	91-L	89.50	LB	D
									B	V	91-D	99.75	HB	D
A 11	SH	1-44	44	37	37	37	2-42	80	B	V	91-X	100.00	C	D
A 11	SH	1-24	24	27	27	27	2-47	80	B	VTR	23-X	195.00	RP	D2
B 3	SH	--	24	27	--	--	--	80	R	VTR	15-X	150.00	C	D2
									S	V	15DX	250.00	C	D2
--	--	--	--	--	1-35	--	--	--	B	--	112-X	150.00	Cp	
											4-C	39.50	A	
											7 Transitone	--		

	Model	Price	
BS	PD-4	24.50	M
BS	P-4	25.50	M
BS	P-6	47.50	oh
EL	P-7	52.50	M
BS	P-8	59.00	M

PIERCE-AIRO INC.   NEW YORK CITY   4 to 12 Tubes

"DE WALD" — 35 Models, 27 Chasses

									Model	Price	
I 4	TRF	--	--	--	--	--	--	B	— Cub Companion		M
A 5	TRF	2-24	--	--	--	1-45	80	B	AC-524 De W.Comp'n	*59.50	M
A 5	TRF	2-35	--	24	30	1-47	80	B	535		oh
								B	536		M
								B	546		oh
D 6	TRF	2-32	--	32	30	2-31	--	B	547-A	*63.50	M
D 6	TRF	2-36	--	36	37	2-33	--	T	DC-632		oh
								T	447		M
A 6	TRF	2-35	--	24	--	1-47	80	T	DC-637		oh
								B	638		M
A 7	TRP	2-24	--	24	27	2-45	80	V	646M		N
D 7	TRP	--	--	--	--	--	--	B	647M		oh
A 7	8H	1-35	24	24	--	1-47	80	B	AC724		oh
								B	DC727		oh
								B	735		M
								B	736		

(continued)

237

PILOT RADIO & TUBE CORP.   (PILOT)   LAWRENCE, MASS. $20.00 to $149.50

28 Chasses   47 Models   4 to 11 Tubes

P	T	C	RADIO	INTERMEDIATE			AUDIO			RECT.	AVC	NS	R	CONT	TUNING	MODEL NUMBER AND NAME	PRICE	CAB.	SPKR.	NOTE
				D	O	IF	D	1st	OUT.											
A	8	SH	1-35	24	27	1-35	24	--	1-47	80	27	--	B	V	--	746M	--	ch	D	--
													B	V	--	747N	--	M	D	--
						(Pierce-Airo)														
--	--	--	--	--	--	--	--	--	--	--	--	--	--	--	--		--	M	--	--
--	4	TRF	--	--	--	--	36	01A	1-7A	--	--	--	RP	--	--	1 Chest-O-Radio	--	MS	--	--
D	4	TRF	1-39	--	--	--	57	--	1-47	82	--	--	B	--	--	Kad	--	MS	--	--
A	5	SH	1-58	24	*	1-58	57	--	1-47	82	--	--	B	--	--	Bac	--	MS	--	--
A	--	--	--	--	--	--	--	--	--	--	--	--	B	T	--		--	CM	D	--
B	--	--	--	--	--	--	--	--	--	--	--	--	--	--	--	50	--	A	--	--
D	--	--	--	--	--	--	--	--	--	--	--	--	--	--	--	52 Motortone	--	ch	--	--
D	5	SH	2-56	24	27	1-35	36	--	2-33	80	--	--	BL	--	--	DC-532	--	M	D	--
A	6	SH	--	36	37	1-39	24	--	1-47	--	--	--	Bp	--	--	DC-533	--	M	--	--
D	6	SH	1-58	58	56	1-58	36	--	2-33	82	--	--	Bp	--	--	533-A	--	CM	D	--
A	6	SH	--	--	--	--	57	--	1-47	--	--	--	Bp	--	--	Bag	--	CM	--	--
A	7	SH	--	--	--	--	--	--	--	--	--	--	Rp	T	--	Kaf	--	C	D	--
--	--	--	--	--	--	--	--	--	--	245	--	--	BS	--	--	Plg	--	C	--	--
--	8	SH	--	--	--	--	--	--	--	400	--	--	--	--	--		--	ch	--	--
A	8	SH	--	58	56	1-35	57	--	1-47	82	--	--	--	T	--	HAH	--	CM	D	h9
A	12	SH	1-58	58	27	2-35	56	--	2-47	82	56	--	--	VT	M	RAM	--	CM	D	h6
B	4	TRF	1-22	--	--	--	01A	01A	1-12A	--	--	--	BS	--	--	K-110 Super-Wasp	*29.50	ch	--	s
A	4	TRF	1-24	--	--	--	27	27	1-27	--	--	--	BS	--	--	K-115 Super-Wasp	*34.50	ch	--	g
A	4	TRF	1-24	24	27	--	--	--	--	80	--	--	S	--	--	V-191	39.50	T	--	q
D	4	TRF	1-36	36	37	--	--	--	--	80	--	--	S	--	--	V-192	39.50	T	--	q
A	5	TRF	2-35	--	--	--	24	--	--	80	--	--	B	--	--	S-167	42.50	M	--	--
D	5	TRF	2-36	--	--	--	37	--	2-38	--	--	--	B	--	--	S-168	42.40	M	--	--
D	5	TRF	2-36	--	--	--	37	--	2-38	--	--	--	B	--	--	S-169	--	M	--	--
A	6	TRF	1-24	--	--	--	24	27	2-45	80	--	--	BS	--	--	K-136 Univ.Sup.Wasp	99.50	T	D	--
A	6	TRF	2-24	--	--	--	24	27	1-45	80	--	--	B	--	--	S-157	*59.50	M	D	--
D	6	TRF	2-01A	--	--	--	01A	01A	2-71A	--	--	--	B	T	VT	C-157 Queen Anne	*79.50	CL	D	--
A	7	SH	1-35	24	27	1-35	27	--	1-47	80	--	--	B	T	VT	S-156	*59.50	M	D	--
													B	--	VT	C-158 Queen Anne	*79.50	CL	D	--
													B	T	VT	S-148	*59.50	M	D	--
													B	--	--	C-151	*74.50	CL	D	--
													B	--	--	C-162	89.50	C	D	--
													B	--	--	S-164	79.50	M	D	--
B	7	SH	1-36	36	37	1-36	37	--	2-38	--	--	--	B	T	--	S-150	65.00	M	--	--
													B	--	--	S-166	75.00	M	--	--

											Model	Price			
A	10	SH	1-35	35	27	2-35	27		2-47	80		27		S449	89.50 M	—	—
													C-152	86.50 CL	—	—
													C-163	89.50 M	—	—
													S-165	79.50 M	—	—
D	10	SH			(5-36,3-37,2-38)						B		C-153 Standard	*116.00 C	—	D
B	10	SH			(5-27,5-36,2-38)						B		C-154 DeLuxe	*139.00 C	—	D
B	10	SH			(5-36,3-37,2-38)						B		T-177	99.50 T	—	—
B	10	SH			(3-27,5-36,2-38)						BS		C-189	119.50 C	—	—
A	11	SH	(3-24,3-27,1-47,2-35,2-80)								BS		T-178	99.50 T	—	D
											BS		C-190	119.50 C	—	D
A	—	TRF			—	—		2-45		27	BS		T-170	99.50 T	—	—
A	—	TRF			—	—		2-45			RS		C-179	119.50 C	—	—
											RS		— All Wave	*99.50 T	—	D
D	4	TRF	(1-36,1-38,1-39,HG-50)								BS	VT	— All Wave	*149.50 C	—	D
D	5	TRF	2-39	—	36	—	2-38	—				VT				
											B		— Duo	20.00 Pr	—	—
A	5	TRF	2-58	—	57	—	1-47	80			R		9257-R Corsair	44.50 St	—	—
											R		8645-R Armada	54.50 C	—	D
A	6	SH	—	24	27	1-35	—	1-47	80		B		9255 Corsair	39.50 St	—	D
											B		8643 Armada	49.50 C	—	D
D	7	SH	—	36	37	1-39	36	3-38	—		BS		1010 Dragon Monarch	59.50 M	—	D
											BS		8810 Dragon Emperor	79.50 M	—	—
											B		7641-R 20th Century	49.50 M	—	—
											BS		8241-R Golden Arrow	72.50 M	—	—
A	7	SH	1-35	24	27	1-35	24	1-47	80		BS		1011-R Dragon Mon.	64.50 M	—	—
											BS		8811-R Dragon Emp.	104.50 M	—	—
											BS		7639 20th Century	44.50 M	—	D
											B		1010 Dragon Mon.	59.50 M	—	D2
A	11	—	—	—	—	—	—	—	—		—		8239 Golden Arrow	67.50 C	—	D
													— Super Wasp	C		

PIONEER PRODUCTS CORP. PLANO, ILL. "PIONEER*" (1932) 4 Models

B	6	—	2 Chasses	(2-30,1-33,3-34)	5 and 7 Tubes	$75.35 to $98.75		
P	7	SB		(3-30,1-32,1-33,2-34)				
				T-53-M	75.35 M	BS V	—	—
				T-33-C	88.60 C	BS V	—	—
				S-33-M	84.25 M	BS V	—	—
				S-33-C	98.75 C	BS V	—	—

PIONEER RADIO LABS. CHICAGO, ILL. (1931) 1 Model

A	6	SH	1 Chassis	(1-24,2-27,1-35,1-47,1-80)	6 Tubes	B	—	—	M	D

239

P	T	C	RADIO	D	O	IF	D	1st	OUT.	RECT.	AVC	NS	R	CONT	TUNING	MODEL NUMBER AND NAME	PRICE	CAB.	SPKR.	NOTE
																PIONEER RADIO MFG. CO. SAN FRANCISCO, CAL. (1951)				
			— Chasses							—				— Tubes		6 Models $29.50 to $79.50				
A													B			Pee Wee	29.50	M	D	—
A													B				35.50	M	D	—
D													B				49.50	C	—	—
A													B				59.50	GC	D	—
A													B		V	Western Airway	79.50	A	D	—
B													B				79.50	A	—	—
																PIONEER TELEVISION CO. JERSEY CITY, N. J. (1932) 7 Tubes				
			1 Chassis							—						1 Model	$39.50			
A	7	—	—	—	—	—	—	—	—	—	—	—	RP	—	—	All Wave	$39.50	ch	D	ts
																PLAZA MUSIC CO. NEW YORK CITY "HAMILTON-LLOYD" 5 to 7 Tubes				
			9 Chasses													15 Models $ -- to $--				
A	6	TRF	5-24	—	—	—	24	—	1-47	80	—	—	B	—	—	—	69.50	M	D	—
A	5	TRF	2-58	—	—	—	57	—	1-47	80	—	—	R	—	—	59 Pal	30.25	Pr	D	—
													B			711	30.50	M	D	—
D	5	TRF	—	57	—	—	57	—	1-47	—	—	—	B	—	—	711	—	Pr	—	—
A	5	SH	1-58	57	*	—	57	—	—	80	—	—	B	—	—	61	32.50	M	D	—
													B			711	32.75	M	D	—
D	5	SH	—	(2-24,2-35,1-47,1-80)							—	—	B	—	—	52	—	C	—	—
A	6	SH	—							—	—	—	B	—	—	30	49.75	M	RP	—
													BL			34	—	M	D	—
													BL			90	—	M	RP	—
A	6	TRF	3-35	—	—	—	24	—	1-47	80	—	—	B	—	—	34	—	M	RP	—
D	—	TRF	—				—	—	—	—	—	—	B	—	—	90	40.00	M	K	—
A	7	SH	—	(1-47,1-56,1-57,3-58,1-80)							—	—	B	—	—	16	—	M	RP	—
																34			RP	D	
																PLYMOUTH RADIO CORP. LOS ANGELES, CAL. (1931)				
			1 Chassis							—						1 Model $ -- to $--				
A	—	—	—	—	—	—	—	—	—	B	—	—	—	—	—	—	—	M	—	—

NEW YORK CITY $7.60 to $37.50

7 Chasses	7 Models							-- Tubes												

											59.50	M	K	D	--	--	c	--
							-- Polo Junior				7.60	M	--	D				
							P.M.R.M. Deluxe				16.50	M	K	D				
							DX3				23.00	M	--	--				
							P.C.R.M.				32.50	T	--	--				
							P.A.R.N.				35.00	--	--	D				
											37.50	--	--	--				

POWELL MFG. CO.   1 Chassis   Models   (1931)

PREMIER ELECTRIC CO.   "PREMIER" (1932) Tubes   CHICAGO, ILL. $ -- to $ --
Models

RADIART CORP.   (RADIART) (1932)   2 Models   CLEVELAND, OHIO $22.50 and $32.50
2 Chasses   4 and 5 Tubes

A 4	TRF	1-58	--	--	57	--	1-47	80	--	T	41-A	22.50	M D
A 5	TRF	--	57	*	55	--	1-47	80	--	VT	32-A	32.50	M D

RADIO CHASSIS INC.   "RCI" (1932)   NEW YORK CITY $ -- to $ --
12 Chasses   14 Models   5 to 8 Tubes

A 5	TRF	1-58	--	--	57	56	1-47	80	B	AC-25	27.50	M
A 5	TRF	2-58	--	--	57	--	1-47	80	2	FVA-35	51.00	M
D 5	SH	--	--	--	--	--	1-71A	--	B	TR-35	36.50	st
D 6	TRF	2-58	--	01A	71A	01A	1-71A	--	B		--	ch
A 6	SH	1-58	57	*	56	--	1-47	80	B	DR-25	29.50	M
D 6	TRF	3-58	--	01A	71A	01A	1-71A	--	B	SHA-36	37.50	M
D 6	SH	--	--	--	--	55	47	--	R	TR-36	39.50	st
A 8	SH	1-58	58	56	1-58	55	2-47	90	3	FVD-36	34.50	M
--	SH	--	--	--	--	--	--	--	B	CH-38	--	ch
--	SH	--	--	--	--	--	--	--	B		--	ch
												MC
												st

(continued)

P	T	C	RADIO	D	O	IF	D	1st	OUT.	RECT.	AVC	NS	R	CONT	TUNING	MODEL NUMBER AND NAME	PRICE	CAB.	SPKR.	NOTE
					INTERMEDIATE			**AUDIO**												
--	--	SH	--	(Radio Chassis)			--	--	--	--	--	--	B	--	--	--	--	M	--	--
--	--	SH	--	--	--	--	--	--	--	--	--	--	B	--	--	-- Treasure Chest	--	St	--	--

RADIO-CHRON CO.   KANSAS CITY, MO. $39.95 to $99.50
"RADA-CHRON"   (1931)   5 to 9 Tubes
8 Chasses   9 Models

P	T	C	RADIO	D	O	IF	D	1st	OUT.	RECT.	AVC	NS	R	CONT	TUNING	MODEL NUMBER AND NAME	PRICE	CAB.	SPKR.	NOTE
A	5	TRP	--	--	--	--	--	--	--	--	--	--	B	--	--	A-1	39.95	M	D	--
A	5	TRP	--	--	--	--	--	--	--	--	--	--	B	--	--	A-2	49.95	C	D	--
A	6	-	--	--	--	--	--	--	--	--	--	--	B	--	--	G-7	69.90	A	D	--
A	7	SH	--	--	--	--	--	--	--	--	--	--	B	--	--	G-17	59.90	M	D	--
A	8	SH	--	--	--	--	--	--	--	--	--	--	B	--	--	K-10	74.90	C	D	--
A	9	SH	--	--	--	--	--	--	--	--	--	--	--	--	--	K-10	69.90	C	D	--
A		--	--	--	--	--	--	--	--	--	--	--	V	--	--	K-10	84.90	LB	D	--
A		--	--	--	--	--	--	--	--	--	--	--	V	--	--	K-20 Queen Anne	94.90	CL	D	--
A		--	--	--	--	--	--	--	--	--	--	--	--	--	--	--	99.50	RC	D	--

RADIO ENGINEERING LABS. INC.   LONG ISLAND CITY, N.Y. $30.00 to $90.40
4 Chasses   4 Models   2 to 4 Tubes

P	T	C	RADIO	D	O	IF	D	1st	OUT.	RECT.	AVC	NS	R	CONT	TUNING	MODEL NUMBER AND NAME	PRICE	CAB.	SPKR.	NOTE
B	3	TRP	1-22	--	--	--	01A	12A	--	--	--	--	S	--	--	--	30.00	K	--	3h
B	2	REG	--	30	--	--	--	30	--	--	--	--	C	--	--	273	33.30	Pr	--	u
B	3	TRP	1-36	--	--	--	36	--	1-38	--	--	--	S	--	--	278	53.40	--	--	--
B	4	TRP	1-35	--	--	--	35	27	1-27	--	--	--	S	--	--	260-S	90.40	--	--	--

RADIO PRODUCTS CORP.   NEWARK, N. J. $15.00 to $25.00
1 Chassis   -- Models   -- Tubes

P	T	C	RADIO	D	O	IF	D	1st	OUT.	RECT.	AVC	NS	R	CONT	TUNING	MODEL NUMBER AND NAME	PRICE	CAB.	SPKR.	NOTE
A	--	--	--	--	--	--	--	--	--	--	--	--	B	--	--	* Miniature&Clock	--	MC	--	l

RADIO SERVICE LABS.   CLINTON, IOWA $--
1 Chassis   1 Model   (1932)   4 Tubes

P	T	C	RADIO	D	O	IF	D	1st	OUT.	RECT.	AVC	NS	R	CONT	TUNING	MODEL NUMBER AND NAME	PRICE	CAB.	SPKR.	NOTE
A	4	--	--	--	--	--	--	--	--	--	--	--	--	--	--	440	$--	M	--	q

RADIO SIGHT & SOUND CORP.   CHICAGO, ILL. $32.50   "MARS"   (1932)   7 Tubes
1 Chassis   1 Model

P	T	C	RADIO	D	O	IF	D	1st	OUT.	RECT.	AVC	NS	R	CONT	TUNING	MODEL NUMBER AND NAME	PRICE	CAB.	SPKR.	NOTE
A	7	--	--	--	--	--	--	--	--	--	--	--	B	--	--	170	32.50	C	1D	--	l

RADIO SURPLUS CORP. — (1932) — NEW YORK CITY $9.95 to $39.50
4 Chasses — 3 Models — 5 Tubes

A	5	TRF	--	--	--	--	--	--	--	--	--	16.65	M	D
A	5	TRF	3-24	--	24	1-35	1-47	1-45	80	--	--	39.50	CL	D
A	5	-	(1-24,1-27,1-35,1-47,1-80)								--	16.75	CL	D
B	2	REG.	(1-32,1-33)							--	SW2 Reliable Jr.	9.95	ch	u

Reliable

RADIOTECHNIC LABS. INC. — (1931) — BROOKLYN, N. Y.
1 Chassis — 1 Model — -- Tubes

-	--	--	--	--	--	--	--	P	--	RTL Television	-	K	-

RADOLEK CO. — (1932) — CHICAGO, ILL.
1 Chassis — 1 Model — Tubes

A	4	--	--	--	--	--	--	B	--	-	14.65	M	D

RAWLS, W.C. & CO. — "RAWLS" (1932) — SUFFOLK, VA.
1 Chassis — 1 Model — -- Tubes $295.00

A	9	SH	--	35	1-35	24	1-47	80	BS	--	TV85 Broadcast & SW Television	295.00	C	Sh/2h
A	8	TRF	2-35	--	--	24	2-45	80	P	--				

RCA VICTOR CO. INC. — "RCA-VICTOR" — CAMDEN, N. J. $37.50 to $995.00
35 Chasses — 59 Models — 4 to 14 Tubes

A	4	TRF	1-24	--	24	--	1-47	80	B	--	R-5 Radiolette	37.50	M	D
D	-	TRF	--	--	--	--	--	--	B	--	R-5 Radiolette	--	M	D
A	7	TRF	3-24	--	24	--	2-45	80	B	E	R-14	91.50	CL	D
									B	E	R-15	--	C	D
A	8	SH	1-35	27	27	1-35	1-47	80	B	E	42	91.50	C	D
									B	E	RE-17	183.50	RP	D
A	8	SH	1-35	24	27	1-35	2-47	80	B	E	R-7 Superette	69.50	M	D
B	8	SH	1-32	32	30	1-32	2-30	--	B	E	R-9	89.50	C	D
A	8	TRF	3-24	--	27	--	2-45	80	B	E	R-7A Superette	99.50	C	D
A*	9	SH	1-24	24	27	2-24	2-45	80	B	E	RE-73	114.50	RP	D
											80	--	-	D
											82	--	-	D

(continued)

(RCA Victor)

P	T	C	RADIO	D	IF	D	1st	OUT	RECT	AVC	NS	R	CONF	TUNING	MODEL NUMBER AND NAME	PRICE	CAB	SPKR	NOTE
A*	9	SH	1-24	24	27	27	--	2-45	80	27	--	B	E	--	86	-	-	D	-
A	9	SH	1-35	24	27	27	--	2-47	80	27	--	B	E	--	RAE-68	495.00	RP	D	n
												B	VT	--	R-11	119.00	HB	D	-
												B	VT	--	RE-16	125.00	RP	D	-
A	10	SH	1-35	24	27	27	--	2-47	80	27	--	B	VT	--		139.50	D	D	-
												B	VT	--		139.50	HB	D	-
												B	VT	--	RAE-26	215.00	RF	D	n
A	12	SH	1-35	24	(4-24,2-27, 4-45,2-80)	27	45	2-50	81	27	--	B	VT	--	M-50	157.00	C	D	-
A	12	SH	1-35	24	27	27	--	4-47	80	27	--	B	VT	--	R-55	178.00	C	D	-
A*	13	-	--	--	--	--	--	--	--	--	--	H	VTR	--	RAE-59	350.00	RP	D2	n
A	13	-	--	--	--	--	--	--	--	--	--	B	T	--	RAE-79a	900.00	RF	P	1h
D	3	SH	1-24	24	27	27	--	--	--	--	--	S	--	--	ER-1240	995.00	R	D2	nin
B	6	SH	--	--	--	--	--	--	--	--	--	--	--	--	RAE-79	121.00	RP	-	-
A	7	-	1-35	24	27	27	--	1-47	80	27	--	B	T	--	M34	-	-	-	-
A	8	SH	1-35	24	27	27	--	1-47	80	27	--	B	T	--	STA-2	39.50	A	D	q3h
A	8	SH	1-58	58	1-58	56	--	1-47	80	56	--	B	VT	--	M-32	49.95	M	D	s
B	8	SH	1-34	32	1-34	34	30	2-30	--	34	--	B	VT	--	R-4	46.75	C	D	-
A	9	SH	--	--	--	--	--	--	--	*	--	B	VT	--	R-6	66.50	T	D	-
A	9	SH	--	--	--	--	--	--	--	--	--	B	V	--	R-70-N Playroom	49.50	T	D	-
B	10	SH	1-36	36	1-36	37	37	2-12a	--	37	--	B	VT	--	R-8 Superette	59.95	C	D	-
			1-58	58	1-58	56	56	2-46	82	56	--	B	VT	--	R-12 New Superette	79.50	RP	D	-
												B	VT	--	RE-19	129.50	T	D	-
												B	VT	--	R-71	36.50	C	D	-
												B	VT	--	R-72	69.50	RP	D	-
												B	VT	--	R-71-B	62.75	RP	D	-
												B	VT	--	RE-30	125.00	HB	D	-
												B	VT	--	RE-18	147.50	A	D	-
												B	VT	--	R-21	99.50	T	D	-
A	10	SH	--	--	--	--	--	--	--	--	--	B	VT	--	M-30	74.50	C	D	d
B	10	SH	--	--	--	--	--	--	--	--	--	B	VT	--	R-74	69.50	C	D	d
-	10	SH	--	--	--	--	--	--	--	--	--	B	VT	--	R-76	93.50	C	D	d
A	11	SH	--	--	--	--	--	--	--	--	--	B	VT	--	R-77	104.50	RP	D	d
A	12	SH	1-58	58	2-58	56	56	2-4	83	56	--	B	VTA	--	R-91	178.00	RP	D	-
												BS	--	--	RB-81	178.00	M	D	-
												B	VTA	--	RE-20	199.50	RP	D	-
															Intravario	-			
															Intravario	-			
															Intravario	-			
A	10	SH										BS	VTA	--	RO-23	117.50	C	D	d
B	10	SH										B	VTA	--	R-78 Bi-Acoustic	139.50	RP	D	n
												B	-	--	RAE-84 Bi-Acoustic	310.00			
															Intravario				

REMLER CO. LTD.   SAN FRANCISCO, CAL.   Intravario   Intravario   P-31

12 Models   10 Chasses $29.90 to $84.50

	SH										4 to 9 Tubes				RP Pr	s sn
A 4	TRF 1-35	--	--	--	--	24	--	1-47 80	--	B	--	21	29.90	M	D	-
A 5	TRF 2-24	--	--	--	--	24	--	1-47 80	--	B	--	11	39.50	M	D	-
A 7	TRF 1-35	24	27	1-35	--	24	--	1-47 80	--	B	--	15	49.50	M	D	-
A 8	SH			(4-24;2-27,1-45,1-80)						B	--	15C	69.50	LB	D	-
A 8	SH			(2-24,2-27,2-47,2-35)						-	--	-	77.50	M	D	-
A 4	SH	57	*	--	57	57	--	1-47 82	--	BP	9	19C	84.50	LH	D	-
A 5	SH	57	*	1-58	57	57	--	1-47 82	--	BP	--	21-3	29.90	M	D	-
A 5	SH		(2-24,1-27,1-35,1-47,1-80)							-	--	12-3	34.75	M	D	-
A 6	SH	58	56	1-58	58	57	--	1-47 82	--	BP	VTN	10	39.50	M	D	-
A 9	SH	58	56	1-58	58	57	56	1-47 82	57	BP	VTN	10-3	42.75	M	D	-
A -	SH	--	--	1-58						BP	VTN	15-3C	59.50	M	C	-
													4.50			

REPUBLIC INDUSTRIES   "SKY-HAWK"   (1932)   ASHLAND, OHIO

2 Models   2 Chasses   5 and 10 Tubes $36.50 and $84.50

A 5	SH	57	*	1-58 57	--	--	--	1-47 80	--	BP	--	MS	36.50	M	D	-
A 10	SH	58	56	1-58 55	--	--	* 56	2-47 80	--	B	VTN	N	84.50	C	D	-

REPUBLIC RADIO CO.   (1931)   CHICAGO, ILL.

1 Model   1 Chassis   -- Tubes

| A - | -- | -- | -- | -- | -- | -- | -- | -- | -- | B | -- | -- | $ -- | M | D | - |

REPUBLIC RADIO MFG. CORP.   (1932)   IRVINGTON, N.J.

1 Model   1 Chassis   6 Tubes   Autotone

| B 5 | SH | -- | -- | -- | -- | -- | -- | -- | -- | B | VR | -- | $ -- | A | - | - |

REVERE RADIO CORP.   "REVERE"   ASHLAND, OHIO

14 Models   - Chasses   5 to 7 Tubes $39.95 to $94.50

| A 5 | TRF 1-35 | -- | -- | 24 | -- | 1-47 80 | -- | B | -- | 39 | 39.95 | Cp | D | - |
| A - | | | | (continued) | | | | B | -- | 39C | 39.95 | M | D | - |

P	T	C	RADIO	INTERMEDIATE D-O	IF	AUDIO D	1st	OUT.	RECT.	AVC	NS	R	CONT	TUNING	MODEL NUMBER AND NAME	PRICE	CAB.	SPKR.	NOTE
A	5	TRF	1-35	(Revere)	--	24	--	1-47	80	--	--	B	--	--	Patrician	47.50	M	D	--
												B			59	59.50	C	D	--
												B			79	79.50	GC	D	--
A	5	TRF	--	--	--	--	--	--	--	--	--	B	--	--		39.50	T	D	--
D	5	TRF	--	--	--	--	--	--	--	--	--	B	--	--		47.50	T	--	--
-	6	SH	--	--	--	--	--	--	--	--	--	B	--	--	47-S	47.95	T	--	--
-	6	SH	--	--	--	--	--	--	--	--	--	B	--	--	55-S Patrician	56.50	C	--	--
-	6	SH	--	--	--	--	--	--	--	--	--	--	--	--		59.95	C	--	--
-	-	-	--	--	--	--	--	--	--	--	--	--	--	--	65-S	66.50	BC	--	--
B	7	SH	--	--	--	--	--	--	--	--	--	B	▽	--	Patrician Tower	74.50	A	D	◀
B	7	SH	--	--	--	--	--	--	--	--	--	B	▽	--	-	69.50	A	--	◀
																94.50	A	--	--

ROOTS AUTO RADIO MFG. CORP.   CHICAGO, ILL.   (1932) $ -- to $ --

2 Chasses   3 Models   7 and 8 Tubes

P	C	INTERMEDIATE	MODEL NO.	PRICE	CAB.	NOTE
P	7	(2-37,2-38)	49	49.50	A	◀
P	8	(3-24,2-37,2-38) or 4}, 3-44,1-BR	69	69.50	A	◀
			79	79.50	A	--

ROSS CORP.   CHICAGO, ILL.   (1931)   -- Tubes

1 Chassis   1 Model

P	C	MODEL	PRICE	CAB.	NOTE
-		Phoenix	59.50	Mn	-

SARA, J & L CO. INC.   NEW YORK CITY   (1932)   "SARA" $35.00 and $43.75

2 Chasses   2 Models   5 Tubes

P	T	C	IF	1st	OUT.	RECT.	R	MODEL	PRICE	CAB.	NOTE
SH	5	57	1-58	W	1-58	80	B	SJ-4K	35.00	oh	D
A	5				1-58	80	B V		43.75	ch	D

SAVIL RADIO ENGINEERING CORP.   NEW YORK CITY   (1931)   - Tubes

- Chassis   - Models $ -- to $ --

P	C	MODEL	PRICE	CAB.	NOTE
A	TRF	Various	:	M	--
D	TRF	Various	:	M	--

SCOTT RADIO LABS. - Models "SCOTT" CHICAGO, ILL. $ -- to $ --

		1 Chassis									12 Tubes			BS		oh	D	S		o	-- to $ --
A	12	SH	1-24	24	27	3-24	27	2-45	80					BS		o	D2	S	Wellington -	0	
A	12	SH												BS		RP	D2	S	DeLuxe	RP	750.00

SEARS ROEBUCK & CO. 63 Models "SILVERTONE" CHICAGO, ILL. $19.95 to $198.00

		32 Chasses							4 to 12 Tubes								
A	4	TRF 1-35								B		1371	Meteor Midget	M	*23.95	D	S
A*	5	TRF 2-35					1-47	80		B	T	1251		M	34.40	D	S
B	5	N					1-45	80		B	T	4985		RP	67.50	D	
A*	6	TRF 2-24			24		2-45	80		B	T	1141		M	46.00	D	
A*	6	TRF 2-35			24		2-45	80		B	T	1151	DeLuxe	M	49.00	D	
										B	T	1161		LB	59.00	D	
										B	T	1155		M	59.50	D	
B	6	TRF 2-32			32	5-	2-31			B	T	1175	Alden	GC	74.50	D	
										B	T	1175		C	54.00	D	
										B	T	1261	Grenada	C	49.00	D	
										B	T	1261	Ambassador	RP	73.75	D	
										B	T	1062		Stm	69.00		
										B	T	1069		LB	37.00	M	
A*	6	SH	24	27	24		1-47	80		B	T	1291		M	54.50	D	
										B	T	1293		M	71.00	D	
										B	T	1297		C	64.50	D	
										B	T	1301		M	55.00	D	
										B	T	1305		C	71.00	D	
										B	T	1391		GC	79.50	D	
										B	T	1401		C	59.75	D	
B	7	TRF 3-32			30	30	2-31			B	T	1402	Musette	CP	39.75	D	
B	7	TRF								B	T	1405		M	44.50		
B	7	TRF 3-24			27		2-45	80		B	T	1404	Wilmington	C	54.50	D	
A*	7	TRF 3-35			24		2-45	80		B	T	1471		Stm	29.95	D	
										B		1072		C	79.00		
										B		1076		C	99.00	D	
A	7	SH 1-35	24	27	24		1-47	80		B	T	4985		RP	112.00	D	
A*	8	SH 1-35	35	27	24		2-47	80		B	T	1097		LB	77.00	D	
A	8									B	M	1311		C	69.00	D	
										B	VT	1331	Berkeley	RP	127.50	D	
										B	T	1481		M	36.50	D	
										B	T	1483		C	39.95	D	
												1321		C	69.00	D	
												1463	Orland	C	54.50	D	
														C	69.50	D	

(continued)

P	T	C	RADIO	INTERMEDIATE D	INTERMEDIATE O	INTERMEDIATE IF	AUDIO D	AUDIO 1st	AUDIO OUT.	RECT.	AVC	NS	R	CONT	TUNING	MODEL NUMBER AND NAME	PRICE	CAB.	SPKR.	NOTE
						(Sears, Roebuck)														
A	8	TRF	3-24	--	--	--	27	27	2-45	80	--	--	B	T	--	4981	198.00	RP	D	n
A	9	TRF	4-24	--	--	--	27	27	2-45	80	--	--	B	T	--	4986	129.00	RP	D	n
A*	10	SH	1-35	35	27	1-35	24	--	2-47	80	47	--	B	T	5	1112 Queen Anne	132.00	HH	D	g
														T		1119 Wynclyffe	115.00	LB	D	ha
		SH					24		2-47	80	47	--	B	VT	M	1430	89.00	C	D	ha
A	4	SH	2-32	--	--	(1-27,2-35,1-80)	27	--	1-33	--	--	--	S	--	--	1601 Shortwaver	23.50	M	D	--
B	4	TRF	2-32	--	--		32	--	--	--	--	--	B	T	--	1621	36.50	M	PD	--
A	6	TRF	2-35	--	--		24	--	2-47	80	--	--	B	T	--	1623	39.95	C	PD	--
B	6	TRF	2-32	--	--		32	30	2-31	--	--	--	B	T	--	1157	24.75	M	D	--
A	6	TRF	2-24	--	--		24	--	2-45	80	--	--	Bp	T	--	1171	29.95	C	D	--
A	6	SH		(2-24,2-35,1-47,1-80)			35	1-47	1-80		--	--	Bp	T	--	1295	49.95	M	D	--
A	7	SH		(2-24,1-35,1-47,1-80)							--	--	B	T	--	1341	19.95	M	D	--
B	7	SH		(3-30,3-32,1-33)							--	--	B	T	--	1507	29.95	C	D	--
A	7	SH		(2-24,1-27,2-35,1-47,1-80)							--	--	F	T	--	1591	24.95	M	GC	--
A	8	SH		(1-24,1-47,1-56,1-57,1-58,1-80)							--	--	B	--	Q	1593	39.50	C	RP	n
A	8	SH		(2-24,1-27,2-35,2-47,1-80)							--	--	B	--	--	1485	49.95	M	M	r
B	8	SH		(2-30,1-31,4-32,1-33)							--	--	B	T	--	1491	43.50	C	C	d
A	9	SH		(1-24,3-46,1-56,1-57,2-58,1-80)							--	--	BS	VT	Q	1563	49.50	M	M	d
A	10	SH		(1-24,1-27,4-35,3-47,1-80)							--	--	BS	VT	Q	1587	49.95	C	M	
A	12	SH	--	58	56	2-58	57	46	2-46	83	57	57	BS	VTN	--	1531	37.50	C	D2	d
																1571	44.75			
																1575	39.95			
																1631	98.00	RP		
																1511	52.50	M		
																1641	59.95			

SENTINEL RADIO CORP., CHICAGO, ILL. $24.50 to $109.50

"SENTINEL" (1932) 4 to 10 Tubes

16 Models   10 Chasses

P	T	C	RADIO	INTERMEDIATE D	INTERMEDIATE O	INTERMEDIATE IF	AUDIO D	AUDIO 1st	AUDIO OUT.	RECT.	AVC	NS	R	CONT	TUNING	MODEL NUMBER AND NAME	PRICE	CAB.	SPKR.	NOTE
A	4	TRF	1-58	--	--	--	57	--	1-47	80	--	--	B	T	--	412	24.50	M	D	--
A	5	SH	--	57	--	1-58	55	--	1-47	80	--	--	B	V	--	513 Personal	34.50	A	D	o
B	5	SH	1-39	56	*	1-39	85	--	1-41	85	--	--	B	V	--	521	39.50	A	D	f
B	5	SH	1-39	36	*	1-39	85	--	1-41	85	--	--	F	V	--	521	39.50	A	D	--
A	6	SH	1-58	57	--	1-58	55	--	1-47	80	--	--	B	V,	--	614	39.50	M	D	d
B	8	SH		(2-30,2-32)		2-34,2-49					--	--	BS	V	--	814	59.50	M	D	--
													BS	V		816	75.00	C	D	
													B	V		815	54.50	M	D	
A	8	SH	1-58	58	56	1-58	56	57	1-47	80	--	--	B	V	--	816	69.50	C	D	

												Model	Price		
A	8	SH	--	58	57	56	2-58	57	57	1-47	80	817	84.50	HR	dr
A	10	SH	1-58	58	56	56	1-58	57	57	1-47	80	826	92.50	C	dr
A	10	SH	1-58	58	56	56	1-58	46	57	2-46	80	827	107.50	HR	
												1016	79.50	C	
												1017	94.50	HB	
												1016	74.50	C	
												1017	89.50	HB	

SERVICE ELECTRIC CO.   "CODE"   (1931)   INDIANAPOLIS, IND.
9 Models   4 to 12 Tubes $29.50 to $560.00
7 Chasses

												Model	Price		
A	4	TRF	1-35	--	--	24	--	1-47	80	B		Black	29.50	M	D
B	4	TRF	1-35	--	27	24	--	1-47	80	BSL		Rodeo	49.50	A	D
A	5	TRF	3-24	--	56	24	(3-SG,1-45,1-80)	--	BSL		Blackhawk	--	M	D
A	6	TRF	3-24	--	24	24	--	1-45	80	B		Cresta	32.50	M	D
												Futura	32.50	M	D
A	7	SH	1-35	24	27	24	1-24	1-47	80	B	120	Cresta	67.50	M	RP
A	10	SH	3-35	24	27	24	1-24	2-47	80	B		Coda	109.50	LB	D
A	12	SH	3-35	24	27	24	2-24	2-47	27	--		Aida	560.00	RP	D

SHELDON RADIO CO.   "SHELDON"   (1932)   LOS ANGELES, CAL.
2 Models   6 and 12 Tubes $59.50 and $150.00
2 Chasses

												Model	Price		
B	6	SH	1-39	36	37	1-39 W	1-41	--	--	B	V	A-6	59.50	--	
A	12	SH	2-35	35	56	2-35 W	2-45	80	*	B	V		150.00	LB	

SHORTWAVE & TELEVISION LABS. INC.   "BAIRD"   BOSTON, MASS.
9 Models   -- Tubes $59.50 to $124.40
9 Chasses

											Model	Price		
--	7	--	--	--	--	--	--	--	--	--	--	95.10	K	tr
--	7	--	--	--	(3-24,2-27,1-45,1-BH,1-Rect)	--	--	--	S	--	35	110.00	T	tr
A	8	--	--	--	--	--	--	--	S	--	25	124.40	K	tr
--	1	--	--	--	(1-45)	--	--	--	BS	--	26	--	K	ts
A	1	--	--	--	(1-45)	--	--	--	--	--	36	*84.30	T	ts
--	1	--	--	--	--	--	--	--	--	--		*100.00	--	tr
A	7	SH	1-58	58	56	2-58	1-47	80	RS	V	155	59.50	T	
A	7	SH	1-58	58	56	1-58	1-47	80	BS	V	200	59.50	--	

249

SILVER-MARSHALL INC.

"SILVER-MARSHALL"   CHICAGO, ILL. $40.87 to $170.00

25 Chasses   36 Models   5 to 13 Tubes

P	T	C	RADIO	D	O	IF	D	1st	OUT	RECT.	AVC	NS	R	CONT	TUNING	MODEL NUMBER AND NAME	PRICE	CAB.	SPKR.	NOTE
A	5	TRF	1-24	--	--	--	27	24	1-45	80	--	--	S	--	--	SM-737 Bearcat	139.60	T	D-M*	va
A	6	SH	1-24	24	27	2-24	27	--	--	--	--	--	B	--	--	SM-714	*87.50	ch	D	va
A	6	SH	1-35	24	27	2-35	27	--	--	--	--	--	B	E	--	716	*69.50	ch	D	--
A	7	SH	--	24	27	2-35	27	--	1-47	80	--	--	B	E	--	F4	59.50	M	D	--
A	8	SH	--	24	27	2-24	27	--	2-45	80	--	--	B	E	--	F5	69.50	LB	D	--
																37	79.90	M	D	--
																38 Cadet	89.90	CL	D	--
B	8	SH	1-32	32	30	2-32	30	--	2-31	--	--	--	B	E	--	39	106.55	C	D	--
																41	149.90	C	D	--
A	8	SH	--	24	27	2-35	27	--	2-45	80	--	--	B	E	--	783	84.50	M	D	--
A	9	SH	1-35	24	27	2-35	27	--	2-47	80	--	--	BL	E	--	40DC	119.90	C	D-M*	--
A	10	SH	1-35-	24	27	2-35	27	--	2-47	80	*	--	B	E	--	724DC	82.50	ch	D	--
																773	-	ch	D	--
A	10	SH	1-24	24	27	2-24	27	27	2-45	80	--	--	B	E	--	726	-	LB	D	k
A	11	SH	1-35	24	27	2-35	27	--	2-47	80	--	--	B	E	--	D-1	89.50	C	D	--
A	3	SH	1-35-	24	27	--	--	--	--	26	27	--	BS	E	--	G-6	109.50	ch	D*	--
A	6	SH	--	58	56	1-58	55	--	1-47	80	--	--	B	VT	M	716 + 683	*159.00	ch	D*	*
B	8	SH	--	32	30	2-34	30	30	2-30	--	--	--	B	--	M	SM714 - 677B	*170.00	ch	D	q
B	8	SH	--	58	56	2-58	55	--	2-58	80	--	--	--	VT	M	726-SW	139.50	T	D	--
B	8	SH	1-32	32	30	2-32	30	30	2-30	--	*	--	B3	T	--	738	*69.50	ch	D	--
D	9	SH	--	24	27	2-35	27	--	2-47	80	27	--	BS	VT	--	KB-21	-	ch	D-M*	k
A	10	SH	--	24	56	2-58	56	45	2-45	82	27	--	Bp	VT	--	727-DC	89.50	ch	D2	hb
A	10	SH	--	58	56	2-58	56	56	2-45	80	56	--	Bp	VT	--	Y-39	40.87	c	D	hb
A	10	SH	--	58	56	2-58	56	45	2-45	82	56	--	B	VT	--	726-DC	49.50	ch	D	k
A	11	SH	1-32	24	27	2-35	27	27	2-47	80	--	--	BS	VT	--	Q 727-SW DeLuxe	139.50	ch	D	--
																SM-727	99.50	c	D	--
																V-30	69.50	ch	D	--
																SM-728	109.50	c	D	--
A	12	SH	1-35	24	27	2-35	27	27	2-47	80	--	--	B	T	M	Twin-Q-25A	89.50	C	D	hc
A	12	SH	--	58	56	2-58	56	45	2-45	82	56	--	BS	T	M	Q-32	58.50	ch	D	hc
A	13	SH	--	58	56	2-58	56	45	2-45	(82)	56	--	BS	T	M	C-24	139.50	C	D	hc
										(80)						728-SW				
																CB-1				
																Triple Q34 DeLuxe				

SIMPLEX RADIO CO. SANDUSKY, OHIO "SIMPLEX" $19.95 to $71.20

19 Chasses — 23 Models — 4 to 7 Tubes

																Price			
A	5	TRF	2-24	--	--	--	--	--	1-45	80	--	B	E-	--	--	--	--	M	D
D,	5	TRF	2-32	--	--	--	--	--	2-31	--	--	B	E-	--	--	--	--	M	D
B,	5	TRF	2-32	32	--	--	--	--	2-31	--	--	B	E-	--	--	39.50	K	M	D
A	5	SH	--	24	1-35	1-35	*	24	1-47	80	--	B	--	--	--	61.20	J	M	D
A	6	SH	1-35	24	1-35	1-35	*	24	1-47	80	--	B	--	--	--	71.20	J	C	D
A	4	TRF	1-58	--	57	1-34	32	57	1-47	80	--	B	E-	--	--	19.95	R	M	D
A	4	TRF	1-39	--	36	1-39	36	36	2-38	--	--	BP	E-	--	--	19.95	R	M	--
D	5	--	--	(2-24,1-35,1-47,1-80)					--	--	--	--	--	--	--	32.50	--	M	D
A	5	SH	32	32	1-34	1-34	*	32	1-33	--	--	B	E-	--	--	26.50	N	ch	D
B	5	SH	39	39	1-39	1-39	*	36	2-38	--	--	BS	E-	--	--	33.50	N	M	D
D	5	SH	57	57	1-58	1-58	*	55	1-47	--	--	BP	VT	--	--	36.50	P	ch	D
A	5	--	--	--	--	--	--	--	--	--	--	BP	VT	--	--	29.50	P	M	D
A	6	TRF	2-58	--	57	1-57	57	57	1-47	80	--	BP	VT	--	--	29.95	P	M	D
A	5	SH	--	--	--	--	--	--	--	--	--	BS	E-	--	--	29.95	P	M	D
A	5	SH	--	--	--	--	--	--	--	--	--	BS	E-	--	--	29.95	Q	ch	D
A	5	SH	--	--	--	--	--	--	--	--	--	BSL	--	--	--	34.50	Q	M	D
A	7	SH	--	--	--	--	--	--	--	--	--	--	--	--	--	39.95	S	-	--
																35.50		LB	--
																46.50		GC	--
																67.50		M	--
																49.50		M	--
																59.50	Special Model	C	--

SONORA MFG. CORP. NEW YORK CITY

1 Chassis — 1 Model — 6 Tubes $75.00

| D | 6 | -- | -- | -- | -- | -- | -- | -- | -- | -- | -- | -- | -- | -- | -- | 75.00 | -- | M | D |

SORBER RADIO MFG. CO. KANSAS CITY, MO. "SORBER" (1932) $74.55 to $93.30

— Chasses — 2 Models — 7 Tubes

| B | 7 | -- | 3-32 | -- | 32 | -- | 32 | 30 | 2-31 | -- | -- | B | -- | -- | -- | 74.55 | -- | M | M |
| | | | -- | -- | -- | -- | -- | -- | -- | -- | -- | B | -- | -- | -- | 93.30 | -- | LB | M |

SPARKS-WITHINGTON CO. JACKSON, MICH. "SPARTON" $45.00 to $585.00

27 Chasses — 35 Models — 5 to 13 Tubes

A	5	TRF	2-35	--	27	--	--	1-45	80	--	--	B	--	--	5	45.00	--	M.	D
A	6	TRF	2-24	--	27	--	--	2-83	80	--	--	B	--	--	9	62.50	--	CL	D
					(continued)											410	45.00	--	M	D

(Sparks-Withington)

P	T	C	RADIO	INT. D	INT. O	INT. IF	AUDIO D	AUDIO 1st	OUT.	RECT.	AVC	NS	R	CONT. TUNING	MODEL NUMBER AND NAME	PRICE	CAB.	SPKR.	NOTE
A	6	TRF	2-24	–	–	–	27	–	2-83	80	–	–	B	–	9A	62.50	M	–	–
B	6	TRF	3-32	–	–	–	32	30	1-31	–	–	–	B	–	51	79.50	M	–	–
A	6	TRF	3-24	35	27	–	27	–	1-83	80	–	–	B	–	52	99.50	LB	D	ps
A	7	SH	1-35	35	27	1-35	27	–	1-47	80	27	–	P	T	55	145.85	–	D	–
A	8	SH	1-35	–	–	1-35	84	–	1-47	80	–	–	B	VT	10	69.50	M	D	nhd
A	10	SH	6-84	–	–	–	27	–	2-83	80	27	–	B	VT	15	99.50	LB	D	–
A	10	SH	1-35	35	27	2-35	27	–	2-45	80	–	–	B	VT	235	*280.00	RP	D	n
													B	VT	25	136.00	HB	D	–
B	13	SH	1-35	35	17	2-35	27	27	2-50	81	27	–	B	VT	26	165.00	HB	D	n
A	5	TRF	3-24	–	27	–	27	–	1-12A	–	–	–	P	–	30	235.00	RP	D	pa
B	6	TRF	2-36	–	–	–	36	36	1-38	–	37	–	P	VTR	45 Visionola	575.00	HT	D	e
B	6	TRF	3-35	–	–	–	36	–	1-38	–	37	–	P	VTR	32	102.60	C	D	f
															35	585.00	RP		
															50	99.50	A		
															40	99.50	A		
															40	99.50	A		
–	5	SH	1-58	24	*	1-58	56	56	1-47	80	*	–	B	VT	12	64.50	C	–	n
A	8	SH	–	24	–	–	56	–	–	–	–	–	B	T	14	69.50	LB	D	–
–	9	SH	1-58	24	*	1-58	56	56	2-47	80	56	–	B	VT	16	114.00	C	D	–
A	10	SH	–	–	–	–	27	–	–	–	–	–	B	VT	18	94.50	HB	D	–
A	10	SH	1-35	35	27	2-35	27	–	2-45	80	27	–	B	VT	20	195.00	RP	D	sg
A	12	SH	(2-24,4-27,3-35,2-47,1-30)										RS	VT	30A	248.00	RP	D	–
A	13	SH	–	–	–	–	–	–	–	–	–	–	BS	VT	16-AW	155.00	C	D	–
A	13	SH	–	–	*	–	–	–	–	–	–	–	B	VT	26-AW	195.00	C	D	–
A	13	SH	1-58	24	*	1-58	56	56	4-47	80	56	–	B	VT	27	129.50	C	D	–
															27A	142.75	HB		
															28	166.75	HB	D2	
A	13	SH	–	–	–	–	–	–	–	–	–	–	B	V	The Triolian Country Home	165.00	C	–	–
B	–	–	–	–	–	–	–	–	–	–	–	–	B	–	51	79.50	T	–	–
B	7	SH	1-39	36	*	1-39	70	37	2-38	–	*	–	B	–	52	99.50	A	–	–
A	4	SH	–	–	–	–	–	–	–	–	–	–	S	–	34	79.50	T	–	q
															60	49.75	–	–	–

STANDARD RADIO CO.   CHICAGO, ILL. $12.95

P	T	C	RADIO	D	O	IF	D	1st	OUT.	RECT.	AVC	NS	R	T	1 Model	PRICE	CAB.	SPKR.	
–	4	–	–	–	–	–	–	–	–	–	–	–	B	–	1 Chassis	12.95	M	D	–

4 Tubes

| | | 1 Chassis | | | 1 Model | | | -- Tubes -- | | | -- | | M | $ | -- |

STEINITE MFG. CO. CHICAGO, ILL.
"STEINITE" (1931) $49.50 to $109.00
6 Chasses — 18 Models — 5 to 8 Tubes

Class	Circuit	Tube complement	B/T	Model	Name	Price	Code	Type
A 5	TRF	2-24 ... 1-24 ... 1-45 80	B	700	Marvel	49.50	M	D
A 5	TRF	2-35 ...	B	421		49.50	M	D
A 6	TRF	2-24 ... 2-45 80	B	425		49.50	–	D
			B	707		64.50	CL	D
			B	605		79.50	LB	D
			B	630		69.50	M	D
A 6	SH	1-24 ...	B			69.50	CL	D
A 8	SH	1-24 24 27 1-35 27 2-45 80	B	605	Monarch	79.50	C	D
			B			89.50	MP	D
			B			99.50	C	D
			B			109.00	MP	A
A 8	SH	1-35 24 27 1-35 27 2-47 80	B	705		59.50	M	D
			B	705		69.50	RP	D
			B	700		67.50	MC	D
			B	712		89.50	M	D
			B	725		99.50	LB	D
			B	GF		99.50	HB	D
			B	706		69.50	GC	D
			B	642-B		79.50	H	D

STERLING MFG. CO. CLEVELAND, OHIO
"STERLING" (1931) $37.95 to $99.50
3 Chasses — 5 Models — 5 and 7 Tubes

Class	Circuit	Tube complement	B/T	Model	Name	Price	Code	Type
A 5	TRF	2-35 ... 24 ... 1-47 80	B	V	Little Symphony	37.95	T	D
A 5	TRF	2-24 ... 24 ... 1-45 80	B	VI		69.50	T	D
A 7	SH	1-35 27 24 1-35 27 1-47 80	B T	VIII		54.50	T	D
			B	VII		69.50	LR	D
			B	VIII		99.50	LB	D

STEWART-WARNER CORP. CHICAGO, ILL.
"STEWART-WARNER" $23.95 to $270.50
14 Chasses — 42 Models — 4 to 11 Tubes

Class	Circuit	Tube complement	B/T	Model	Name	Price	Code	Type
A* 4	TRF	1-35 ... 24 ... 1-47 80	B	501A	Metropolitan	34.95	M	D
D 4	TRF	1-36 ... 36 ... 2-53 --	B	501C		34.95	M	–
A* 6	SH	1-24 27 24 1-35 27 1-47 80	B T	500-A	Apartment	52.95	M	D
			B	503-A	Tudor	65.75	C	D
			B	505-A	French	71.75	C	D
			B	507-A	DeLuxe	82.75	C	D
			B	509-A		67.75	LP	D

(continued)

P	T	C	RADIO	INT. D	INT. IF	AUD. D	AUD. 1st	AUD. OUT.	RECT.	AVC	NS	R	CONT	TUNING	MODEL NUMBER AND NAME	PRICE	CAB.	SPKR.	NOTE
D	7	SH	(Stewart-Warner)	36	37 / 1-37	36	37	2-33	--	--	--	D	--	--	500C	52.95	M	--	--
				--								B	--	--	503C	65.75	LP	--	--
												B	--	--	505C	71.75	LB	--	--
A*	8	TRP	3-24	--	--	27	27	2-45	80	--	--	B	--	--	507C	32.75	LP	--	--
												B	--	--	509C	104.75	C	--	--
A*	8	SH		24	27 / 1-35	24	--	1-47	80	--	--	B	--	--	12	104.75	C	--	--
												B	--	--	14	87.75	C	--	--
												BS	T	--	504-A Tudor	93.75	C	D	n
												BS	T	--	506-A French	104.75	C	D	q
												BS	T	--	508-A DeLuxe	90.75	LP	D	--
												B	T	--	510-A No.2 Portable	148.50	RP	D	--
A*	2	SH		24	27			--			--	S	M	--	512-A	23.95	-	--	--
-	6	-													R301-A				

A	6	SH		57	56 / 1-58	W	--	1-47	80	*	--	B	V	--	R-40-A Table	52.45	M	D	--
A	6	SH		58	56							B	V	--	R-43-A Tudor	67.45	C	D	--
A	7	SH	1-58	57	56	W	--	1-	80	*	--	B	V	--	R-45-A Tiffin	79.95	C	D	--
												B	V	--	R-47-A Combination	81.95	RP	D	--
A	8	SH		58	56 / 1-58	W	--	1-47	80	*	--	B	V	--	63	68.95	M	D	--
												B	--	--	64	74.95	C	D2	--
												--	--	--	65	83.95	LP	D2	--
A	11	SH		58	56 / 1-58	27	--	2-47	82	57	--	BS	V	G	R-44-A	96.95	C	D	--
												BS	V	G	R-46-A	167.25	C	D	--
												BS	V	G	R-48-A	---	C	D	--
A*	11	SH	1-58	58	56	27	--	2-47	80	57	--	BS	VTA	G	50	149.95	C	D2	6h
												BS	VTA	G	51	194.50	RP	D2	6h
												BS	VTA	G	58	270.50	RP	D2	6h
A	11	SH		--	--	--	--	--	--	--	--	BS	VTA	G	R-50-A	119.75	C	D	6h
												BS	VTA	G	5-51-A	129.75	C	D	6h
												BS	V	G	R-58-A		C	D	6h
												BS	G		55				
															56				

6 Chasses / 6 Chases

STORY & CLARK – Models "STORY & CLARK" (1931) CHICAGO, ILL.
4 to 10 Tubes

$ -- to $ --

P	T	C	RADIO	Int.	IF	D	OUT.	RECT.	R	R	MODEL	PRICE	CAB.	SPKR.	NOTE
A	4	TRP	1-35	-- --	35	-- --	1-47	80	B	B	#44	--	C	D	6h
A	5	TRP	2-35	-- --	35	-- --	1-47	80	B	B	* -	--	--	D	--

$ -- to $ --

											Price			
A 7	SH	1-35	35	27	1-35	27	--	1-47	80	B	--	--	A	--
A 7	TRF	3-24	--	--	--	27	--	2-45	80	B	--	--	A	--
A 9	SH	1-35	35	27	1-35	27	27	1-47	80	B	T	C	A	79.50
A 10	SH	1-35	35	27	1-35	27	27	2-47	80	R	E	GC	A	89.50

*77 Miniature
*78 Console Petite
*74 Colonial
*75

STROMBERG-CARLSON TEL. MFG. CO. ROCHESTER, N.Y. $139.00 to $660.00
15 Chasses — 27 Models — 4 to 10 Tubes

											Model	Price		
A 7	TRF	3-24	--	--	--	--	--	2-45	80	B	10 DeLuxe	271.35	C	A
D 7	TRF	--	--	--	--	--	--	--	--	B	11 Convertible	297.35	C	A
A 8	SH	1-24	24	27	1-24	--	--	2-45	80	B	10 DeLuxe		C	A
A 9	TRF	3-24	--	--	27	27	--	2-45	80	B	11 Convertible	175.00	C	A
A 9	SH	1-35	35	27	2-35	27	--	2-45	80	B	25 Standard	210.00	C	A
A 9	SH	1-35	35	27	2-35	27	--	2-45	80	B	12 Grand Console	370.65	C	A
A 10	SH	1-35	35	27	2-35	27	*	2-45	80	B	14 Multi-Record	660.00	RP	A
										B	19	195.00	C	A
B 4	TRF	3-24	--	27	--	--	--	--	--	P	20	225.00	HB	A
A 4											22 Telektor	375.00	C	A
A						MQ					27	365.00	A	pe
A 9			--	58	56	--	MQ	--	80		2		R	v

											14-AX Telektor	197.00		
A 10	SH	1-58	58	58	1-58	--	QV	--	--	B	32		ML	
A 10	SH	1-35	35	27	2-35	27	M	--	80	B	37	139.00	C	e
A	SH	1-58	58	55	1-58	55	M	--	80	B	38	167.50	LR	e
							M		57	B	39	187.50	LB	n
							M			B	40	225.00	HB	r
							M			B	24 Telektor	550.00	RP	r
							M			B	38	167.50	LR	r
							M			B	39	187.50	C	n
							M			B	40	225.00	HB	qs
A 4	SH	3-24	(3-37 | 1-80)			--	--	--	S	41	395.00	RP	--
											10	--	St	

SUPERADIO MFG. CO. CHICAGO, ILL.
1 Model — 1 Chassis (1931) -- Tubes --

											Model	Price		
A	TRF	--	--	--	--	--	--	--	--	B	The Minuette	34.65	M	D

$34.65

255

P	T	C	RADIO	D	O	IF	D	1st	OUT	RECT.	AVC	NS	R	CONT TUNING	MODEL NUMBER AND NAME	PRICE	CAB.	SPKR.	NOTE
					INTERMEDIATE			AUDIO											
			SURREY COURT & FULLERTON											CHICAGO, ILL. (1932)					
			1 Chassis				1 Model							9 Tubes		$79.50			
A	9	-	--	--	--	--	--	--	--	--	--	--	ES	-	-	79.50	C	D	-
			TALKIOLA CORP.											"TALKIOLA" NEW YORK CITY		$495.00			
			1 Chassis				1 Model							(1931) -- Tubes					
A	-	-	--	--	--	--	--	--	--	--	--	--	B	-	-	495.00	C	-	-
			TATRO, L. PRODUCTS CORP.											"TATRO" DECORAH, IOWA					
			6 Chasses				12 Models							7 to 9 Tubes		$ -- to $ --			
D	9	SH	1-36	37	37	2-36	37	36	2-38	--	--	--	B	T	C-932	--	--	--	--
R	7	SH	1-44	44	37	1-44	85	--	2-38	--	*	--	B	V	Ensign	--	M	--	--
D	7	SH	1-44	44	37	1-44	85	--	2-38	--	*	--	B	V	Lieut.Commander	--	T	--	--
D	8	SH	1-44	44	37	1-44	85	BR	2-38	--	*	--	B	V	D-70	--	LB	--	--
D	9	SH	1-44	44	37	2-44	85	BR	2-41	--	*	--	B	V	E-73	--	LB	--	--
D	9	SH	1-36	36	37	2-36	37	--	2-38	--	--	--	B	VT	E-83	--	C	--	--
													B	VT	Commander	--	C	--	--
													R	VT M	Admiral	--	C	D2	--
													B	VT	Captain	--	C	--	--
													B	VT	F-913	--	LB	--	--
													B	VT	F-923	--	LB	--	--
													B	VT	C-932	--	LB	--	--
			TELEVISION PRODUCTS OF AMERICA											NEW YORK CITY					
			1 Chassis				1 Model							-- Tubes		$39.50			
-	-	-	--	--	--	--	--	--	--	--	--	--	S	-	See-All	39.50	K	-	tr
			TRANSFORMER CORP. OF AMERICA											"CLARION" CHICAGO, ILL.					
			17 Chasses				25 Models							5 to 14 Tubes		$29.95 to $129.50			
A	5	TRF	2-55	--	--	--	--	24	--	1-47	80	--	S	--	40	39.50	M	--	--
A	7	TRF	3-24	--	--	--	--	27	--	2-45	80	--	B	T	61	67.50	M	--	--
A	7	SH	1-35	35	27	1-35	24	--	1-47	80	--	B	T	70	79.50	B	--	--	--
													B	T	80	67.50	M	--	--
													B	T	81	84.50	C	D	--

		SH	1-35	55/35	27	24	80	24				price		
A*	8	SH	1-35		27	24				B	T	69.50	LR	D
A*								1-47		B		49.95	M	D
A										B	VT	79.50	C	D
A*										B	VT	99.50	C	D
A*										B	VT	89.50	HR	D
A										B	VT	129.50	HR	D2

		SH	1-35	55	27	24	80	24				price		
	6	SH				24				B		39.95	M	D
A	6	SH	1-35	1-35	*	57	1-35			B	T	52.50	C	D
A	6	SH		24				80		B	T	29.95	M	D
	7	SH				57						49.95	M	D
A	8	SH	1-35	24	27	56	58	80	*	BS	VT	67.50	C	D
A	8	SH	1-58	57	27	56	56	80	*	B	VT	39.95	M	D
A	8	SH		57	*	56		2-47	*	BS	V	41.95	M	D
A	9	SH								B	T	-	-	
A	10	SH			27	27	56			B	VT	79.50	RP	D
A	10	SH	1-35	57	27	1-35	56	2-47	*	B	VT	89.50	RP	D
A	12	SH	1-35	57	27	1-35	56	4-46	90	B	VT	49.95	ch	D2
A	14	SH	1-58	58	56	2-58	56	2-46	82	B	VTA	69.95	C	D2
										MOU		129.50	C	D2

Models: 84, 85, 90, 91, 94, 95, 100, 101, 220, 120, 121, AC-240, 241, 340, 140, 160, 260, 260-C, 280, 300 DeLuxe

TRAUL RADIO CO. 2 Models

"ULTRADYNE" (1931)   BROOKLYN, N.Y. $32.50 to $94.45

2 Chasses — Tubes

		SH									price		
A	-	SH	(3-24,1-27,2-35,1-47,1-80)							BS	32.50	K	D
A	8									BS	94.45	ch	D

L-32 Senior, L-33 Junior

TRAV-LER RADIO & TELEVISION CORP. 21 Models

"TRAV-LER"   ST. LOUIS, MO. $22.50 to $350.00

15 Chasses — Tubes

											price		
A	4	TRF	1-24						1-47	80	B	22.50	M	D
A	4	TRF	1-35				1-47	80	P	29.95	M	D
A	5	TRF	2-35				1-47	80	B	49.95	M	D
D	7	TRF	3-32		12A	12A	1-47	1-71A		B	59.95	LR	D
-	8	-	-			27				B	74.50	C	D
A	9	SH	1-35	24	27		2-47	80	*	B	89.50	M	D
A										P	49.95	M	D
A										P	59.95	L3	D
A										P	69.50	HR	D
A											70.00	K	
A											70.00	K	
A											150.00	K	D
											175.00	ch	
-											99.50	K	

L, K, K, DX, S, S-9, S-9, S-9 — Trav-lette

(continued)

P	T	C	RADIO	INT. D	O	IF	AUD. D	1st	OUT.	RECT.	AVC	NS	R	CONT	TUNING	MODEL NUMBER AND NAME	PRICE	CAB.	SPKR.	NOTE
			(Trav-ler)																	
A	-	-	--	--	--	--	--	--	--	--	--	--	P	--	--	S-8	124.50	-	-	tr
B	8	SH	1-36	36	37	1-36	37	37	2-38	--	--	--	B	--	--		49.95	A	-	-
A	9	SH	1-58	57	56	--	55	56	2-46,1-80)	80	*	--	B	V	Q	S-10	59.50	M	D	d
A	10	SH	(1-24,4-2),-2				,5,2-47,1-80)			90			B	V	Q	S-10	69.95	M	D	-
													BP	V			89.95	LB	-	tr
B	-	-	--	--	--	--	--	--	--	--	--	--	B	V	--		350.00	C	-	-
B	8	SH	1-58	--	--	--	--	--	--	--	--	--					38.00	A	-	-

TROJAN FACTORIES LTD. LOS ANGELES, CAL. "TROJAN" $24.50 to $69.50
10 Chasses   13 Models   4 to 8 Tubes

P	T	C	RADIO	INT. D	O	IF	AUD. D	1st	OUT.	RECT.	AVC	NS	R	CONT	TUNING	MODEL NUMBER AND NAME	PRICE	CAB.	SPKR.	NOTE
A	4	TRF	1-35	--	--	--	24	--	1-47	80	--	--	B	--	--	Tiny	29.75	M	D	-
A	5	TRF	2-35	--	--	--	24	--	1-47	90	--	--	B	--	--	Baby	47.50	M	D	-
A	6	TRF	2-35	24	--	--	24	27	1-47	90	--	--	B	--	--	Junior	59.50	M	D	-
																Junior	79.50	C	D	-
A	7	THF	3-35	24	--	--	24	27	1-47	80	--	--	B	--	--	Giant	69.50	M	D	-
A	8	TRF	3-35	24	--	--	24	27	2-47	80	--	--	B	--	--	Giant	89.50	C	D	-
A	4	TRF	1-58	--	--	--	57	--	1-48	80	--	--	B	--	--	4A Tiny	24.50	M	D	-
A	5	TRF	2-58	--	--	--	57	--	1-48	80	--	--	B	--	--	5C Baby	37.50	M	D	-
																5C Baby	47.50	C	-	-
A	8	SH	--	27	27	2-35	27	--	2-47	80	--	--	B	--	--	8-H Giant	59.50	M	-	θ
A	8	SH	--	56	58	2-58	56	38	2-48	80	--	--	B	--	--	8-H Giant	79.50	C	D	f
B	8	SH	2-37	36	36	--	36	38	2-38	36	--	--	B	VR	--	9-H Motor	59.50	A	-	-

UNITED AIR CLEANER CORP. CHICAGO, ILL. "SENTINEL" $37.50 to $99.50
21 Chasses   23 Models   4 to 10 Tubes

P	T	C	RADIO	INT. D	O	IF	AUD. D	1st	OUT.	RECT.	AVC	NS	R	CONT	TUNING	MODEL NUMBER AND NAME	PRICE	CAB.	SPKR.	NOTE
A	4	TRF	1-35	--	--	--	24	--	1-47	80	--	--	B	--	--	111	37.50	M	D	-
A	5	TRF	2-35	--	*	--	24	--	1-47	80	--	--	B	--	--	115	38.50	T	D	-
A	5	SH	--	24	27	1-35	24	--	1-47	80	--	--	B	E	--	116	39.50	T	D	-
A	6	SH	1-24	24	27	1-24	24	--	1-45	80	--	--	B	E	--	108	57.50	N	D	-
A	7	SH	1-35	24	27	1-35	24	--	1-47	80	--	--	B	E	--	108A	69.50	T	D	-
																108A	79.50	C	D	-
A	8	SH	1-24	24	27	1-24	27	--	2-45	80	--	--	B	E	VT	106 Portrola	89.50	SS	D	-
A	8	SH	1-35	24	27	1-24	24	--	2-47	80	--	--	B	T	VT	109 Louis XVI	89.50	C	D	-
A	9	SH	1-35	24	27	1-35	27	24	2-47,1-80)	80	*	--	B	T	VT	114	89.50	C	D	k
A	10		(2-24,3-27,2-35,2-47,1-80)										B		VT	118	99.50	LB	D	-

UNITED AMERICAN BOSCH

"AMERICAN BOSCH" — SPRINGFIELD, MASS. $32.95 to $169.50

39 Models — 20 Chasses — 5 to 12 Tubes

Model	Type	Price		
116	CL	56.50		
124	T	59.95		
124	CL	56.50		
110	M	46.75		
110	C	62.50		
120	C	79.50		
125	M	89.50		
125	C	49.95		
140	C	64.50		
140	M	79.50		
145	-	89.50		
127	HB	73.50		
150	D2	99.50		
5	ch M	43.50		
5A Personal	T M	53.50		
5B	CL M	69.50		
5C	MC M	53.50		
31-G	C	87.50		
31-H	C	67.50		
73-A	C	79.50		
73-B	C	95.00		
20-J	C	89.50		
20-K	C	99.50		
20-L	C	139.50		
133-A	C	87.50		
200-A Personal	st	49.95		
200-B Personal	st	49.95		
200-C Personal	st	49.95		
205-A Personal	st	32.95		
36-A	T	45.00		
36-A	C	56.00		
236-A Personal	st	43.95		
91	-	65.00		
91-H	A	69.00		
9:20	A	88.50		
100	A	89.00		
40-B	C	95.00		
40-G	C	89.00		
40-H	C	60.00		
40-J	C			

(continued)

United American Bosch

P	T	C	RADIO	INT D	INT O	INT IF	AUD D	AUD 1st	OUT	RECT	AVC	NS	R	CONT	TUNING	MODEL NUMBER AND NAME	PRICE	CAB	SPKR	NOTE
-	8	SH	--	--	--	--	--	--	--	--	--	--	B	VT	-	40-L	139.50	C	D	-
B	8	SH	1-32	32	30	1-32	34	30	2-49	--	--	--	B	VT	M	226-F The Fireside	99.95	C	D	-
D	8	SH	1-39	39	37	1-39	39	71A	2-LA	80	--	--	B	T	-	224-D Metropolitan	84.95	C	D	-
A	8	SH	--	58	56	2-58	56	56	2-47	80	*	--	B	VT	Q	242-E Empire	74.95	C	D2	-
-	-	-	--	--	--	--	--	--	--	--	--	--	B	V	Q	242-S The Salon	69.95	C	D	-
A	10	SH	1-58	58	56	2-58	56	56	2-45	80	*	--	B	VT	M	230-M The Mansion	89.50	C	D2	-
A	10	SH	--	58	56	3-58	56	56	2-45	80	*	--	BS	VT	M	230-P The Patrician	95.95	C	D2	-
													BS	VT	M	260-C World Cruiser	124.50	C	D2	-
													B	VT	M	260-R World Rover	99.50	C	D2	-
A	12	SH	1-58	58	56	2-58	58	56	3-46	82	*	58	B	VTN	M	312-C Grand Concert	139.50	C	D2	d
													B	VTN	M	312-G Grand Opera	169.50	C	D2	d

UNITED ENGINE CO. LANSING, MICH. $24.95 to $119.50

(1931) 4 to 8 Tubes — 5 Chasses, 8 Models

P	T	C	RADIO	INT D	INT O	INT IF	AUD D	AUD 1st	OUT	RECT	AVC	NS	R	CONT	TUNING	MODEL NUMBER AND NAME	PRICE	CAB	SPKR	NOTE
4	TRF	1-35	--	--	--	--	--	--	1-47	80	--	--	--	--	--	5	24.95	C	Mn	-
1	-	--	--	--	--	--	--	--	--	--	--	--	--	--	--	P-75	39.50	m	-	-
1	-	--	--	--	--	--	--	--	--	--	--	--	--	--	--	8-11	57.00	M	-	-
																	79.50	C	D	-
8	SH	--	(1-24,2-27,2-35,2-47,1-80)	--	--	--	--	--	--	--	--	--	--	--	--	8-31	82.50	C	D	-
																8-181	89.50	HB	D	-
																Colonial	119.50	GG	D	-

UNIVERSAL AUTO RADIO CORP. CHICAGO, ILL. $49.50 to $79.50

"UNIVERSAL" 5 to 7 Tubes — 7 Models, 7 Chasses

P	T	C	RADIO	INT D	INT O	INT IF	AUD D	AUD 1st	OUT	RECT	AVC	NS	R	CONT	TUNING	MODEL NUMBER AND NAME	PRICE	CAB	SPKR	NOTE
B	6	TRF	2-35	--	--	24	24	37	1-38	--	24	--	B	VR	-	50 Standard	59.50	A	D	a
B	7	TRF	2-35	--	--	24	24	37	2-38	--	24	--	B	VR	-	DeLuxe	69.50	A	D	a
B	5	SH	1-44	39	1-44	W	W	--	1-41	--	*	--	B	V	-	57	49.50	A	-	a
F	6	TRF	2-35	--	24	24	37	2-38	--	--	*	--	B	VR	-	60	69.50	A	D	a
B	7	TRF	3-36	--	37	37	37	2-38	--	--	*	--	B	VR	-	70	79.50	A	-	-
B	7	SH	1-44	39	1-44	W	37	2-41	--	--	*	--	B	V	-	77	69.50	A	D	-
				(1-37,1-38,3-39,2-LA)									-	-	-	-	-	A	-	-

UNIVERSAL RADIO & TELEVISION CORP. NEW YORK CITY $29.95 to $69.50

(1931) 5 to 8 Tubes — 4 Models, 3 Chasses

P	T	C	RADIO	INT D	INT O	INT IF	AUD D	AUD 1st	OUT	RECT	AVC	NS	R	CONT	TUNING	MODEL NUMBER AND NAME	PRICE	CAB	SPKR	NOTE
A	15	TRF	2-35	--	--	24	--	24	1-47	80	--	--	B	-	-	42	29.95	M	D	-

Cls	Tb	Chassis									Model	Name				Price			
A		TRF 3‑35	—		27	1‑47	80	27	—	—			B	V	—	39.95	M	D	—
A											86			V		52.50	LB	D	—
A											93			V		69.50	HB	D	—

U.S. RADIO & TELEVISION CORP.   CHICAGO, ILL. $17.95 to $150.00
16 Chasses   24 Models   "APEX" & "GLORITONE"   5 to 12 Tubes

Cls	Tb	Chassis									Model	Name	B	V		Price	Code	D	
A*	5	TRF 2‑24	—	—	—	1‑47	80	27	—	—	26B	Gloritone	B	—	—	59.50	C	D	—
A	5	TRF 2‑24	—	27	—	1‑47	80	27	—	—	26P	Gloritone	B	—	—	49.95	M	D	—
A*	5	SH —	24	*	—	—	—	—	—	—	27		B	—	—	-	M	D	—
A*	7	SH 1‑35	27	1‑35	—	1‑47	80	24	—	—	99A		B	VT	—	39.95	C	D	—
		SH 1‑35	24	1‑35	*	1‑47	80	27	—	—	99B		B	VT	—	49.95	M	D	—
A	7	TRF 2‑24	—	—	—	2‑45	80	—	—	—	7A		B	T	—	47.50	C	D	—
											7B		R	T	—	59.95	M	D	—
A*	8	SH 1‑35	27	1‑35	27	1‑47	80	27	—	—	32A	Apex	B	VT	—	64.50	C	D	—
		SH 1‑35	27	1‑35	27	2‑47	80	27	—	—	32B	Apex	B	T	—	79.50	M	D	—
A	10	SH 1‑35	27	1‑35	27	1‑47	80	27	—	—	8A	U.S. Apex	B	VT	—	67.50	C	D	—
											8B	U.S. Apex	B	VT	—	79.95	M	D	—
											10B	U.S. Apex	B	VT	—	99.50	LB	D	—
A	4	SH 57	57	*	—	1‑47	80	24	—	—	24	Gloritone	B	—	—	17.95	M	D	—
A	5	SH 57	57	*	—	1‑47	80	—	—	—	5‑A	Gloritone	BP	—	—	34.50	T	D	—
											25‑A		BP	—	—	33.50	T	D	- 3
A*	5	SH 1‑35	27	1‑35	*	1‑47	80	24	—	—	7AX		BS	—	—	-	M	D	—
A	7	SH —	57	2‑58	56	1‑47	80	—	—	—	7‑D	Apex	B	VT	—	52.50	T	D	d
A	9	SH 1‑58	57	1‑58	*	2‑46	80	57	—	—	9‑A	Apex	B	VT	—	49.95	T	D	d
											9‑B	Apex	B	VT	—	63.50	LB	D	d
											19‑B	Apex	B	VT	—	69.95	LB	D2	d
B	9	SH —	58	(6‑30,2‑33,1‑34)		—	—	—	—	—	69		B	VTN	GM	69.50	C	PD	d
A	10	SH —	56	1‑58	56	3‑46	82	57	—	—	10C		B	VTN	GM	107.50	HB	D2	d
A	12	SH 1‑58	58					57	—	—	120‑B	Apex	B	VTN		150.00	HB	D2	d

VAN SICKLEN CORP.   ELGIN, ILL.
2 Chasses   2 Models   "VAN SICKLEN"   6 and 7 Tubes $89.50

Cls	Tb	Chassis									Model		B	V		Price	Code		
B	6	TRF 1‑35	—	—	—	24	27	2‑71A	—	—	Motoradio		B	V	-	89.50	A	-	h1
B	7	—	—	—	—	—	—	—	—	—	Motoradio		B	—	-	89.50	A	M	—

VIRGINIA LINCOLN FURNITURE CO.   MARION, VA.
1 Chassis   1 Model   "VIRGINIA‑LINCOLN" (1931)   7 Tubes $99.50

Cls	Tb	Chassis									Model		B	V		Price	Code		
B	7	SH —	—	—	—	24	27	2‑71A	—	—	2510		B	T	-	*99.50	GC	D	—

WALTON RADIO CORP. — ANN ARBOR, MICH. (1931) — — Tubes
1 Chassis — 1 Model — $23.50

P	T	C	RADIO	\[INT\] D	O	IF	\[AUDIO\] D	1st	OUT.	RECT.	AVC	NS	R	CONT TUNING	MODEL NUMBER AND NAME	PRICE	CAB.	SPKR.	NOTE
A	-	TRF	--	--	--	--	--	--	--	--	--	--	--	--	Wal-Tone	23.50	T	D	-

WARE MFG. CORP. — NEW YORK CITY (1931) — 7 Tubes
1 Chassis — 2 Models — $

P	T	C	RADIO	D	O	IF	D	1st	OUT.	RECT.	AVC	NS	R	CONT TUNING	MODEL NUMBER AND NAME	PRICE	CAB.	SPKR.	NOTE
A	7	SH	1-35	24	27	1-35	24	--	1-47	80	--	--	B	--	SBF	--	M	D	-
													B	--	SBF	--	CL	D	-

WELLS-GARDNER DIV. — GULBRANSEN CO. — CHICAGO, ILL.
See:--Gulbransen Co.

WESTERN TELEVISION CORP. — CHICAGO, ILL. — "VISIONETTE" (1932) — — Tubes
$59.50 to $150.00 — 3 Chasses — 3 Models

P	T	C	RADIO	D	O	IF	D	1st	OUT.	RECT.	AVC	NS	R	CONT TUNING	MODEL NUMBER AND NAME	PRICE	CAB.	SPKR.	NOTE
A	-	--	--	--	--	--	--	--	--	--	--	--	P	--	Visionette	59.50	K	-	tr
A	-	--	--	--	--	--	--	--	--	--	--	--	BS	--	Visionette	85.00	T	-	tr
														--		150.00	T	-	tr

WESTINGHOUSE ELECTRIC & MFG. CO. — MANSFIELD, OHIO — "WESTINGHOUSE" (1931) — 4 to 9 Tubes
$37.50 to $260.70 — 5 Chasses — 11 Models

P	T	C	RADIO	D	O	IF	D	1st	OUT.	RECT.	AVC	NS	R	CONT TUNING	MODEL NUMBER AND NAME	PRICE	CAB.	SPKR.	NOTE
A	4	TRF	1-24	--	--	--	24	--	1-47	80	--	--	B	--	WR-14	37.50	M	D	-
A	8	SH	1-35	24	27	1-35	27	--	2-47	80	--	--	B	T	WR-10A Columette	69.50	N	D	hr
A	8	SH	1-35	24	27	2-47	80	--	2-47	80	--	--	B	T	WR-12 Columaire	88.50	CN	D	hr
A*	9	SH	1-24	24	27	2-24	27	--	2-45	80	27	--	B	T	WR-5 Conventional	157.20	HB	D	-
													R	TR	WR-6	194.80	HB	D	-
													B	TR	WR-6	259.20	HB	D	-
													B	T	WR-7	--	RP	D	-
													B	TR	WR-7	194.20	RP	D	-
													B	TR	WR-8 Columaire	260.70	CN	D	-
													B	VT	WR-8 DeLuxe	125.00	CH	D	-
A	9	SH	1-35	24	27	1-35	27	--	2-47	80	27	--	B		WR-15		GC	D	

WHOLESALE RADIO SERVICE CO. INC. — NEW YORK CITY — "Tru-Test" "LaFayette"
$16.50 to $ — 3 to 10 Tubes — 7 Chasses — 7 Models

P	T	C	RADIO	D	O	IF	D	1st	OUT.	RECT.	AVC	NS	R	CONT TUNING	MODEL NUMBER AND NAME	PRICE	CAB.	SPKR.	NOTE
A	5	TRF	--	--	--	--	--	--	--	--	--	--	B	--	Tru-Test	*16.50	M	D	-
A	6	TRF	3-24	--	--	--	24	--	1-45	80	--	--	B	--	LaFayette	--	M	D	-

A	10	SH	--	--	--	--	--'	--	--	--	B	VT	--		Lafayette	#45.50	ch	D	a
A	-	TRP	--	--	--	--	--	--	--	--	S	--	--			#29.50	ch	-	g
A	3	SH	24	27	--	--	26	--	--	--	S	--	--			-	-	-	-
A	5	SH	(2-84,1-27,2-55,1-47,1-80)								B	M	--		Lafayette	21.50	M	D	-
A	7	SH	--	--	--	--	--	--	--	--	B	M	--		Lafayette	-	M	D	-

WILCOX-GAY CORP.   "WILCOX-GAY" (1932)   5 to 10 Tubes

CHARLOTTE, MICH. $31.00 to $84.00

5 Models   5 Chasses

A	5	SH	57	*	1-58	57	--	1-47	80	--	B	BP	2S5-30			31.00	T	A	b
A	7	SH	1-58	56	1-58	55	--	1-47	80	*	B	I,V	2-T-5-30			35.00	T	A	b
											B	V	2-V-7-51			45.90	C	A	b
											B	V	2-V-7-510			59.70	C	A	b
A	10	SH	1-58	58	1-58	56	56	2-47	80	66	B	V	2-W10-515			84.00	C	A	b

WONDER-BAR RADIO CO.   "WONDER-BAR" (1932)   5 and 6 Tubes

NEW YORK CITY $149.50

2 Models   2 Chasses

D	6	TRP	2-14	--	14	17	2-71A	--	--	--	B	--	46			149.50	BR	-	-
A	5	SH	--	*	1-35	24	--	1-47	80	--	B	--	51			149.50	BR	D	-

WOODSTOCK ELECTRIC CORP.   "" (1931)   -- Tubes

$ -- to $ --

-- Chasses   2 Models

--	--	--	--	--	--	--	--	--	--	--	B	--	--			--	M	-	-
--	--	--	--	--	--	--	--	--	--	--	B	--	--			--	MC	-	-

WORLD BATTERY CO.   (1931)   6 Tubes

CHICAGO, ILL. $38.00

1 Chassis   1 Model

B	6	TRP	--	--	--	--	--	--	--	--	-	--	--			38.00	KA	D	-

ZANEY-GILL CORP.   (1931)   6 Tubes

CHICAGO, ILL.   LOS ANGELES, CAL. $49.50 to $ --

1 Chassis   3 Models

A	6	TRP	3-24	--	27	--	1-45	80	--	--	B	T	54		Mighty Midget	#49.50	M	D	-
											B	T	54		Queen Anne	#69.50	CL	D	-
											B	T	54			-	CL	D	-

ZENITH RADIO CORP. CHICAGO, ILL. $49.95 to $290.00   "ZENETTE"   11 Chasses   32 Models   6 to 13 Tubes

P	T	C	RADIO	INT. D	INT. O	IF	AUD. D	1st	OUT.	RECT.	AVC	NS	R	CONT	TUNING	MODEL NUMBER AND NAME	PRICE	CAB.	SPKR.	NOTE
A*	6	TRF	2-35	--	--	--	24	--	1-47	80	--	--	B	--	--	LP Table	49.95	M	D	--
A*	6	TRF	2-24	--	--	--	24	--	2-45	80	--	--	B	--	--	L Table	49.95	M	D	--
A	7	SH	1-35	24	27	1-35	27	--	1-47	80	--	--	B	T	--	B Zenette	73.30	M	D	K
																A Zenette	73.30	M	D	K
A*	8	SH	1-35	35	27	1-35	27	--	1-47	80	24	--	B	T	--	C Zenette	99.80	HB	D	K
																D Zenette	109.80	HB	D	K
A*	10	TRF	3-24	--	--	--	24	27	2-45	80	--	--	B	T	--	LH Zenette	49.95	T	D	--
																WH Zenette	69.95	LP	D	--
A*	10	SH	1-35	35	27	1-35	27	27	2-45	80	24	--	B	T	--	MH Zenette	79.95	HB	D	--
																AH Zenette	79.50	M	D	--
A*	13	SH	2-35	24	27	2-35	27	27	2-45	80	24	--	B	T	--	CH Zenette	99.80	LB	D	--
																RH Zenette	125.00	HB	D	--
																90 Zenette	135.00	C	D	--
																82 Hypermetron	235.00	HB	D	2h
																89 Hypermetron	265.00	C	D	2h
																91	155.00	C	D	--
																92	195.00	HB	D	--
A	7	SH	1-58	24	27	1-58	27	--	1-47	80	--	--	B	VT	--	103 Ultra	290.00	C	D	3h
													B	--	--	210	49.95	T	D	--
													BL	--	--	210-5	55.00	T	D	--
													B	--	--	220	62.50	T	D	--
													BS	--	--	250	73.00	T	D	--
													B3	--	--	260	92.00	LB	D	--
													B	V	--	270	123.50	RP	D	--
													B	V	--	230	55.25	T	D2	--
A	8	SH	1-58	58	56	1-58	57	--	1-59	80	57	--	B	VT	M	240	78.75	LB	D2	--
													B	VT	SM	245	102.50	LB	D2	--
A	10	SH	1-58	58	56	1-58	56	--	2-59	80	57	--	B	VT	SM	410	105.00	LB	D2	--
													B	VT	SM	411	124.00	LB	D2	--
													B	VTN	ASM	420	145.00	LP	D2	--
A	12	SH	1-58	58	56	1-58	56	56	3-59	80	57	57	B	VTN	ASM	430	166.00	HB	D2	--
																440	184.00	HB	D2	--